OLD FORGE

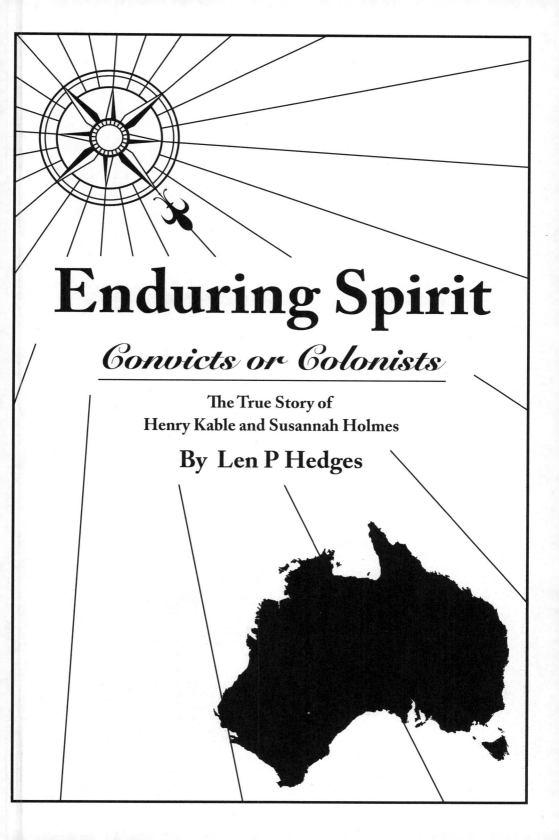

Enduring Spirit

Convicts or Colonists

The True Story of
Henry Kable and Susannah Holmes

By Len P Hedges

First Edition 2009

Designed by
Jupper Peep
studio@jupperpeep.com
www.jupperpeep.com

Published by
Old Forge Publishing
39 Backgate
Cowbit
Lincolnshire
PE12 6AP
oldforgepub@aol.com
www.oldforgepublishing.org
01406 381313

ISBN 978-1-906183-08-0

Printed for Old Forge Publishing by
the MPG Books Group,
Bodmin and King's Lynn

Contents

Acknowledgements

Researching the basic facts for this book was one of the most enjoyable aspects of writing the story of Henry Kable and Susannah Holmes. The following were invaluable sources of many of the facts contained in the finished manuscript.

Robert Hughes book 'The Fatal Shore' is a masterly overview of the First Fleet's momentous journey to Australia and is a must for serious students of this subject. 'The Convict Ships' by Charles Batson and 'English Prison Hulks' by W Branch Johnson were also very helpful, as was June Whittaker's 'The Raking of the Embers'.

The journals of two officers who sailed in the First Fleet, 'The journal of Arthur Bowes Smythe', surgeon on the Lady Penryn and Lt Ralph Clark's 'Journals and Letters' gave a marvellous in depth look at conditions on that incredible journey.

Locally, the staff at Norwich Museum were very helpful and provided great insight into jail conditions in the 1780s. Jenny Rainbow at the Norfolk Records Office pointed me in the right direction to dig out original records of prisoners residing in the Norwich Castle jail towards the end of the 18th Century and their convictions, all of which helped enormously.

I must also mention Derek James of the Eastern Evening News whose article on Henry Kable and Susannah Holmes first provoked my interest in this remarkable story.

Lastly, but certainly not least, my heartfelt thanks go to my wife Jan, who offered forthright comments and slogged through mountains of handwritten pages to produce the first legible outline of the book.

Enduring Spirit

Convicts or Colonists

Chapter One

Young Henry Cabell watched the judge put the fold of black cloth on his ill-fitting wig. It was hot and close in the panelled courtroom, despite the fresh winds blowing in from the flat fields of Norfolk.

Henry stood next to his father, a man of forty-five years but seemingly much older. He gripped the metal rail around the top of the dock like a vice; the big vein in his neck throbbing as it always did when he was troubled.

"Abraham Carman, Henry Cabell and Henry Cabell the younger, you have all been rightly convicted of the heinous crime of burglary in the County of Norfolk, England. You wilfully deprived a respectable widow, Mrs Hambling of Alburgh near Harleston, of all her worldly possessions and intended to sell them for your own gain and profit. You stripped her home of every movable; even taking hangings from bedsteads and covers from windows. We have heard how you extracted meat from pickle cases and consumed wine from her meagre cellar. This was a mean spirited, planned robbery from a widow whose home you knew to be empty."

Pausing only to adjust the black cloth on his tightly curled wig he rapped the bench with a gavel and stared fiercely at the men in the dock.

"I sentence each of you to be hanged by the neck until dead. May the Lord have mercy on your souls!"

Henry's father threw back his head and howled like a wolf, an agonised cry from the pit of his stomach.

"Not my son! Not my son!"

Judge Eyre watched him in mild surprise and rapped his gavel on the bench again. "Take them down." He spoke in a flat monotone; he had said the same words many times before.

Abraham Carman, manacled by feet and hands, turned to father and son, face drained of blood. "We'll be reprieved, count on it."

The guard, a tall gaunt man, gripped Carman by the collar and hauled him down the dock steps. "And pigs might fly," he said grimly.

The three men were thrown in a dark cell below the Court, the only light coming from a mean window below street level. Thick cast iron bars squeezed the light further. The place stank. A sentence of death had a way of opening a man's bowels.

Henry's father sat on a wooden ledge, his head in his hands, and elbows on his knees. Great sobs racked Abraham Carman's thin frame, the big man was in deep shock.

Young Henry held Carman's hand and stretched his lips in a mirthless smile. He was devastated by the verdict. He knew that theft of goods worth more than forty shillings drew a sentence of death but during his short stay in Thetford lock-up the old lags had told him time and again 'no plunder on you when taken – no conviction'.

The thought of death by hanging had never entered his head, but now he had to confront the possibility. He held his head in his hands, a mirror image of his father. He forced himself to think of the King's Pardon. He had heard the old lags talk of it and resolved to discover all he could about transportation from the gaolers. The few prisoners he had met spoke mostly of their own circumstances and hopes, liberally laced, he suspected, with alcohol and ignorance. Someone, surely, would give him advice on how to win the King's Pardon; anything but death on a rope.

His chance came when the gaoler peered through the barred opening in the early hours of the morning.

"What about the King's Pardon? I had nothing on me when taken."

"Don't count on it, son. I've not heard of one person being sent to America for months and months. Years even. They don't want our scum no more. Count on nothing but the rope."

Henry's heart sank like a stone in his chest. "No hope, are you sure?"

"Not a bleeding chance, boy!"

Henry spent the night pacing about the cramped cell, examining every brick and bar. His mother occupied a great deal of his thoughts. He hadn't seen her since the night of the robbery. What would she think of them now? She always attended church on Sundays, to hear the good word. He guessed she would have been too proud to go since the robbery. He bitterly regretted agreeing to that mad escapade. He hadn't given himself enough time to consider the consequences. He had acted without thought; a failing of his.

Abraham Carman and his father slept on, huddled together like two big kids in a bed.

He thought about escape – hence his thorough examination of the cell during the bleak hours, but concluded there was no hope of breaking out. The stinking hole was as tight as a drum. His best chance was likely to be on the journey to the place they would be kept before hanging.

Through the grating to the street outside the sound of heavy wheels crushing their way over the hard ground woke Abraham Carman.

At the front of the building three heavy carts rumbled to a halt. Two drivers jumped down and huddled in the building's entrance.

"Where are you taking your lot?" The slighter of the two asked.

"Cambridge Bridewell," the second man answered, stamping his feet and rubbing his hands at the same time, "Yours?"

"Eight, to the dungeons at Norwich Castle, and good riddance too."

The third Wagoner appeared and immediately hammered on the tall oak doors.

"Come on you buggers I 'int got all day!"

To their surprise, the door was opened right away. The court clerk glowered at them, face lit by the lantern he was holding.

"Who's first?" he growled.

"Me, I've to git to Norwich," the slight figure spoke through his muffler.

"You others wait here," the clerk threw over his shoulder as he motioned the driver in.

He unlocked another barred door and disappeared into the gloom beyond. Ten minutes later he was back, leading a straggle of eight men each chained to the one in front. All had heavy leg irons clamped to each ankle, forcing them into a ponderous gait. The cumbersome crocodile of men and metal assembled in the hall. Even the dull light in that dreary place caused them to squint.

The driver signed a document under the careful eye of the clerk and the strange procession clanked its way to the front of the building. The double doors were flung open and the early morning sun slanted in. A collective groan went up as the prisoners squeezed their eyes against this assault upon their senses.

The group shuffled forward to the leading cart and a guard shoved the first man up the box step.

Each cart was constructed in the same way. A strong wooden hut with barred windows had been built on the back of a stout cart. A small door at the rear led to rows of benches on each side. When the fourth prisoner had clambered in, the guard unlocked the chain attaching him to the fifth man in the line. The driver locked the loose chain to a hefty bolt let into the wooden bench. He did the same when the eighth prisoner had squeezed into the cramped hut on wheels. After barring the heavy door and securing it with a peg, he positioned himself on the roof of the hut. His legs dangled over an opening which was crossed hatched with iron.

Young Henry found himself next to one of the side windows. By craning his neck he could see the countryside as the cart crunched its way along the road. Heat in the confined space quickly built up and every man began to sweat profusely. As they passed through villages the prison cart was recognised. Men, women and children walked beside it, jeering and laughing at the human cargo.

It took over five hours to travel the thirty miles from Thetford to Norwich. As the cart trundled through the medieval gates of St Stephens, Henry thought he caught a glimpse of his friend Bobby, straining to see over the crowds lining the edge of the dusty road, but it was impossible to be sure. A few minutes later, the cart trundled over the bridge to stop outside the heavy gates to Norwich Castle.

"Out yer git, and look lively."

They were not lively; they stumbled out one by one, dragged down by chains and exhaustion.

There had been no chance of escape during the journey, manacled one to another and bolted to the cart. Henry stared at the towering walls of the old castle that was Norwich Gaol and his heart sank.

The prisoners clanked their way into the cold courtyard. One of the guards, a squat figure with a square head, cracked a wooden stave against the ground.

"You men see the gate as you came over the bridge?"

One man nodded, the others waited fearfully.

"That's where you lot will be dancing the Newgate hornpipe wearing a collar of the finest hemp!"

Some prisoners hung their heads, one or two glared angrily at t heir tormenter.

Henry peered round, noting a two storey structure built against wall. From the roof of that there was only another twenty feet or so to the battlements.

Chapter Two

On the day the three Alburgh burglars were sentenced, Susannah Holmes started a new job in Surlingham near Norwich, a pretty village of straggling houses by a Broad. The Broads, a series of connected lakes, had been formed by extensive peat workings in the distant past.

Susannah Holmes trudged up the wet drive to the big house owned by Jebez Taylor. The ground was low and marshy around the Broads. Before she had a chance to bang the big knocker, her friend Jessie opened the door.

"Always use the back door, Susannah," she whispered.

They went quickly up the broad stairs and on to the narrow steps to the attic. Susannah unpacked her possessions and carefully put them into the wooden chest at the bottom of the narrow bed. She was sharing the tiny attic with Jessie who said the previous girl had 'upped and left'. She knew that Susannah had been desperate to find a position since her last employer had died.

"Better hide that necklace, Mrs Taylor don't like no fancy things on us girls," said Bessie.

Susannah removed the coral necklace that her brother had given her on her twentieth birthday, two weeks previously, March the first, 1783. Carefully, she placed her most treasured possession in the chest at the end of the bed. Harry was her only family now her parents had died.

Susannah was a trim attractive girl with a buxom figure. Usually her green eyes danced with laughter but times had changed since she had been out of work. She had been maid to an elderly lady for four years, until a heart seizure had carried her away. At the funeral, the old lady's son told her she was no longer needed and she had to leave the house that day. By good fortune, her brother had come home from the sea a few days earlier and she had lodged with him. Work was scarce in rural Norfolk and their savings had soon disappeared.

The job working with her friend Bessie had come unexpectedly when their prospects seemed especially bleak. Her brother was still out of work but now at least she could provide him with food. Bessie had told her the only other servant in the house, Mrs Choke, the cook was generous with leftovers.

"Always bob and curtsey when Mrs Taylor is about, she's a bit sharp but don't mean no harm I'm sure. She don't like us girls to have nothing to do," Bessie's words broke into her thoughts.

"What about the Master?"

"We hardly ever see him, he's too busy in business. He buys cloth from local weavers and sells it in London, sometimes he don't come back for days."

Susannah looked down into the damp garden. A thin mist hung in the air at the end nearest the broad.

The house hunched low in the marshy ground, grey bricks melancholy with the grime of time. Prone to the wind and rain that found no resistance over the expanse of water to the east, it huddled as best it could in the lea of a line of lime trees, permanently stooped having submitted long ago to prevailing squalls from the North Sea.

It was a stolid house, constructed, it was said, as a vicarage for a church that was never built. The low mists and blustery winds got into the joints of the property like rheumatism. Small windows and casements alike creaked and groaned at these sly invasions but could do nothing to prevent them entering the fabric of the house, it was a dark abode.

Bessie was a short, dumpy girl of middling proportions. Her light brown hair was usually scrunched into two untidy buns covering her ears. This had the dual effect- both giving the strong impression of a pork pie on each side of her head and rendering her ears ineffective. Bessie was always asking people to repeat themselves.

There was a creak on the stair and the door opened without a sound, Mrs Taylor's face appeared between it and the doorframe.

"New girl, come." The head was withdrawn and took its owner to the front parlour.

At the door of the parlour Susannah straightened her starched pinafore and adjusted her hair before entering.

"Always knock before you enter, girl." Mrs Taylor did not even look up.

Susannah bobbed, apologising.

"Leave the room and come back in, this time knocking first."

Susannah left the room hastily, her face burning. Hardly daring to pause, she knocked sharply on the panelling.

"Come."

"Can you read, girl?"

"Yes, Madam, I can."

"This is a list of your duties. I shall inspect your work every day; there is no room in this house for slack work or slack behaviour. Do not waste the day gossiping with Bessie, that girl needs little distraction. Your duties are to clean this house until everything sparkles. Most particularly you are not to fraternise with anyone in this household. Do you understand?"

"I understand, Madam."

Back in the hall, Bessie beckoned her into the drawing-room.

"She can be a bit of a tartar, but we can look out for each other," Bessie squeezed Susannah's hand. "She gives everybody a lecture before they start, it's just her way."

"Don't worry Bessie, I'm glad to have a roof over my head. I can't afford to lose this job, me and Harry haven't eaten a decent meal for ages."

The next few days passed painfully for Susannah who found herself at the sharp end of criticism from the Mistress, who seemed to be everywhere, checking on what she had done and finding fault with it.

Bessie did her best to mollify her friend but it was obvious, even to her that the Mistress had 'taken agin her.'

Towards the end of her first week, Susannah and Bessie were in the kitchen with the cook when suddenly the back door flew open, banging against the end of the sink, and a figure, all boots and overcoat, barged in.

"Why do you have to imitate a hurricane every time you come into this kitchen? You'll have that door off its hinges one of these days, mark my words," the cook shouted.

The gardener's boy took off his cap and slumped heavily at the table, ravenously eyeing a pile of toast.

"Better give him a round of toast, else we'll never hear the end of it." The cook sighed.

Seizing the topmost chunk, the boy chomped at the edge, biting and tearing. A second slice vanished as if by magic.

"Get out of here before you eat us out of house and home." The cook pulled the boy towards the door but was not quick enough to prevent him grabbing another slice of toast.

They heard him scrunching his way through the thick bread as he strode down the path outside.

"He's is a nice lad, but be careful with that one," Mrs Choke said darkly.

The two girls looked at her in surprise.

"Whatever do you mean, Mrs Choke" Bessie asked.

"There's a reason that the maid afore you left so sudden," she nodded mysteriously at Susannah.

Bessie stood up quickly, causing her chair to fall on the kitchen floor.

"That in't true, he wasn't friendly with her at all." Tears sprang to her eyes.

"I heard the Missus with my own ears after church one Sunday. She was shouting at the girl, saying she was over familiar and had to go!"

"He in't like that." Two tears rolled down Bessie's face, shiny with traces of butter.

"It stands to reason girl, he's the only one round here likely to get familiar with anyone."

"Don't take on so, Bessie. Just cos the Missus said the girl was over familiar don't mean it's true," Susannah whispered.

"I suppose you're right lass, Mrs Taylor would say you was over familiar with the cat if you stroked it more than twice." Mrs Choke tousled Bessie's hair.

"You've been here a long time, Mrs Choke, you must know everything that happens in this house," Susannah said.

"I'm stuck in this kitchen almost all day, but I know what's what. There's no shenanigans with the Missus and her husband and she don't like to see anyone else partaking of the smallest pleasure."

"The Missus and her husband have separate bedrooms," Bessie whispered confidentially.

"Susannah knows that, she's helped you clean 'em these last few days."

"She's the one with the money you know," the cook went on, "it's her father's business. Mr Taylor runs it now of course but the Missus is always reminding him who holds the purse strings. He bears it all pretty well, I'll say that for him."

"He's cheerful when he goes away on business," Bessie said.

"And made to suffer when he gets back." Mrs Choke spooned the pudding mixture into a baking tray. "The Missus has a bed cold enough to chill any man's desire."

When Susannah went to bed that night she combed her hair in silence, a worried frown on her face.

"You've got lovely hair Susannah, it's all coppery brown and so long. I wish mine was like that."

Susannah stared at her reflection wondering if her hair was the cause of her troubles, Mrs Taylor made her wear a cap that concealed every strand. The last week in the Taylor household had been hard. She tried her best but could do nothing right it seemed. Every table ornament had to be re-polished or dusted again. Grates always needed cleaning twice according to the eagle eye of her new employer. The two frocks she owned had to be lowered by dropping the hems in case the Master should catch sight of her ankles on the stairs.

A few days later, Susannah was feeling a little better. The Mistress had gone to attend her mother who was sick. The Master, Jebez Taylor, had returned from London and was much easier on the girls. To their delight, he had given Susannah and Bessie permission to go into Norwich on their half day off.

Saturday was market day in Norwich. Bessie was friendly with Joe, who took vegetables to the market every Saturday, and had arranged a ride.

Soon the two friends were bumping along the rutted road, squeezed into the back of the flat cart between sacks of potatoes and parsnips. It was a lumpy journey, the cart jostling and lurching, but this merely added to the girls' good humour.

It took over an hour to get to Norwich. The cart rumbled up Bracondale past the big houses, then down through the old city gates into the narrow highway of St Stephens. At the bottom, they could see the great castle that was being used as a prison. Joe reined in the tired horse by the market place. Stalls, handcarts and trestles stretched back up the hill by the flint-faced Guildhall.

"Be back here by three o'clock – no later else you'll miss your ride home!" Joe wagged his finger in their faces.

Bessie stretched up and kissed him lightly on the end of his nose.

"Get away, you silly mawther," he grinned, rubbing his nose with the back of his hand.

They decided to treat themselves to tea and scones at a little corner shop they had spotted by the wheelwright. Susannah wanted to see where the Lord Mayor lived, as she had heard it was close by. Soon they were walking down a small alley past the Bridewell, a dark flint-faced building with strong bars stretching across the windows. At the bottom of the alley, by the big church, they turned left onto Charing Cross, busy with coaches and carts.

A few minutes later, they were staring at a large house set back from the road. A man in a tall hat was closing the coach house doors.

"Is this where the Mayor lives?" called Susannah.

"Not any more, this is where the County Judges stay when they are up for the quarter sessions, or when they come to inspect convicts in the Bridewell and Castle."

They gawped for a while at the grand building, then climbed the slight hill by St John's church in the Maddermarket. As they passed the churchyard, which was a good ten feet above the alley, they heard a man swearing, and a girl cried out. Bessie was all for hurrying away. Susannah left her in the alley and went through the little wicket gate before running up the few steps to the churchyard above. By the gravestones on the far side, almost hidden by an overhanging tree, a man and a woman were struggling. Susannah was shocked to see the man punch the girl who fell to her knees.

"You bleeding harlot!" Between each word he punched the girl about the face. Susannah rushed in and rained blows on his head with her umbrella.

"Leave her alone, she's hurt bad!"

The man, about fifty years old, light coloured hair plastered back, was sweating profusely. He was a large man with an overhanging belly. His belt, circling a vast stomach, hung open and he had to hold up his pantaloons with one hand. He used his other blood-smeared hand to seize Susannah.

"Another of the buggers!" he yelled.

Instinctively, Susannah stabbed at him with her umbrella, poking him in the eye. He staggered backwards, cursing. The girl on the ground grabbed his legs and began screaming. With that, he seemed to have had enough, he shook off the girl and pushed Susannah against a gravestone, her umbrella in tatters. The sweating man stumbled down the steps to the alley below, just managing to keep his pantaloons up. They heard him roar under the archway by the church in a cloud of oaths.

The girl sat back on her heels, hands covering her face, blood seeping through her fingers.

"I'll call a watchman, there must be one nearby."

"No, wait,"

Using her Sunday best handkerchief, Susannah wiped away the blood from the girl's face. An inch long gash, situated just below the hairline, was leaking at an alarming rate. One eye was red and puffy. Bessie's frightened face appeared above the top step by the gate.

Between them they got the girl to her feet and sat her down on a low grave like a stone coffin set above the ground. At a nearby trough, filled to the brim with cold rainwater, Susannah rinsed her handkerchief and washed the worst from the girl's face.

"Ta," she held Susannah's hand and squeezed hard.

"What's your name? We must get you home."

"Liz is my name – I'll get myself home, it isn't far."

"We must get you to a magistrate – that man shouldn't get away with what he's done!"

"I know who he is."

Bessie and Susannah exchanged glances. Liz peered at her reflection in a small puddle. The cut had stopped bleeding but her face was beginning to swell.

"That bugger gave me a right pissbawler, I must have seen every star in the bleeding sky."

Bessie stepped back in surprise, and looked around the churchyard, as if expecting a cleric to appear.

"This is God's place, you mustn't swear like that!"

Liz, holding the sodden red cloth to her eye, squinted around at the gravestones.

"There are many here that would love to hear me say anything!"

"You've had a fright, you don't know what you're saying," Susannah sat down and hugged the girl. With that all the fight seemed to leave Liz and she began to sob uncontrollably. Susannah held the shaking figure as tightly as she could.

"You're ever so kind," she bawled into Susannah's ear.

Bessie looked round uneasily and began hopping from foot to foot. She looked over the low stonewall at the back of the cemetery into the narrow street below. People hurrying by were staring up at the churchyard. Bessie sprang back from the wall.

"Who was that man? You said you knew him," Susannah said gently.

"I see him about once a month, he's always tight with his pocket book."

Bessie looked blankly at Liz, "Is he a special friend?"

"There's nothing special about that fat old sod!"

"So you don't love him?" Bessie whispered.

"Love him? Love is what men don't feel for their wives. Round here love costs a shilling and takes ten minutes."

Bessie backed away holding her hands to her mouth.

"Why did he hit you?" Susannah asked.

"The old bugger didn't pay me the full price. I thought I'd help myself to a bit extra on the sly, like."

Bessie was staring, horrified, at Liz, both hands firmly clamped over her mouth.

"Bessie, have you got a handkerchief I could use to clean Liz's face?"

Bessie shook her head violently from side to side.

"Don't worry; I can manage with this one, though it's in a bit of a mess. I can wash it and bring it back here next week." Liz squeezed Susannah's handkerchief, and thin red drops spattered on the grey stone below.

"You keep it, I can get another."

"You've been kind where many would not have been, I won't forget." Liz hugged Susannah.

"Are you sure you'll be alright? I could walk with you to your home."

"No, really, you've done enough, thanks my dear."

Liz tidied her clothing and straightened her hat making her way gingerly down the narrow steps to the alley, and under the arch towards the market place. Bessie peered over the low wall at the departing figure.

"Well, I never," she whispered.

"Come on Bessie, let's go to the cattle market up by the castle prison."

Susannah grabbed Bessie's hand and led her down the steps from the churchyard.

Fifty yards away in a private room above the Cat and Fiddle two men turned away from the window as the girls disappeared from view.

"Anyone you recognise, John?"

John Custance, Squire to the village of Weston, nodded his head. He was a handsome man, finely chiselled features below a dark head of hair. A thin moustache curled around his top lip. A bright yellow cravat emphasised the fine tan of his skin.

"I've seen the one that took the beating. She came before my court a couple of years ago. If I remember correctly the foul creature had burgled a place at Hethersett that belonged to a weaver. I remember her particularly as I was called to the Bridewell about a month after she was incarcerated there. She had a tongue sharper than a viper and the chief turnkey wanted permission to clamp her in a scolds bridle."

"Did it work?"

"It did, the metal piece that protrudes into the mouth rubbed her tongue raw, she wasn't much trouble after that."

The squire went to the open log fire and warmed his hands.

"Now, Sir Harbord, where were we in our discussion?"

Sir Harbord Harbord BT, Member of Parliament for Norwich stared out of the window again. He was a tall man, elegantly dressed in a long green close fitting coat with gold buttons. A white cravat hung loosely over a frilled shirt. Soft white cuffs matched the shirt. His light coloured pantaloons were pulled tight at the knee. White silk stockings led to a pair of highly polished shoes with enormous brass buckles.

"Our valiant citizens are getting concerned about the prisons filling up. This petition they want me to take to Parliament indicates their disgust at the delay in transporting prisoners. You, John, as a magistrate and a trustee of the prison will know better than most about the conditions there."

"Our citizens are worried about their health," Custance replied, "ever since the Hulks Act of 1776 prisons have been filling up. Our ports confine many undesirables in the hulks around our coasts and, and many more are squeezed into prisons not designed for the purpose. The result is overcrowding, poor food and vile conditions. Typhus is the real terror, the real reason petitions are raised and sent to MPs such as yourself!" John Custance prodded the logs in the grate with a thin poker; a shower of sparks fell onto the tiled hearth.

Sir Harbord paced about the room, hands clasped behind his back.

"It's true, ever since we have been unable to send our unwashed and unwanted to America, prisons have overflowed. The Thames and southern ports are dotted with hulks of rotting ships, home to a festering tide of humanity."

"Parliament, Sir Harbord, must realize that people are terrified of the typhus outbreaks in prisons and hulks. They fear an epidemic and want rid of the prisoners."

"I'll see what I can do," Sir Harbord sighed, "the new Transportation Bill is being drafted now. It should become law about the middle of next year. The trouble is we don't know yet where to send people for transportation. Damn that insurrection in America!"

John Custance looked out of the window. The girl was back again, cuts and bruises thinly disguised under a layer of face powder.

"I must be going, I have to catch the coach to London." Sir Harbord picked up his top hat and made his way to the door.

"I have some business to do, too," John Custance looked down at the girl who had taken up her usual position by the church wall.

Bessie and Susannah were in the market place waiting for Joe the wagoner to turn up. They had had an exciting day, not least the frightening incident with the girl in the churchyard. Bessie had not stopped talking about it for two hours.

Finally, Joe creaked up in his cart. The horse immediately deposited an enormous pile of dung at their feet. It looked round dolefully, sneezed and shook its great head. Joe took a sack from the back of his cart and shovelled the pile into it.

In terms of growth, Joe's ankles and wrists were considerably in advance of the rest of him and consequently, the ends of his pantaloons were some distance from his boots. Similarly, the cuffs of his rough jacket stood some way off his wrists and seemed nearer his elbows.

Helping Susannah and Bessie up into the cart, he carefully wiped a spot of horse dung from the flat surface with his sleeve. The two girls made themselves as comfortable as they could, looking doubtfully at the sack of manure. A head of steam rose slowly from the contents.

"This isn't the Coronation cart, you know!" Joe threw another cover over the steaming sack.

To turn the cart, Joe had to get out and walk the horse backwards for a few yards. Once they were travelling forwards, Bessie shook Susannah's arm.

"Look, is that the girl we helped?"

Emerging from a hostelry in the narrow road between the market place and the castle were a man and a woman. As they reached the bottom of the road the girl saw the two figures in the cart and winked theatrically at Susannah.

"That is Liz, her eye is almost closed now." Bessie was fascinated.

She was on the arm of a well-dressed man with dark hair and a thin moustache wearing a bright yellow cravat.

Chapter Three

Young Henry woke up in a panic, banging his skull on something hard and it took him a minute or two to remember where he was.

Abraham Carmen was in the bunk immediately above. He was chained a deaf mute they had met at the Thetford Assizes the previous day. Four men were in the bunk beds on the other side of the cell. Attempting to sit upright, he found the fetter on his leg was still chained to his father's leg iron.

All eight in the cramped space had been condemned to death or prison at Thetford. Soon after arriving at the castle, they had been bundled into a cell deep below the castle keep. The men had filled in the dark hours the previous evening by exchanging whispered stories about their crimes and sentences.

Suddenly there was a great clanging on the cell door. A dim figure was raking a heavy wooden stave over the bars enclosing the small window in the door.

"On your feet, look lively now!" The turnkey crashed his stave across the bar again.

"Stand up there, git into line."

The prisoners somehow fell into a line between the layered beds hinged to the walls and held by heavy chains. The door creaked open and a grimy hand beckoned them out. Each pair of men, shackled together, had somehow to keep in step up the stone stairway.

"The governor always sees new prisoners first thing, to acquaint 'em with the rules and regulations of this salubrious establishment."

Soon they stood blinking in the light reflected off the walls of the keep. From the side of the yard, two men emerged and trudged up to the prisoners. The stockier of the two, a man with a thick neck, produced a wooden box and threw it onto the hard ground. The shorter man stepped onto the box and cleared his throat.

"My name is Gynne, George Gynne. I am your Gaoler."

He looked around at the men before him. Most stared at the ground but one or two screwed up their eyes to study the speaker. He was short and stout, waistcoat and trousers straining to contain the fleshy figure within.

"I receive nothing from the authorities for the dubious privilege of entertaining you in this desirable residence in the heart of the great city of Norwich. Indeed I pay our under-sheriff over thirty one pounds per annum for the pleasure. Thus I am not only your gaoler but also your landlord. This means you must pay me for your living expenses while you are here. You will be issued with a small loaf of bread each day and given cheese to share between you. You can use the pump in this yard for your drinking water. All this is free." He waved his hands in an expansive gesture.

"However, the more prisoners there are, the less there is to share around. The turnkeys will give you the price of extra rations as and when they become available. They are not always available, reliant as we are on traders who want to be paid before they hand over victuals." He paused again and looked around. "If any man wants bedding and a bed to himself the charge is two shillings per week, to be paid in advance."

There was an audible gasp from some of the prisoners.

"If bedding is provided and two share then the charge is one shilling and sixpence. Three men sharing the same bed need only pay ninepence each per week."

Henry caught his father's eye and they exchanged a grim look.

"Easement of irons – that is removal of the chains linking your legs is a paltry three pence per week!"

The gaoler announced this as an unmissable bargain.

"Those with the skills will be allowed to work. The appropriate materials such as lace, leather, cotton and thread can all be bought from the turnkeys. The public are allowed to purchase your goods twice a week through the gratings on the east side of the castle."

He jumped off the box and walked briskly back to the main building. The Chief turnkey stepped forward and favoured the felons with a grin once more.

"Savage by name and savage by nature," he declared, "there'll be no smarmy back talk to me, and I'm not a lily-livered liberal sort of a man. Keep your trap shut and do as you're told and your life will be tolerable, otherwise," he glared round at the prisoners, "it won't!"

A prisoner held up his hand. Savage strode over to him.

"Excuse me sir, I'm not sure I can afford to live here, the terms are not acceptable. If you will kindly let me out I will find my own lodgings."

Instantly, Savage knocked him down. A low growl arose from the other prisoners.

"You in't likely to be living anywhere soon." He kicked the fallen figure, and scowled at the rest of the men, "anyone else want to try a bit of lip? I'll oblige with the same remedy."

Resentment rose like a pain in young Henry's chest, his father held him back by the chain. The guard picked up the box and walked away whistling.

Abraham Carmen, the deaf mute, together with Henry and his father went to sit by the huge outer wall of the keep, to tear at the half sized loaf they were given.

They all turned their pockets out. Between them they had seventeen shillings. Henry's father was entrusted with this treasure.

"I'm thinking we should all pay three pence each to have these blasted chains taken off," Carmen said to a round of nodding.

"A bit of extra grub to go round wouldn't go amiss, I'm starving," Henry rubbed his stomach.

They paid the fee for easement of irons and soon the four men were stomping about the cold yard enjoying the relative freedom of being without chains. Ankle clamps were left on, each weighing about ten pounds.

They walked round the yard examining their prison. It had once been a great Norman castle but was now just a roofless shell. The huge outer walls, some forty feet high, still stood. It was constructed on a massive mound in the centre of the busy city.

A few buildings leaned against the east wall and from these, windows looked on to a large enclosed yard. A heavy oak door studded with iron led to the dungeons below. In the south wall, facing the bridge over which they had arrived the previous day, were four openings, cross-hatched with iron as thick as a man's wrist. The other two sides had arrow slots, too far up to see out of, built when there were two more storeys above ground level.

The Cabells, Abraham and Smith the mute man, having opted not to pay for bedding, found themselves being taken back through the door which led to the dungeons. As soon as the inner door to the dungeons was opened, a putrid stench swept over them.

"God almighty, what's that?" gasped Abraham.

The turnkey, holding a rag to his face, shoved them down the steep steps.

"Always the same when you come from the open air. The stink sickens stomachs and turns grown men green."

As if to prove the point, Smith vomited down the stairs, adding a further flavour to the fetid atmosphere.

At the bottom of the steps, the turnkey selected a huge key to open a heavy studded door set in the damp wall. The door banged shut behind them and all four stood peering into the deep gloom. A wax candle faintly disturbed the darkness. It was not the cell in which they had spent the previous night. This was far worse. The smell was indescribable, a raw mix of sweat, excrement, ammonia, stale bodies, tallow and smoke, over laden with the rancid odour of stagnant water. Smith threw up again, this time against the door.

Something stirred at the back of the rectangular room. Young Henry, peering into the shadows, was startled to see four pairs of eyes staring back. Four filthy creatures squatted on the floor, each wrapped in a blanket so only their heads showed. The four heads glared at the newcomers from under matted hair.

"God Henry, what have we come to?" his father said softly.

Henry's stomach lurched from hunger to despair and back again

"I'm thinking that we should spend some money on bedding," Abraham whispered.

The newcomers slept fitfully that night, fearing the old lags, and what they might do.

The grey dawn light did not penetrate the deep dungeon. To the prisoners, first light was that of the turnkey's lantern. He played another discordant tune on the door.

"Stand clear o' the door!" The turnkey marched in and emptied a small sack of loaves on the floor. He then threw something wrapped in a grey cloth on the loaves. A squabble immediately broke out as the old lags fought over the bread and cheese wrapped in the cloth.

One of the original inmates crouched in the corner eating like a hungry hound, biting at the dry crust and tearing off mouthfuls, all the time glancing about as if expecting another dog to run at him and snatch a morsel from his jaws.

"They're worse than stinking rats in a trap," Henry hissed. "We must get out of these dungeons; they're cesspits of death and disease!"

Abraham tugged at Henry's sleeve. "We go for bedding and a cell above ground?"

"We do, and I'm thinking extra food."

As soon as the chief turnkey turned up, they paid their dues for the change of cells, bedding and the extra food. Thirty minutes later, they were settled into a new cell, sharing a scrawny meat pie.

"This is a dump, but after last night it's a mansion, a mawthers delight." Abraham grinned, the first time a smile had cracked his face since the quarter sessions in Thetford.

"We've got to be careful, the money has already shrunk like meat in a skillet," Henry Senior replied.

"Let's eat now, and worry later. There is plenty of time to worry, I reckon."

Henry stared out of the barred opening at the roof of the lean-to attached to an outer wall. He calculated it wouldn't take a lot to get on the roof but the sheer climb to the top of the battlements looked insurmountable. He would need a rope.

Henry thought back to that February morning when it had all began. They lived in a tied cottage in the village of Mendham by the border separating the counties of Norfolk and Suffolk. Henry's father had been stood off from his job on the farm and had received notice to quit the cottage. The farmer, a friend of the family for years, had given them four weeks to find other lodgings.

"Sorry Henry, times are hard. I've got to sell the farm."

After the farmer left, Henry packed his leather punches needed for his work on the leather stall in Norwich market. He could hear his mother and father talking in the room above. There were few secrets in a farm cottage.

Recently his mother had been getting up later and later. A hacking cough had turned into something worse. When Henry had taken up a cup of tea for her the previous morning he had been alarmed to see the pillow sodden with sweat, her face glistening and grey. When his father returned they sent for the doctor.

The doctor arrived by pony and, trap and after examining the patient, had come down into the cramped kitchen.

"It's consumption I'm afraid, she needs proper care, these old cottages are full of damp."

"I've got little money Doctor, I'm out of work. My son is the only one earning."

"At the very least, man, she needs the right care. If not....." He spread his hands in an expressive gesture.

Henry's father held his head in his hands, suddenly looking an old man.

"How much do I owe, Doctor?" he said wearily.

"Pay me when you get work, Cabell." The doctor sighed, knowing he had little chance of ever getting his fee. "But your wife needs proper care and attention, away from this damp cottage."

He got up and shook both their hands, rammed on his stovepipe hat and was gone. Henry and his father looked at each other in silence for a while.

"Don't worry son, I'll think of something."

The woman from the cottage next door came in without knocking, removing a heavy cape. Another sustained bout of coughing came from the room above. They listened to the long racking sounds that ended in a muffled explosion of phlegm.

"That's a death rattle, mark my words." At least Mrs Morson had the decency to keep her voice low.

Henry's father clamped his jaw a little tighter and his lined face whitened a touch. "I'm going for a job."

Henry wished his father luck and, for the first time in his life, they shook hands. Henry Senior hooked his old cheesecutter hat onto the back of his head and pulled it low over his eyes. He nodded and bent out of the low door, too emotional to speak.

That evening the fate of Henry and his family's would be sealed.

Henry worked all day on the leather stall. Norwich hosted the market for the county of Norfolk and was the second most important centre of commerce after London. Flemish people, fleeing from persecution in the Low Countries, had settled in the area and brought with them cloth-making skills that had transformed the local economy. The abundance of cloth had led to other jobs such as cutting and sewing trousers, jackets and ladies clothing. Some of the skills were being used by an enterprising few to make articles from leather and a shoe making industry had begun to take root.

———

Saturday was market day. Drovers from far and wide brought their herds for sale at the cattle market, overlooked by the imposing Norman castle standing on a prominent knoll in the centre of the city. The fruit and vegetable marketplace was also in sight of the castle. For the last few years, the castle had been used as a makeshift prison when America refused to take any more transportations.

When Henry arrived home that evening his father was sitting in the only easy chair in the living room. His friend Abraham Carman lounged against the little table.

"Did you get that job?"

Henry's father shook his head, his lips a thin line across his worn face.

Their neighbour had left a rabbit stew which they ate in silence. Henry sat for a while with his mother who slept fitfully, her shallow breathing marked by an ominous rattle in her throat. He could hear Abraham talking in a low voice in the room below and eventually went down, to find his father peering out of the latticed windows into the gathering gloom.

"Go up to the top woods and check those snares I set, Henry."

Henry looked at his father in surprise, usually he wouldn't let anyone set rabbit snares but himself. When he got back his father told him to check on his mother. She was sleeping, her hair spread like wet straw over the white pillow.

Below, the men were talking in fierce whispers but Henry could still hear nearly all what was said. Abraham was having the most trouble in keeping his voice down.

"It's easy I tell you, I took the woman to Norwich myself. I've got the cart for the whole weekend, we load up and go straight to Ipswich. I know someone who will take the lot from us."

There was urgency in Abraham's voice that made Henry listen intently.

"You need the money for victuals and your wife's medicine. I need a hand with the heavy stuff. We do this and all your worries will be over. We'll need someone to keep the horses quiet."

"Not my son!" His father's voice came back loudly.

Henry went lightly down and opened the door. The two men looked up in surprise.

"What do you want me to do?"

"Not too much, Henry, and you'd be helping your father out of a pickle.

We just want you to hold the horses and keep them quiet while your father and me relieve an old dear of a few things she don't need."

Henry looked at his father who stood white faced, gripping the back of a wooden chair.

"I'll do it," he said shortly.

Nobody realised what a momentous decision it was. It would change all their lives, and all their deaths.

"When?"

"Tonight, it must be tonight,"

After telling father and son to meet him by the church at the end of the villageAbraham slipped into the cold night

"I knew Abraham was a bit of a rogue, but this....."

His Father shrugged his shoulders. "He calls it his part time job"

"And you, father?"

"I've helped him once before, he knows when I need money."

At the appointed hour they both put on heavy overcoats. Neither spoke. They took a track behind the village to the church, avoiding the path that would have taken them past the local alehouse.

The heavy cart with the two horses was concealed just off the country road in a small wood. Abraham stood by the lead horse softly stroking its long muzzle. With barely a word, the three swung into the cart. Henry sat in the back not knowing whether it was fear or excitement that was making his blood race. Every creak of the leather harness, every scrape of wheel on hard surface, was magnified in the still night air.

The journey seemed to take hours but at last Abraham reined the horses back.

"You sit here, Henry, we'll go and have a look at the old dear's place."

Tension gripped Henry's stomach and held it taut as a drum. Up to this moment he had been helping his father in a family crisis, now realisation hit him hard. Something touched him on the leg and he let out a small cry.

"It's only me," Abraham's voice came from the blackness to Henry's right, "Take the cart into the orchard and keep those horses quiet."

Over the next twenty minutes the cart got more and more full. Henry helped when they came with a heavy item of furniture. Despite his inbred fear of the law, Henry felt a strange thrill as the three of them laboured in the darkness. His father worked silently but Abraham gradually discarded caution.

At last Henry's father decided that no more would fit on the cart and they should go.

"One more, there's a big vase by the front door." Abraham staggered back to the house.

"He's drunk more than a bottle of wine," whispered Henry Senior, "I'd better get him."

Suddenly there was a shout from the house, followed quickly by another. A lantern was lit and the unmistakeable shrill of a watchman's whistle filled the air. Henry heard his father shouting.

"Go, Henry, go!"

He walked backwards through the orchard before turning and fleeing through the next field. The cottage behind him had become a maelstrom of noise and lights. People seemed to be everywhere, running behind and in front of the cottage.

He ran full pelt for fifteen minutes without once looking behind him until finally, exhausted, he sank into a clump of thick bushes. After catching his breath he made his way home avoiding the roads; it took almost three hours.

After changing into fresh clothes, he gathered as many of his meagre possessions as he could. Finally he went upstairs to see his mother. Silently he kissed her on the cheek before leaving the room. Pausing only to leave half of his money on the kitchen table, he melted into the darkness behind the house.

As he slipped out of the far side of the trees he discovered a plump rabbit clamped in a snare he had set earlier. He headed towards Norwich, and the only person who might be willing to help.

Morning came, wrapped in a cold mist, made more miserable by a damp drizzle that crept down the back of his collar like a serpent. Henry trudged on, a wretched figure of despair, trapped in misery. At last he came to the edge of Norwich where the London road and the road to Ipswich form a broad fork. In the grey light of morning Henry could just make out the twin turrets and pointed archway of St. Stephen's Gate. In the surrounding fields, patch after patch of spiders' nightly work veiled the wet grass. Dew laden webs thick upon the misty greenery like a light covering of snow.

In Calvert Street it was Robert Edge who noticed the muffled figure standing in the narrow passageway opposite.

"Bobby," he called to his son from the back room, "is that young Henry stamping his feet over there?"

"He's got a coat like that but it's hard to tell, he's too far back in the alley."

They both stared out at the shadowy figure silhouetted in the back entry. A few minutes later Bobby brought Henry through the front door.

"Why are you skulking in the shadows young Henry and what are you doing in Norwich on a Sunday?" Robert noticed the tears brimming on the edge of the boy's pale blue eyes. "You look perished lad, come and stand by the fire."

Robert Edge went into the back room, leaving Henry by the burning coals.

"Mother, young Henry is in the front room. I'm guessing his mother has died, she's been ill for a while. Make the lad a pot of soup, he's frozen through."

Mrs Edge, a plump woman, hurried through, "Is it your mother, Henry?" she asked the shivering figure by the fire. Henry kept his head down.

"Never mind lad, you can tell us about it later. Come through when you've got yourself warm. Bobby, help your friend with his overclothes."

Henry struggled with the buttons, his hands numb with cold. Fumbling inside his coat, he fished out the rabbit and presented it to Mrs Edge.

"For you," he said quietly.

It wasn't long before Henry was wolfing down the hot soup and bread. Almost as soon as he finished the food he laid his head in his arms and fell into asleep at the table.

The family left him there and gathered in the kitchen. Bobby related the story Henry had told him earlier. Robert Edge looked grim.

"Robbery's a bad affair, and this one sounds like a hanging business!"

"The boy did it for his parents, he can't be blamed," Mrs Edge said quietly.

"The law takes no notice of why a thing is done, only who does it. This is a hanging, mark my words."

"Then we have to help the boy," her voice was quietly determined.

"And get ourselves hanged too?"

The family talked in fierce whispers for some time. Finally Robert said, "Alright, but we only help him to get away to London, no more."

Chapter Four

wo men were to be transferred from another cell later that day to share the quarters occupied by Henry, his father, Abraham Carmen and the deaf mute. At the morning exercise period a man wearing a stovepipe hat came over the yard to sit with the four new prisoners. He spoke with a cultured voice.

"My name is John Euston, highway robber at your service." The man grinned easily, and leaned back against the wall. "Why are you in this edifice of sin?"

"Burglary." Henry Senior replied.

"More than forty shillings worth stolen?"

"That's about the size of it."

"Death by hanging then. Waiting for the King to serve the sweet dish of mercy?"

Henry's father nodded mutely.

"The King, working as he does through the myriad hands of many administrators, lawyers and sundry other people, seems to be an indifferent server. Sometimes mercy appears, sometimes it doesn't. There seems to be neither rhyme nor reason to those incarcerated, awaiting the King's pleasure."

"My son is strong, they'll take him to America."

"People are sentenced to transportation but nobody goes. Thus these scurvy gaols grown swollen with lice and felons."

"Nobody going to America?" said Henry Senior.

"They don't want our labour, tainted as it is by crime. No, they have a different sort of slave now, much cheaper to buy and cheaper to work."

"Who is cheaper than a man that has to work seven or fourteen years for his freedom"

"Negroes dear sir, Negroes from the continent of Africa."

"I've never heard of such a thing," Henry Senior snorted.

"I have, father," young Henry said quietly.

Smithy, disgruntled at not knowing what was being said, wandered off. Just then a long scream echoed round the enclosed yard. Henry Senior scrambled to his feet and looked around. "In heaven's name, what's that?"

"That sir, was a woman, if you favour a loose description of the female. There are women in this prison, held over there." He waved a grey handkerchief vaguely towards the far side of the yard.

"What's wrong? Why did she scream?"

"Possibly our dear turnkey Savage is extracting a payment of some kind. Do sit down, there is nothing you can do."

"Are there many women here?" Henry's father asked.

"Six or seven. They are creatures of the lowest kind; you'll hear more vile blasphemy from them than any soul would believe was possible.

"They mix with the men here then."

"No, their occupation of this outside space is at different times to us. However, our enterprising turnkeys do organise the occasional visit to the men's cells at night – for a price of course."

"God, this is a rum old place we've come to."

A ragged figure detached itself from a knot of prisoners by the wall and made its way across the courtyard. The man had a curious way of walking with his knees in front of his feet. Each step was a sort of slouching bend, so he proceeded in a series of slow springs across the uneven stones. At last he arrived by the four prisoners and stood surveying them keenly.

"Do sit down, Fuller, you're blocking out what little sky we can see. Come and meet our new cellmates." Euston said.

"Shut up you old shirtlifter," the ragged man said affably. Nevertheless, he squatted by the others and stretched out a hand.

"Fuller is the name, although sometimes it's Cunningham as it 'as a better ring."

"Fuller was apprehended at Castle Acre near Kings Lynn, having broken into a cart and depriving an honest tradesman of ribbons, lace and stockings as well as bread, pickles and cheese," Euston explained dryly.

"I was starving, I'd travelled from London and hadn't eaten for days.

When your stomach's churning and your innards aching you have to put something inside 'em. It don't matter to your belly how you fill it, but you must, even if it's with someone else's victuals!"

"Who's that over there?" Fuller pointed to a figure wandering the outer walls. The deaf mute, who they had named Smithy as he had indicated his trade was blacksmith to a local squire, had become more and more agitated since their arrival in the prison. During their hour of exercise he had taken to patrolling the walls staring at every flint with interest.

They watched as the ragged figure made his way amongst the other prisoners, seeming not to notice any of them, so intent was he on studying the sheer walls.

"Let him be, his ordinary life probably grinds him to powder. This prison must be just about the harshest grinder of all!" Young Henry said quietly.

Suddenly a shout from the far side made them all stand up.

"It's Smithy, he's climbing the wall like a bleedin' fly!" Abraham Carman yelled.

They lurched over to the wall, chains and fetters a discordant cacophony of dull clanks. Smithy had managed to climb about ten feet above the ground. Bloodied fingers gripped the sharp edges like talons; one toecap clinging to the rough flints while the other scrabbled for a minute hold. He inched himself up a fraction but it was clear he was doomed to fail.

Savage and two other turnkeys pushed their way through the cheering prisoners.

"Right, you scum, git back!" He waved his short stave in the faces of the front rank.

Soon a semicircle of space opened up around the three guards. Satisfied, Savage turned his attention to the desperate figure clamped to the flint wall.

"You thick headed clod, come down or I'll break your legs," he roared, and began banging his baton on the stones.

Henry tapped his father on the shoulder, raised a finger to his lips and nodded towards the lean to at the opposite end of the yard. His father understood immediately.

"Careful son," he whispered.

Checking there were no turnkeys watching, Henry made his way to the lean to. His metal capped boots against the cast iron drainpipe were impossible to muffle but his noisy ascent was drowned by the excited prisoners watching Smithy. On the sloping roof he stood up gingerly, heart thumping. The wall rising above the roofline of the lean-to seemed impassable. Sweat dripped from his chin as he checked the crowd cheering Smithy on the far side. His father was the only one looking in his direction. Without warning, his hobnailed boots slipped on the black roof and he slid down the tiles. It was impossible to halt on the shiny slates and he shot off the roof. The gutter slowed his fall but broke under his weight and he landed in a heap on the ground.

The next thing he knew he was being dragged away by his Father and Abe Carman. They didn't stop until they had hauled Henry back to their cell. Nobody seemed to have noticed as the yard was still agog at the deaf mute's attempt to climb the wall on the far side. Henry lay on the straw palliase still dazed by the fall. Abe Carmen examined him as if he was inspecting a bullock in the market place.

"Looks alright to me – no bones broken."

"Son, don't you try that again, you could have broken your neck!" His father wiped a trickle of blood from Henry's nose and helped him to a sitting position.

"I must get my hands on a long rope, it's the only way!" Henry whispered through swelling lips.

"You bleeding idiot, you'll get us all in trouble, then we'll have too much rope around our gullets!" Abe snarled.

Outside, the others were still cheering on Smithy. The filthy figure clung to the wall but his face streamed with tears as he whimpered like a dog. Savage, finding he was too short to score a direct hit on Smith, made a prisoner crouch down by the base of the wall. Using the man as a stepping-stone, he slashed at the figure above and managed to strike the mute's ankle who then promptly fell on the turnkey.

This raised a cheer from the onlookers but they quickly fell silent as the chief turnkey turned his fury on to the fallen figure. The fight finished abruptly when the turnkey smashed his baton over the back of John Smith's head. Quickly, the other turnkeys herded the subdued prisoners back to their cells.

As soon as they heard the heavy lock turned, Euston, the highway robber, pulled himself up to look through the bars.

"Your silent friend is getting a hell of a beating out there, now he's being chained up. God almighty, they've got more chains on him than a ship in harbour!"

"He'll be for the dungeons now. The next light he sees will be through the hangman's noose." Fuller spoke from the back of the cell.

"I bag his mattress," said Abraham.

Euston dropped from the bars, "I hope this doesn't mean they will cancel the visits later today. I'm counting on seeing my lawyer."

Friends, relations and lawyers were allowed a weekly visit. The new arrivals had not been released from their cell the previous week so this day was regarded as a special privilege for them.

Henry sat down on his straw mattress and held his swollen face in his hands. Henry's father put his arm around the boy's shoulder.

"Don't fret lad, they won't cancel the visits. People come from miles around. The lawyers won't put up with not earning their fees, you can be sure of that."

Euston noticed Henry's bloody nose but said nothing.

At one o'clock, the big gates by the drawbridge opened to allow visitors to flood across the hanging span, as it was known. Robert Edge surged forward with the crowd. It was the first time he had been in a prison. Mrs Edge had made him come with little parcels of food for Henry and his father.

All were made to line up to pay threepence each for the privilege of visiting. The gate turnkey lurked in the confines of a small room hung with leg irons and chains, unevenly spaced between faded posters proclaiming prison rules, rather in the manner of Christmas decorations. Only there was nothing festive in those human clamps, no goodwill in the cold chains. Robert Edge passed the turnkey who logged visitors in and out, inspecting each through the barred window of his cramped room. Soon he was forced to hold his nose as the stench of prison assaulted his nostrils. Stumbling out into the yard from the dark passage he took in the scene in front of him.

The compound was a noisy, depressing, disorderly babble of trade and litigation. A potman was selling beer to prisoners and visitors alike. Lawyers and litigants spoke through nosegays and gaolers jangled about with great bunches of keys on leather belts. It was a hotchpotch of despair and hope, a strange mixture of fetters and dreams of freedom.

"Mr Edge, Mr Edge!" Robert made his way through the babble to the ragged young man waving a dark neckerchief.

"My God, Henry – you are so gaunt! What has happened to your flesh?"

"No rabbit stews here, Mr Edge, no suet puddings either!"

"No, of course not lad. I'm sorry, it was the shock of seeing you."

"This is my father, Henry. I'm named after him."

"I'm sorry that we meet in this Godforsaken place, Mr Edge. My son shouldn't be here, he was only doing me a kindness."

"What's done is done, now Mrs Edge has given me instructions of the strictest kind to make sure that you and your father have these victuals." He unwrapped a thin cloth to reveal apples, plums and two large pies, and looked on dumbfounded as both men grabbed the fruit. The apples, including cores, were consumed in a flash. Even the stones in the plums were not thrown away, but were carefully stored in the cloth for a later treat.

"We will keep the pies for later, Abe will like a bite of these. Maybe we can even send a slice to Smithy in the dungeons," Henry Senior said.

"Have you heard if you're marked for transportation to America?"

"Not yet, but young Henry's sure to go."

Henry looked at his father and remembered the conversation with Euston, their cell companion.

"What did the paper say about us coming here?"

"You was front page, anyone would have thought you was the biggest vagabonds in the county. Don't worry lad, I know different."

"How is Bobby? Does he speak of me?"

"He remarks upon you every day. We miss you on the leather stall, even customers ask after you, lad."

"I didn't know how happy I was until I found myself in this filthy cesspit."

"I have a shilling here for you Henry, it's the last of your wages." Edge slid the coin over to Henry, looking around to see if there were any turnkeys nearby.

"Thanks Mr Edge, it will come in handy. Money is the only certain speaker in this place."

A potman selling beer interrupted them, a thick leather strap was looped over his shoulder to hold a metal bucket which was shaped to fit his hip. This left his hands free to dish out beer with a long handled ladle and to collect the money. "Homemade ale, a penny a mug!"

Both Henrys shook their heads. Robert Edge licked his lips.

A ragged figure detached itself from a group surrounding the potman and reeled sideways, having little control of his legs. It was Fuller, their cellmate, whose peculiar gait now had the added disadvantage of too much ale. Fuller spotted them and began his lolloping walk that took him to a point ten yards off his target into a clutch of people who seemed to be having a communal weep. Fuller collapsed them into a heap and a fight broke out.

Robert Edge pulled the two prisoners away from the fracas.

"Henry, it strikes me that you could do with earning a few coppers to pay for food in this bleak place. I'll bring in some leather and tools and you can make a few purses, like you used to."

"We can do a bit of trade every week through the west windows, I've seen the others do it," Henry said.

A turnkey came out of the door by the gate and rang a bell. He ignored the heap of men fighting in the dirt.

"I'll send young Bobby with the leather next week," Edge threw over his shoulder as he followed the trail of visitors through the door leading to the gate.

"He's in a hurry to go." Henry observed.

"Can't blame him, this place is a rare mix of stench of felony," his father muttered.

Others around them were engaged in tearful embraces and lingering goodbyes.

"We've got the pies to look forward to." They both brightened at the thought and went to find Abraham.

The pies were eked out to last the next two days. Abraham Carman managed to pass a slice to Smithy in the dungeons. Then it was back to the usual fare, a thin mixture of maize and oatmeal called 'stirabout' by the prisoners. It was dished out once a day.

Chapter Five

Weeks passed and the whole prison was waiting to hear who amongst them had been reprieved. Bets were placed daily on who would escape the hangman's noose.

The two Cabells, Carman and John Euston sat huddled by the east wall. It was a cold day so they had their grey blankets wrapped around their shoulders.

"My guts are aching for a bit of decent grub," Abraham said.

"We should hear soon about the King's mercy." Henry tried to keep his voice even.

"Waiting for news of a reprieve and lack of victuals both have a similar effect on your stomach." Euston looked at Henry's father who had been suffering from dysentery for the last two days. Henry Senior smiled weakly, his grey face scruffy with grizzled whiskers.

A boy of about twelve years ran past them and hid round the corner of a building, shortly followed by a man they knew as Sam. He had been in the Castle for almost two years and his clothes were not much more than rags. He always wore a hat shiny with grease.

The men watched him clunk past, looking this way and that, until he went out of sight.

"Sam Creasy," said John Euston, "lowest of the low. He's in for rape and robbery. I remember it well because I knew the woman he raped up by Wormegay. Now he's a Madge Cull, a Fluter."

"Madge Cull? Fluter?" Henry asked.

"He means the man's a shirtlifter," Abraham put in shortly.

"This prison, all prisons, are base levellers," Euston said with disgust.

"No segregation according to type here. Civil debtors with rapists, Boys with madge culls. These are common sewers of crime and disease."

A cry of fear and pain made the men look up. John Euston was first to realise the significance. "The boy!" he shouted.

Henry was on his feet in a moment and ran round the corner as fast as his fetters would allow.

"You foul bastard!" His fist cracked into Creasy's skull and the man dropped to his hands and knees like a sack of corn. Henry aimed a kick between the Creasy's legs before turning to the boy who was trying to pull up his trousers. Shaking and crying, the boy buckled his belt.

The other three came around the corner. Abraham Carman delivered a sharp kick to the man writhing in the dirt. Hauling on his collar, he dragged Creasy to the centre of the yard and flung him onto the hard surface.

"Shirtlifter!" he yelled, and kicked him again. Two turnkeys ran to the fallen man and grabbed him by the hair.

"Stand back there! Hold fast!" One held his baton up to stop the prisoners, who had quickly gathered round. The bell that signalled the end of the prisoner's time in the yard cut the excitement short. Savage, the Chief turnkey, was standing by the door as they shuffled in.

"That boy's not lodged with Sam Creasy is he?" growled Henry.

Savage barged him down the dark passage. "I decide where you scum are billeted, and don't forget it."

Carman helped Henry up and into the cell. The doors banged shut and the men slumped down in their straw mattresses.

"I'll do for that Savage before I'm finished, I swear to it," Carman grunted. "God, this leg's infected now!" He eased his filthy leggings out of the iron fetter.

Euston and Henry went over to look. Carman's ankle was raw and bleeding. Throughout prison leg irons were garlanded with cloth to ease flesh scrubbed raw by unforgiving bolts and sharp metal edges.

"Trouble is, the cloth around the irons gets scabby in this squalor," Euston said.

"When Mr Edge brings me leather I can make you a better collar for those irons. Leather is easier to keep clean and it won't wear away so quick." Henry said.

Henry began to unravel the cloth from the clamps around Carman's ankle. They were both engrossed in this task when the door was unlocked and a turnkey entered with an urn of warm gruel. Every man scrambled to get a helping of the thin soup.

"Why are we getting extra grub?" Fuller demanded, squinting through the black eye he had gained in the fight earlier.

"Its Governor Gwynne's idea, nothing to do with me." The man replaced the lid of the urn and dragged it out of the cell.

Euston looked thoughtfully at the turnkey before settling on his mattress. He did not join in the chatter about the about the reason for the unexpected meal.

Not long after, there was a commotion in the passage and the door was flung open again. Governor Gwynne, Savage and a turnkey came in. Another turnkey stood in the gloom of the corridor, shoulders wreathed in heavy chains.

"I have received news of your sentences," the governor announced. He unrolled a heavy parchment, the turnkey held a lantern by his face. All prisoners stood up.

"Henry Cabell, the younger, His Majesty King George has extended his royal mercy and you are to be transported to the American colonies for a term of seven years."

"Thank God and the King." Henry's father said softly.

"Amen to that," echoed Abraham Carman.

"And my father and Abraham?" Henry's voice was tight in his throat.

The Governor carefully rolled up the first parchment and handed it to the Chief turnkey.

"Henry Cabell and Abraham Carman, you are to be hung by the neck until dead in the City of Norwich on March 31st in the year of our Lord 1783. May the Lord have mercy upon your souls."

Henry and his father fell into each other's arms, tears streaming down their faces. "Don't cry father, it pains me so."

"My tears are for your life, son. Mine is done, finished."

Abraham Carman was shaking like a jelly and could not speak. He could barely stand up. Without warning he slumped forward and the two Cabells grabbed him. All three stood in a sobbing huddle lit by the yellow glow from the turnkey's lantern.

"Right, let's be having yer," Savage stepped forward to part the three men.

"Wait!" Governor Gwynne said angrily. "Let them bide awhile."

After a few minutes the Governor disentangled Henry from his father. Abraham Carman still could not control his legs, and his face was ashen. He had wet himself. The turnkey by the door brought in the chains. Carman and Henry Senior were swiftly festooned in iron.

As he was being led out of the cell, Henry's father called out, "Son, quick, over here."

Young Henry stepped forward only to be stopped by Savage.

"Let him pass, man," Governor Gwynne said sharply.

"Son, my jacket pocket – take the money. It's no more use to me and Abe," he whispered.

Henry shook his head but could not speak. The Governor fished out the small bundle from Henry Senior's pocket. He put the money in Henry's hand and closed his fist around it.

"Your father is right, Cabell, make use of your good fortune."

The prisoners watched as the Governor, turnkeys, and two condemned men set off in a slow procession. Euston emerged out of the gloom and led Henry to the back of the cell. "You knew the appeals were in, didn't you?" Henry whispered.

"Aye lad, I knew."

Chapter Six

It was Sunday morning and the girls were helping Mrs Choke with breakfast. Bessie crouched closely over the coals toasting bread, in imminent danger of roasting her own nose too. Mrs Choke hacked slices from a large loaf to add to the growing pile. She had a curious way of cutting the bread. Grasping the loaf to her chest as if it were the head of a recalcitrant boy, she sawed at it with a fearsome looking carving knife, working from the outside in. The result was always dangerous to her ample bosom as she was apt to cut through the fabric of her apron, a heavily starched garment extending from throat to knees.

"The master came home late last night. He'll be wanting a good solid breakfast after that fancy stuff down in London," she announced.

"What's he like, Mrs Choke?" Susannah had yet to meet the elusive master.

Mrs Choke looked carefully into the hall, satisfied, she closed the door and came back to the scrubbed table.

"He's a good man but is squashed under a mighty powerful thumb." Mrs Choke jerked her own thumb at the ceiling. "You probably didn't hear him come in last night because he comes in quiet as a dormouse and creeps up the stairs to his own bed."

Bessie was studiously engaged in roasting a sausage in front of the blazing fire, but the twin aims of glancing about and listening to the adjacent conversation only succeeded in lighting the sausage like a flare. Susannah extinguished it in an instant by plunging the blackened morsel into a handy glass of red wine.

"Perhaps he creeps upstairs because he don't want to wake the missus," Bessie said, slapping more butter onto toast.

"A cold marriage bed feed the fires of temptation, mark my words!" Mrs Choke said, folding her arms under her ample bosom and staring at the ceiling.

"Whatever can you mean, cook?" Bessie asked.

"Never mind, you're too young to know."

Suddenly the door opened and Mrs Choke plunged her hands into the sink and began vigorously scrubbing a saucepan. Looking up, Susannah saw a gaunt faced man peering at her over steel framed glasses. His sparse hair was neatly combed with a rigidly straight parting down one side. A prominent nose perched sharply over a thick black moustache.

"You must be Susannah, our new maid." His voice, in complete contrast to his appearance, was strong and beautifully modulated. Adjusting his glasses, he looked Susannah carefully up and down. "I'm sure you will be a great help in this household my dear."

Susannah was suddenly aware of her red hands and covered them with a dishcloth. Bessie thrust the toasting fork behind her and managed to stick another sausage into the fire where it immediately caught alight again.

"Breakfast will be ready at eight o'clock as usual, Mr Taylor." Mrs Choke wiped her hands on her starched apron and began chopping a large tomato.

"Very good, Mrs Choke." He raised his eyebrows at Bessie's efforts to rescue the sausage from the coals and smiled again at Susannah before leaving the kitchen.

"That was the master." Mrs Choke's whispered unnecessarily.

"Lovely voice," Susannah murmured.

The next day in the brooding darkness of the little church, Bessie and Susannah sat quietly watching the last of the congregation file out. Bessie coughed, the sound echoing from the wooden rafters above. Mrs Choke had dosed her with a liberal pint of tar water just before they had left for church. Tar water, recommended as a restorative against many ills, was a popular medicine. Bessie had been exuding strong vapours all through the service so their neighbours in the pew, a farmer and his wife, had crammed themselves in the end by the stained glass window.

The two girls left the church, blinking at the bright day. A dog approached, sniffing at Bessie as though she were a freshly painted fence.

"There's my brother." Susannah hurried over to the figure sitting on the low wall. "What are you doing here, Harry?"

"I've got a job as a parish watchman at Rockland St Mary."

Relief flooded through her slim frame. "You'll make a fine watchman, Harry."

"The Squire himself gave me the job. There's a one bed roomed cottage too, I'm to start tomorrow."

"I'm so pleased." She squeezed his hand and kissed him lightly on the cheek.

"Who is this young man?" Mr Taylor's deep voice made them both jump.

"This is my brother, sir."

Mr Taylor gave Harry a cursory glance up and down. "I'm glad you're happy, Susannah."

"Jebez, we have to discuss the church fund with the vicar." Mrs Taylor's voice came from the church gate. "There is no time to spend with the servants."

Mr Taylor raised his top hat, smiled at Susannah, and left without another word. Mrs Taylor strode off down the lane, stern faced and regal followed by her husband, a thin figure with white silk legs and a comprehensive cloak.

Harry and the two girls watched until they disappeared into the vicarage. "I can't stop Susannah. I've a deal of cleaning to do at the cottage. I just wanted you to know I won't be scrounging off you any more."

"You've helped me many a time Harry, I was glad to repay your kindnesses."

They arranged to meet at the same time and place two weeks later, and waved until he was out of sight. They hurried home to give the good news to Mrs Choke. The gardener's boy was there, cramming a sandwich the size of a doorstep into his mouth.

The cook gave Susannah a warm hug when she heard the news.

"He's got work, be thankful for that."

"He's the only family I've got left."

The gardener's boy stared owlishly at Susannah as a large tear rolled down her cheek. He stood before the flaring grate, hands crossed behind his back, palms towards the flames. After a moment or two, the dampness in his clothes was drawn out and steam began to rise in a cloud. Soon he was smoking so hard behind that Mrs Choke was obliged to drag him away from the fire, fearing he was alight.

Bessie hugged Susannah. "Don't worry, he'll write soon."

"He's not got many words."

The Castle was a strange mixture of fear and excitement on the eve of the executions. In Governor Gwynne's parlour, Chief Savage and two other turnkeys were listening to the Governor. Reverend Jackson and another man stood at the back.

"We have all performed this unpleasant task before, but it is necessary to ensure each knows what is expected. I don't want a repeat of our last hanging when the mob broke through the gates and took the bodies by force."

One of the turnkeys held up his hand. He was an older man with a turn in his eye.

"What about that Eckleston woman, the one who killed her two bastard children? The mob hung onto her legs, stretched her neck more than a yard I'd say."

"A slight exaggeration, nevertheless the point is well made. We must ensure the crowd is kept well back from the gates, which will of course be locked and chained."

Rev Jackson held up a tentative hand. "I shall visit the condemned to seek expressions of their guilt and repentance."

"There's nothing the crowd likes more than a dismal ditty," The turnkey grinned.

"Tis a speech of repentance, not a dismal ditty," the Reverend corrected him.

"There'll be a big crowd, probably thousands. They'll want to see 'em dance." Chief Savage's words were met by nods all round.

The Governor frowned, "It is not a music hall act Mr Savage. The reason we encourage the public to view the event is to reform those who see it, and deter those who might be tempted into crime and blasphemy."

"Amen," said the Reverend.

"It's a relief to have an experienced hangman, I expect you will be inspecting the prisoners today Mr Bowles."

"I weighed 'em up before this meeting. Only the scraggy mute will need a half sack of sand to pull him down. I'll strap it on his body at the back so the crowd can't see it."

"The law demands we give the bodies to the Royal College of Physicians to practice their medical arts upon. It also requires us to leave them hanging for a number of days as a solemn lesson to the citizens. However, we will leave only one felon swinging for the dubious delights of the people of Norwich – have you selected the one Mr Savage?"

"It'll be Cabell, Carman's too tall and the mute's too short for the iron bodice."

"If there is nothing else to discuss, I'll see you all here tomorrow at dawn."

Savage coughed, "Do I have permission to take the women to the men prisoners tonight? It'll take their minds off the hangings tomorrow forenoon.

"You may, but only to those with money to pay. We don't want another free-for-all."

"It'll be the usual split of the money, Governor?"

"Of course, bring my share to me tonight."

In the little house in Wagon and Horses Lane, Mrs Edge raked the fire and settled the cast iron kettle on top.

"Are you going to the hanging tomorrow, Robert?"

"I am." Robert was staring out of the window at the Castle, about three hundred yards away.

"I'm coming too," their son said quietly.

"Don't go, Bobby, it's a terrible thing to see people die, even if they are wicked."

"I'm going, Henry's dad dies tomorrow, its the least I can do."

"It wasn't long ago that boy lost his mother to consumption. He'll be alone in the world when they take his father," Mrs Edge's eyes misted over.

"Young Henry will do well in America, he can turn his hand to anything. They say many a fortune has been made in the new country." Robert knocked his pipe out on the fender.

"You had both better get your heads down early tonight. I'll make a parcel of food for young Henry, you might get a chance to pass it to him."

Henry glowered at the men by the barred window. They were laughing and playing a game of counters. The counters were made from different coloured bits of leather cut from the tongue of a pair of boots.

Fuller, one of the men transferred to the cell earlier, was collecting money from the third man. Another burst of laughter brought Henry to his feet. John Euston laid a hand on his arm.

"Let it be, Henry. They are excited about the women coming to the cell tonight. No disrespect is meant to your father."

"My father dies tomorrow, these bastards bray like asses."

"They feel the tension too, Henry, it's their way of getting over that fearsome prospect. Remember, all men in this filthy hole have faced the hangman at some time."

"Are the women brought in every time there's a hanging?"

"Aye, without fail. They'll rut like dogs 'till dawn."

"Are you not joining in?"

Euston eyed his young companion. "The whole spectacle is not to my taste, lad, anyway, I've seen these animals rut before, it gives me no pleasure."

They all jumped when the turnkey announced his arrival by banging his stave on the door. The yellow light of the turnkey's lantern led the Reverend Jackson into the gloom.

"Which of you is Henry Cabell the Younger?"

The others left Henry standing in front of the black robed minister.

"I've been praying with your father, Henry. He wants you to know that he faces the prospect of death with no fear in his heart."

Henry fell to his knees and the Reverend placed his hands on the boy's head.

"Your father truly has a strange calm about him this evening. He asks 'what is the greater hardship, to end life dancing on the rope of justice, or to live in squalor and poverty year after grinding year.'

Henry covered his face unable to hold back great racking sobs. The Reverend kneeled down and talked directly to the boy's cupped hands.

"Your father was most insistent I tell you to embrace a new life in the lands across the seas. For you, Henry, this is the beginning, not the end. God bless you, my son."

"Amen to that, Vicar." Euston's voice echoed eerily from the leaden shadows.

From the bridge by the gates facing Castle Hill a frenzied hammering began. Fuller cocked his ear towards the sound. "Gallows – they're putting up the gallows," he whispered.

All three looked over to Henry who sat squat legged with his hands over his ears. Euston had one arm round Henry's shoulders. Raising his other hand he placed a finger on his lips and shook his head. The others noisily restarted their game.

In the attic of the house of Jebez Taylor the two servant girls were looking out of the little window at the stars. From the lane the sound of a mare's metal shoes on the hard surface rang out in the still night, sounding like a ghostly blacksmith plying his trade in the darkness.

"Tom will be going to Norwich at first light, to see the hangings," Bessie said quietly.

Susannah shuddered and pulled her shawl tighter round her shoulders. "Those poor men," she whispered, "but they must be wicked."

A fresh breeze rippled through the Lime trees and filled the attic. Shutting the window against the sudden cold, the two girls got into bed and snuggled down.

As Bessie was blowing out the flickering tallow, a turnkey in Norwich prison was showing two women into the cell where young Henry Cabell crouched red eyed in the corner. The younger of the two, a woman in her early twenties, stood looking round with her hands on her hips.

"Right, which of you buggers is first?"

The three men by the window made a dive at her. The fetters each was wearing didn't help their lunge and she easily sidestepped the rush. They landed in a heap by the second woman. She was holding a candle up to her face, which had been smeared unevenly with white powder. She drew back her lips into a lop-sided grin; two teeth were missing from the front.

"Hold your horses lads, we've got all night." She leered seductively at the heap by her feet. Her face was lined and worn, her hair, streaked with grey, fizzled straight out as though she had just received an almighty shock.

The three men made another dive at the younger woman.

Two hours later, Liz Pulley gingerly eased herself to sit by Euston and Henry Cabell. Across the cell the other prisoners and the older woman were lying on three straw mattresses pushed together.

Fuller snored open mouthed, his trousers below his knees were caught up in ankle clamps. The light from the single candle licked eerily over his white legs. Another prisoner, resting on his back, with his head on the woman's lap, sucked on her long, pendulous breast sagging conveniently into his mouth.

The woman, sitting against the wall, was sound asleep while the third prisoner kneaded her other breast as if he was a baker making a country loaf.

"Your friend seems to have had her fill," Euston said, nodding towards the female prisoner.

"Aye, she knows what she's about. Madge has been a whore for over twenty years."

"And you?"

"I'm only training to be a trollop."

"You seem to have attained a high level of competence for a learner," Euston said sarcastically.

"Who's the young shaver by your side, John? Is he one of your dandy boys, a shirtlifter like yourself?" She spoke with rancour, as if making a general enquiry about his health.

Euston shook his head and a wry smile creased his face. "The lad is in no mood for such shenanigans; his father faces the gallows tomorrow forenoon."

"Ah, he'll be young Cabell then. I was sentenced at the same quarter sessions down at Thetford as him and his father."

Henry rolled over and faced the woman, disgust evident in his face. "No women came up from Thetford with us."

"Madge and me had the pleasure of an outside seat on the regular coach to Norwich. I reckon they didn't think the men would be safe to travel with the pair of us."

Henry turned away and buried his face in the loose straw.

"Miserable bugger," Liz muttered.

Chapter Seven

March 31st 1783 dawned on the City of Norwich. The first slanting rays of the sun picked out the tall gallows stretching from one side of the bridge to the other. The gates to the castle already locked and chained.

Castle Hill, as it crosses the deep moat-like fortifications of the ancient structure, becomes a bridge. It was on this bridge, just behind the gates, that the sturdy oak gallows stood. Two uprights were bolted into the sides of the gatehouses at the entrance to the castle. A heavy crossbeam spanned the width of the narrow bridge, three nooses hung stiffly from the crossbeam.

Down in the dungeons a gaoler made his way carefully down the stone steps to the cramped cell holding the three condemned men. His lantern threw fitful shadows on the wet walls. He never liked visiting 'the pits' as they were known. Today, tension tightened his throat so when he called out to the prisoners his voice squeaked like a young boy's. Nobody answered as he unlocked the door and peered into the dim room. Cursing, he shaded the lantern with one hand as the flame almost died; suddenly it flared again and revealed two men lying on a straw mattress at the back.

He banged his baton on the vaulted ceiling. The two men stirred and sat up, chains rattling heavily against flagstones. The flame fluttered again and the figure of the third prisoner loomed out of the darkness to his left. The turnkey tried to step back but his feet seemed to be glued to the floor.

"God Almighty!" He shrieked, his voice a high falsetto. Terror made him rip his feet from the stickiness on the flagstones and he leapt back to the door.

"God Almighty!" He said again and held his lantern to the figure on his left. John Smith hung stiffly from a hook in the wall. Deep cuts garlanded his neck, blood, congealed and darkened, ran down his rough shirt, his heavy boots stood neatly on a small ledge. The blood had stained his feet a black red. Only his toes touched the cold stone of the cell floor and were stuck to the huge pool of congealed blood that had trapped the gaoler moments earlier.

Abraham stared at the figure. "Smithy's done himself in." His breath came in short gasps and he vomited against the wall.

Henry Senior crouched on all fours, blinking at the lifeless figure swaying on the metal hook. He pulled himself upright and pointed at the petrified turnkey. "Get help, man."

The turnkey backed out of the door and scrambled up the steep steps. The door swung open, the huge key still in the lock. Henry Senior made a move to the open door but was pulled up short by the chain holding his ankle manacles together.

Within moments, the turnkey returned, accompanied by Governor Gwynne, Chief Savage and Reverend Jackson. Only Savage approached the body, illuminating it with his lantern as he did so.

"He's slashed his throat, looks like he's almost cut out his Adam's apple."

"What did he use?" The Governor croaked.

Savage lifted up Smith's hand with his baton. Something glinted in his fist.

"The bugger's sharpened the edge of his spoon, looks like." Savage let the hand fall back. The spoon dropped to the ground and stuck upright in the sticky mess.

"How does he remain standing?" whispered Reverend Jackson, almost as white as the corpse.

Savage prodded the body with his baton so that it swung away.

"He's stuck a wall hook through the back of his collar."

"Just like a beast in the slaughterhouse." Reverend Jackson fell to his knees and began to pray. Governor Gwynne pushed him towards the body.

"Help Chief Savage get that thing off the wall and into a coffin."

Savage turned to Cabell and Carman and snarled, "You two, get over here and lend a hand."

Carman started forward but Henry Cabell Senior held him back.

"You get no help from us," he stated flatly.

Savage grabbed Cabell and raised his baton. "Control yourself Savage," Governor Gwynne shouted, "These men die today, is that not enough?"

In the little house in Wagon & Horses Lane, Robert Edge stood in front of his wife, flicking hairs from his coat.

"Young Henry's father hangs today. It's only right I dress in my Sunday best."

Mrs Edge gave Bobby a large apple, two thick slices of bread and a hunk of cheese wrapped in a thin white cloth. "Give these to young Henry if you see him."

"We won't get anywhere near him Mother. Nobody gets near the Castle on hanging days."

Father and son went down the lane towards the Maid's Head Hotel and turned right, passing by the gates to the Cathedral. As they went through the area known as Tombland, a solemn peal of four bells rang out from the Cathedral and was repeated over and over again.

They walked in silence towards the great castle that rose before them, dominating the whole city. Already a steady stream of people was making their way to the entrance by Castle Hill where the scaffold stood. From all quarters solitary bells rang out, orchestrated by a mournful peal from the cathedral.

A few people were setting up stalls of fruit and cakes by the outer walls of the Norman Castle. They were, in the main, traders from the market place.

At the corn chandler's on Castle Meadow, a permanent veil of dust floated about, seeking somewhere to settle. A young assistant, keeping one eye on passing trade, hunted around for the dust to alight so he could send it off again, swirling on to some other ledge.

By mid morning, the hostelries were doing a roaring trade. The early crowd was merry, supping ale and speculating on the day's entertainment. The narrow streets were crowded with walkers and wagons. Full stagecoaches groaned up the hill from the River Wensum. Outside, passengers hung on boards at the back or sat by the driver.

In the area below Castle Hill normally used for the weekly cattle market, the crowd was gathering, jostling for the best view of the gallows.

Already pamphleteers were selling broadsheets with sketches of the condemned criminals. The sketches bore little resemblance to the actual felons.

One broadsheet depicting Carman and Cabell went into lurid details of their crime against 'the widow Hambling'. Each man, it seemed, had favoured the printer with a last minute confession.

The boy hawking the second broadsheet – the main drawing showing John Smith squeezing the throat of his victim – had few customers. Word had leaked that he had cheated the hangman. The absence of the deaf mute from his own funeral party was cramping the boy's sales, until he changed his flysheet to 'The man who wasn't there!'

A clergyman was standing on a box, praying to the Lord and urging the crowd to be generous of spirit and forgive the felons so that they might be received into the Kingdom of Heaven. His curate was busy in the throng, dunning donations from unsuspecting watchers.

As noon approached, the crowds became tighter. Farmers and fruit sellers, ostlers and haberdashers stood side by side, vying for space with drunks and drapers, washerwomen and whores.

Here and there self-appointed rabble-rousers inflamed those that would listen with dire warnings of deaths and disease caused by criminals, filth and degradation.

The mob, full of gin, was becoming raucous, baying for justice and revenge against the felons. Some were calling for protection against the curse of typhoid being passed on by prisoners to honest citizens.

A buzz of excitement ran through the crowd as officials began gathering on the Castle mound. Local dignitaries and Members of Parliament were provided with a cart by the entrance so that they might observe the spectacle of death by hanging, separate from the heaving hordes outside the gate.

Squire Custance stood between Jacob Preston, M.P. for Norfolk and Sir Harbord Harbord who had a pair of horse pistols stuck in his belt.

Stretching to better see the mass of voyeurs, the squire held a handkerchief scented with lavender to his face.

"There will be more pockets picked and sundry crimes committed in this mob today than we deal with on the bench in a whole year, I'll warrant" he shouted at Jacob Preston.

The M.P. nodded sadly. "Aye, felons regard today as an opportunity for trade not as a deterrent to wickedness" he bawled back.

Suddenly there was a great crescendo of peals from the churches around. At fifteen minutes to noon the peals ended. The crowds fell silent and the great double oak doors to the castle opened.

The throng of bodies crammed closer by the gallows in the shadowland of impending death. Children were hoisted onto parents' shoulders for a better view, pamphleteers and prostitutes continued to hawk their wares in the crushing crowd.

A strange procession emerged from the prison. At the head was Governor Gwynne, closely followed by two turnkeys, each holding a chain attached to the waist of the condemned men.

An iron fiddle secured Henry Cabell and Abraham Carman. This curious contraption encircled their necks and stretched out in front where it was bolted to include the wrists, making them look as if they were praying. Reverend Jackson walked between the two men; bringing up the rear was Chief Savage and two more turnkeys.

The whole party turned left out of the prison and slowly walked in a macabre march to the beat of a lone drummer standing by the gallows. They paraded right around the Castle Keep, causing a ripple of excitement to surge through the seething masses outside the castle grounds as the procession passed by.

It took ten minutes to circle the Castle and arrive back at the bridge leading to the gallows. Here the iron fiddles were removed and the prisoners arms tied behind their backs. The Governor, Reverend Jackson, Henry Cabell, Abraham Carman and Chief Savage walked across the bridge to the heavy cart drawn up under the gallows.

The crowd by the gate fell back as the hooded hangman emerged from the gatehouse and climbed onto the cart.

He was at pains to appear professional in his duties. Slowly, like a circus performer before an attentive audience, he took down the spare noose, originally intended for Smith, and flung it between the coffins stored on the cart. He went from one prisoner to the other sizing up each man carefully, sometimes standing in deep contemplation with his chin on his knuckles or gazing thoughtfully with hands on hips. A rumour went round that he was a cattle buyer and used the same procedures to assess cows and sheep.

"It's a wonder he doesn't prise open their mouths to inspect their teeth" Squire Custance whispered.

The hangman adjusted the crude apparatus to accommodate each man. In the keep male prisoners had been compelled to view the hangings. Every barred opening was filled with fearful eyes, fascinated and repelled by the gruesome spectacle.

Henry Cabell the younger stood with his back to the wall, eyes shut tight, fists clenched.

In the crowd Bobby Edge could not see beyond a tall man standing in front, so his father relayed the events as they unfolded.

"The Scragger's making a right meal of it Bobby," he said to his white-faced son.

"God in Heaven!" Bobby said, "I wonder what it's like to be hung?"

The tall man turned round "What's it like? It's to piss when you can't whistle lad!" He laughed at his own joke. It was a nervous laugh.

Ceremoniously, the hangman placed the heavy nooses around the prisoners' necks and adjusted them daintily as if arranging necklaces.

Stepping up between the two men Reverend Jackson addressed the crowds.

"This scaffold, this altar of sin, stands before you as a warning against the quagmire of crime that sucks both victim and felon into evil. Give ear to the great bells of this Cathedral City that toll to tell all who listen to keep to the path of righteousness. These two creatures strayed from that path and committed evil acts against their fellow men. Today they pay the penalty and prepare to meet their maker with the mark of the rope upon their throats."

Carman was in a state of dreadful agitation shaking like a leaf.

"For God's sake Reverend, get a move on," Cabell whispered hoarsely from the side of his mouth.

Reverend Jackson glanced at the two men; one bristle chinned and staring grimly ahead, the other trembling violently, sweat running in rivulets down his face.

"May the Lord bless their souls and forgive their sins" he almost shouted.

He stepped down from the coffins then leaned forward and touched Carman's leg, who shied away like a frightened foal. "Your confession, man" he whispered urgently.

Carmen cleared his throat with a nervous cough.

"Purge me with hyssop and I shall be clean,
Wash me and I shall be whiter than snow.
Hide thy face from my sins. Amen."

Carman blurted out the words, spittle flying from his lips. It was all he could remember from psalm 51, known as the hanging psalm, which the Reverend Jackson had taught him.

"Cabell, your turn, man."

Henry Cabell took a deep breath and swallowed hard.

"I'm not sorry to leave this hellhole of a prison, with filthy indignities heaped upon men in the name of justice. Starved of victuals and belly aching from raw hunger, poverty and punishment have been our companions. I am sorry I done wrong and I ask forgiveness of God in Heaven."

The crowd was silent on hearing these words; several men near the front began to weep like children.

Without warning, the hangman swept Carman off the side of the cart. The crossbeam was positioned about two feet ahead of the cart and for a moment he hung there. Then he began a desperate dance, a silent, jerking marionette. A dark brown stain spread from his crotch and soiled his rough leggings.

A second or two later, Henry Cabell followed to dance his deadly hornpipe; eyes bulging and face purpled, the rope biting savagely at his windpipe. His body spun like a top, first one way then the other.

A great shout went up from the crowd and many turned their faces from the awful scene. Others stared in fascinated horror.

In the keep, as the crowd's first roar of fear and terror subsided, Henry Cabell the younger put his head back and howled his anguish to the leaden skies. The sound echoed around the tall walls. Elizabeth Pulley, in the women's cells across the yard, shivered.

"That's what I heard at Thetford Assizes when we were sentenced." She pulled a grubby shawl tighter around her shoulders, "the exact same cry, I swear."

Two hours later Governor Gwynne and Squire Custance looked past the gallows at the dwindling crowd. A few morbid souls were pressed against the gate gazing up at the bodies. A cold wind wound up Castle Hill, causing both corpses to sway in fatal choreography.

"It's time you got those men down, Governor."

"Only Carman's coming down, then he's off to hell in a handcart."

Seeing the Squire's startled look the Governor smiled uneasily. "I mean his body is to go to the College of Physicians for dissection."

"And Cabell – what about him?"

"He swings in a gibbet, as a reminder of the wages of sin. I usually leave 'em up for about a week."

Later, as the sun crept lower in the sky, Robert Edge and his son stared at the turnkeys strapping the body of Henry Cabell in the cast iron gibbet.

"It's time we went home, son. This has been a sad day all round."

In the prison, young Henry Cabell was to refuse to come out of his cell during the whole of the month of April. The only person he would talk to was Euston, the thin highway robber, himself awaiting appeal against his own sentence of death.

Chapter Eight

Winter had begun to introduce itself slowly and the iron hand of a deep frost gripped the ground as Susannah and Bessie made their way to church. Bessie was a striking caricature of fashion that had finished a full twelve months before. On her head she wore a wide brimmed hat with a veil obscuring her face, the kind people usually wore at funerals.

"Only four weeks to Christmas, Bessie, and then just days to 1784. It's been hard, I never thought I'd last many weeks at the house when the missus took against me."

"She still watches you like a hawk," Bessie replied, "She don't like anyone with a smile on their clock."

"Mrs Choke reckons her purse is too full and her eyes too green."

"Let's not fill our heads with old vinegar face – we have an outing to look forward to today."

Susannah's brother had promised to show them round Rockland St Mary. They were to meet him and his friend Sam Rush after church. Susannah had met her brother once or twice since he had got the job as parish watchman at Rockland, but she had never been there, nor had she met his friend Sam, the watchman for her own village.

The service passed slowly for the two girls. The vicar railed and cajoled the hapless congregation until he finally released them from the dusty church, suitably cleansed of the last seven days of sins.

Bessie, for a change, was the first to tumble out of the church into an afternoon of unexpected sunshine warming the earth, throwing off the huddling coat of frost.

Harry was by the lynch gate waiting for them. A little further down the road Sam Rush stood by a pony and trap he had borrowed. Sam was an inch or two short of middle size but he had a warm smile and the girls liked him immediately.

"Sam's been a watchman for three years and has helped me get to know the ins and outs of the job," Harry told Susannah.

"Parish watchmen have to stick together, you never know when you'll need a bit of help," Sam grinned.

Suddenly Mr Taylor appeared, as if from nowhere. "Good day to you Susannah, is this your young man?"

Susannah blushed deeply. "You've met my brother before, sir, and this is his friend."

Mr Taylor looked keenly around the little group before raising his hat an inch or two. "I trust you will not be late back Susannah."

Before she could reply they were interrupted by a commotion from the other side of the street. A small man, much wizened about the face, and wearing a hat several sizes too large, lurched out of the Woolsack Inn and set off at an angle of forty five degrees to the line of the thoroughfare. His path took him to the church gate where the sight of the vicar brought him to an unsteady halt.

"Drunk again, Ebeneezer Groom." The cleric said sternly.

"Me too, vicar!" The man roared and launched himself down the street once more.

When Susannah turned to speak to Mr Taylor he had gone. She caught sight of him on the far side of the crowd of worshippers spilling from the church. He was in the firm grip of his wife who was staring over her shoulder at Susannah.

They set off for Rockland St Mary with Susannah glancing anxiously behind.

"She don't like me, not one little bit," she declared.

Bessie squeezed her hand. "Let's not worry about old miseryguts, we should enjoy our day off."

"Bessie's right sis, I've got a feeling nothing's going to change that woman. She's got a face like a wet week."

"Tell us about your job, Sam," Susannah said, forcing a weak smile.

"Every night I walk around the village listening for villains. Checking doors and windows, especially places like the blacksmiths and saddlers. The inns are on my list too. If the Squire asks me to, I go up to the woods to look for poachers. Old Mrs Borders at the manor house is unnaturally nervous so I always give her door a rattle and enquire through the shutters how she is keeping."

"Sam has a few chicken and geese too," Harry called over his shoulder.

"Aye, we need something to pay regular like. I want to be a thief taker full time – they rake in a fair few bob. A thief taker goes wherever a decent crime is occasioned and keeps at it until the felon is taken. When he's committed the thief taker collects a handsome reward."

They made good time. Harry made smart use of his tickler and soon the horse was sweating and flecked with foam. Harry's cottage was in a row of four. It was a 'one up, one down'. Before long, the girls were scrubbing and cleaning the place from top to bottom.

It didn't take long as Harry's possessions were on the sparse side. Upstairs he had inherited a bed and a chest of drawers. Two chairs, a square topped table and an elderly chaise lounge overfilled the ground floor room.

As a reward for their efforts Harry served them all lemonade in assorted receptacles. Bessie refused to remove her veil and delicately drank lemonade through it.

Harry insisted on showing them the tools of his trade. He had been supplied with a heavy cape for cold nights, a whistle and a wooden baton. He explained that he received extra pay if he apprehended a felon. The amount varied according to the severity of the crime.

For their part, the girls gave vivid descriptions of the vinegary Mrs Taylor and the downtrodden Master. Bessie gave a colourful account of how she had heard Mrs Taylor accusing her husband of spending money on 'trollops'.

"I don't think he goes with such women, he's too much of a gentleman," Susannah declared, "and I don't think she should pick on us so much. We work hard all day. If I could get another position I'd go like a shot."

"Oh you wouldn't, would you?" Bessie looked crestfallen.

"Like a shot."

In no time at all they had to make their way back. Early winter lay cold and sullen upon the earth. The warming effect of the afternoon sunshine had disappeared and the ground was once again rock hard, but the pony made little of the conditions and they arrived in good time. Sam promised to let the girls know when he could borrow the rig again and they all agreed to repeat the outing as soon as convenient.

The girls waved until Sam and Harry were out of sight. As the two girls passed the front door it opened and the master beckoned them enter.

"Jebez!" Mrs Taylor appeared at the top of the stairs, "what is going on?"

They all jumped at the angry words, Bessie lost her hat, then a shoe in the confusion.

"Merely a little humour my dear," Jebez Taylor answered.

"You cannot invite servants into the front hall!" Mrs Taylor stormed down the stairs and brushed him aside.

Bessie had lost her other shoe and was scrabbling about on the floor. Mrs Taylor pushed Susannah down the hall. "Help Cook with the tea."

Impatiently she turned to Bessie who was on her hands and knees, shoeless and with her hat on back to front. "Stupid girl, you look ridiculous, get another bucket of coal for the front parlour this instant!"

Bessie began to cry and proceeded down the hall on all fours. Mr Taylor squeezed Susannah's hand in passing as if to apologise for his wife's behaviour. Susannah got to the kitchen door and held it open, enabling Bessie to shuffle in on hands and knees, tears dripping on the pantiled floor.

The row had woken Mrs Choke, who had been dozing in a chair by the kitchen range. They helped Bessie up to sit at the table, both stockings holed at the knees.

"I'll get you a nice cup of tea, my girl," Mrs Choke glared at the hall door as she put the kettle on the low coals.

Even when the bedroom door slammed shut they could still hear Mrs Taylor's voice screaming at her husband.

That evening Jebez Taylor set off to London. He was to be away for two weeks. Susannah brought out a portmanteau and met him on the path. He drew her into the shade of a large laurel bush.

"My dear, I am sorry my little pantomime got you into trouble," he briefly pressed her hand to his lips.

"Please, Sir," Susannah pulled her hand away in embarrassment, "there's no need."

"Nevertheless," he inclined his head and walked away to the waiting cart.

Neither of them noticed Mrs Taylor glaring out from the net curtains by the front parlour window.

The next morning Bessie scuttled into the kitchen looking worried, "Missus wants you right away, Susannah, she's looking awfully fierce."

Susannah closed the parlour door behind her. Mrs Taylor sat behind her husband's large mahogany desk. Her eyes burned like coals, and her lips turned down at the corners.

"You wanted me, Missus?"

"No, I don't want you, Jezebel, I'll have no trollops in my house, get your things and go!" she shouted.

"What have I done? I've nowhere to go to!" The colour drained from Susannah's face.

"I've seen you, with my husband, I know what's going on!" Mrs Taylor grabbed Susannah by the hair and pushed her out into the hall.

"Don't you dare set foot in my house again, you filthy hussy. Get out, get out, get out!"

For the next few minutes the house was in chaos. Susannah sobbing and near to fainting, with Bessie bawling in sympathy and Mrs Choke trying to restore some calm.

"What's happened, girl, what's the Missus saying?"

"She said I was a trollop," wailed Susannah.

"Leave her to me, I'll see to it," Mrs Choke adjusted her white cap and straightened her large pinafore. She marched out of the kitchen and rapped sharply on the parlour door. Without waiting for a reply she went in and shut the door behind her.

Five minutes later she was back in the kitchen where Susannah and Bessie were clutched together, still weeping.

"It's no good, girl, she's got it into her head there's something going on with you and the Master."

"There's nothing going on, Mrs Choke, I'm a good girl!"

"It in't no use, my lovely, once an idea settles in her noggin there's no shifting it."

"She had no call to say I'm bad."

"Rhyme and reason have no place in her head when her anger is up. We have to get you fixed up while her temper goes off the boil."

Bessie began to wail even louder but Mrs Choke sent her upstairs to pack Susannah's chest. The gardener's boy was despatched to fetch Sam.

Susannah remained in the kitchen white faced while Bessie gathered her meagre possessions together. Mrs Choke and Bessie helped Susannah down the path to Sam at the gate.

"Take her to her brother's place. He can put her up until things can be sorted out," Mrs Choke gave Susannah a hug, "I'll have another try when she's calmed down. I wish the Master was here, he'd talk sense into her."

But next morning an even bigger blow was to fall. Mrs Taylor sent for Sam. "That girl has stolen from this house. You must fetch these items and bring them back." She handed him a list.

"Are you sure there's no mistake? There's a fair amount on this list."

"Don't be impertinent."

"I took her from the house myself, she had only a small box."

"Do your job. You are the Parish Watchman I believe."

Sighing, Sam folded the piece of paper and left.

At Harry's cottage, Sam picked his way heavily up the little path, knocked and entered. Susannah was sitting on her hope chest staring out of the window, her eyes red rimmed.

"How is she bearing up?" said Sam.

"She hasn't said a word since you brought her here last night." Said Harry.

"I'm here on business, Harry. I've got to look in her hope chest. Mrs Taylor reckons she's pinched a deal of stuff."

At this, Susannah began to weep bitterly, shoulders shaking with every sob. They got her onto the chaise lounge and Sam opened the little chest. From the bottom he fished out a bundle and laid the items it contained onto the table.

"One pair of sheets, one silk cloak, linen gown, two handkerchiefs, two silver spoons; exactly as this list given to me by Mrs Taylor!" Sam looked sadly at Susannah. "Are these yours?"

Blankly, Susannah stared at the articles, shaking her head from side to side.

"You are a very stupid girl," he said harshly.

The next morning, the magistrate, a gaunt man, stared at Susannah over a pince nez perched precariously on a sharp nose.

"Miss Holmes, the list from your employer matches exactly with the items found in your possession. What explanation do you give?"

"I don't know how they got there, that's the God's truth. Please sir, I'm not a thief."

"Do you think someone put them in your box? Another servant perhaps?"

"No, Sir," Susannah whispered.

The magistrate took off his glasses and placed them carefully on the ledge that lay before him.

"Susannah Holmes, I commit you to appear at the next Quarter Sessions at Thetford. In the meantime you will be held at Norwich Castle, take her away."

A low wail broke from Bessie at the back of the room. Harry put his arm around her and helped her out into the weak sunshine. The Squire and Vicar watched as Sam put Susannah in the same pony and trap in which they had enjoyed an outing the previous day.

"I expect she took the stuff to get back at Mrs Taylor when she was dismissed."

"More likely to make money, Vicar." The magistrate sighed.

Chapter Nine

John Simpson looked around the buildings hunched together inside the walls of Norwich Castle.

He was finding it hard to get used to the miserable air of decay, the makeshift windows barred and shuttered, every surface covered with a thick coat of dust. Unlocking the door to the first building he held his breath against the flush of fetid air that was sure to rush out.

Usually his wife gave him a patch of linen steeped in bluebells to counteract the smell, but today he had forgotten it.

He stood just inside the dark room, blinking his eyes in the gloom. A figure on a filthy mattress sat up still wrapped in the heavy prison blanket.

"Can't a body get a bit of bleeding kip in this pox ridden place?" the woman demanded, rubbing her eyes.

"If there's any pox here, Liz, you brought it in yourself," he answered.

"Oh, it's you, Mr Simpson. I thought it was that bastard Savage."

She stood up, stretched, and two full breasts fell out of her open blouse, she tucked them back, taking her time.

"Here," he said, "I've some cream for the young girl you said was plagued by infection."

She unwrapped the wax paper and sniffed the concoction. "You sure you want nothing for this, I can get my tits out if you want?"

"No, no, there's no need," he held up his hands in alarm as she began unbuttoning her blouse.

"You're a toff, no mistake."

"Is there enough?"

"Aye, young Mary's fanny is only small."

He stopped with his hand on the door, "You're not letting that girl go with men!"

"It's not a man, it's the bastard Savage."

"For God's sake, the girl's barely thirteen."

Liz Pulley looked up, suddenly serious. "A sore fanny's a small price to pay for a full belly in this rat hole."

He went out, breathing deeply in the morning air. Slowly he made his way across the yard to the men's side. For him, early morning was the best time of the day. There was still a freshness about, unspoilt by the stench of unwashed bodies, nor filled with the profanities of tough and frightened felons.

He went to the cell that housed Henry Cabell and four others. Cabell had been a handful ever since his father had been hung eight months earlier. In the short time Simpson had been a turnkey, Cabell had been incarcerated twice in the dungeons, wreathed in body chains, the fate of those who fought or fell foul of the rules.

Simpson had been trying to divert Cabell's aggression to more constructive purposes. He was a natural leader and the authorities needed someone in each cell to keep order. A turnkey's job was almost impossible if the men were constantly fighting amongst themselves and dangerous if the belligerence was directed at them.

It helped that what little money Cabell possessed when he first came in had gone. Necessity had forced him to make articles for a man who had once employed him on Norwich marketplace. Young Henry was a good worker and skilled in leatherwork, and the weekly contact with the stallholder Edge and his son was helping Cabell get over the sight of his father struggling on the gallows. He was a tough young man but liable to lose his temper if crossed, in consequence other felons treated him warily.

Simpson banged on the cell door before unlocking it. The cramped room was reasonably neat, each man had his own bed space and personal possessions were tucked under the mattress.

Cabell had the most favoured spot, hemmed in at the back by the window.

"Line your men up for the morning wash, Cabell. Grub will be here shortly."

Henry Cabell nodded curtly and rinsed his face and hands in the cold water. He flicked the surplus liquid from his hands and dried his face by giving it a cursory rub with his sleeve.

"Let's have a look at that cut on your cheek, Cabell."

With his baton under Henry's chin, Simpson turned the boy's head so that he could see the wound. It had been inflicted in a fight two days earlier and was infected.

"Try this," he reached in his pocket and produced a little twist of wax paper. "This is made from the juice of house leek mixed with the best milk cream. My wife swears by it for cuts and scratches."

"I'm obliged, Mr Simpson, but there's little chance of dodging infection in this place."

John Simpson watched him apply some of the lotion to his cheek and carefully store the rest in his pocket.

Simpson smiled to himself. Every scrap of cloth, paper or food was scrupulously saved. Nobody was in fortune's favour in this place.

His wife was a herbalist and people came from miles around to buy her preparations. Furze blossom potion for high temperatures, elderflower leaves for scrapes, angelica – a remedy for inflammation, colts foot for coughs, the list was endless. He had started to bring the residue of old concoctions into the prison when his wife wanted the jars for new medicines. He knew prisoners wouldn't mind old potions as long as they were free.

Fuller, whose mattress was next to Euston's, scratched his head feverishly.

"Fleas again, Fuller?" demanded Euston.

"The little blighters seem to favour a full head of hair."

"Hold you head in the water bucket a minute or two – after everybody's had use of it," Henry Cabell said gruffly.

John Simpson went out into the corridor and locked the cell door, to be met by Chief Savage.

"All's well on your watch?"

"It is, young Cabell's taken charge in there," he jerked his thumb back down the passage.

"Cocky bastard," Savage answered, striking the barred window as he went past as a reminder to all that he was there.

Simpson was a tall meagre man of middling years, lean of face and movement. He had a pair of bristling eyebrows, black and bushy that would have kept rain from his face in the event of a light shower. His daughter, a girl of fifteen years, had told him of the post at the castle. She was domestic servant to Savage, the Chief turnkey, and had heard him speak of it.

He'd been glad of the job, having been out of work for nearly a year after leaving the army. Only the pennies his wife earned from her medicines and his daughter's wages had kept them in food.

He had almost quit during those first few days at the prison. His stomach heaved when he was shown the dungeons where the air was foul and floors awash with sewage. Conditions in the cells were better but still grim. All were overcrowded and filthy, disease and despair common companions to many felons.

"Don't start feeling sorry for any cove in here!" Savage had snapped when he caught sight of John Simpson's disgusted looks.

"These scum will have the teeth out of your head and the coat off your back if they'd profit by it. They can earn money if they've a mind to! Most whine and lay around like dogs. If they rouse themselves it's to fight and squabble, usually over some minor grievance, likely as not imagined. If they've a coin in their pockets it will go to the potman when he brings in the beer – they'll not buy victuals! All kinds of villains end up in here, highwaymen and haberdashers, cowmen with coiners, we make no distinction! All are treated the same! Those that can earn we don't discourage. For every shilling they get, make sure you take three pence. Two pence to the Governor with half a pence each for you and me!" He grinned. "I can't say fairer than that!"

John Simpson was to learn that this was one prison rule that the chief turnkey was most particular about keeping.

In the lean-to reserved for female prisoners conditions were generally better, but he had been shocked by the lewd behaviour and profanities of the women. The worst was Elizabeth Pulley, a young woman of twenty-two years who swore like a King's trooper, a curse coming with every other word.

That first day she had invited Simpson to 'come and feel my fanny – it won't cost you a farthing," he had pushed her away with the end of his baton. Her raucous laughter had echoed in his ears for minutes after he left the cell she shared with three other prisoners.

The problems had mounted when the Governor was forced to allow female and male prisoners the same exercise time each day. Overcrowding had meant that there were not enough turnkeys to supervise two periods of exercise and the mixture of sexes in the yard had led to difficulties in keeping order. The men in particular were more likely to break into violence if they had a female audience. The women were generally less trouble although one or two would usually try to augment their income one way or another in the company of the men.

John Simpson was the turnkey on duty at the gate when Sam brought Susannah Holmes to Norwich Castle. Briefly he read the charges on the magistrate's paperwork.

He looked over the top of the stiff document at the girl. She had a handkerchief clamped to her mouth but could not stop sobbing.

"Anything known?"

"Nothing known."

He nodded, knowing this meant a first offender. A second turnkey was watching proceedings whilst cleaning his ears with the aid of a thin stick. Simpson knocked the man's feet from the table, "Take her to Pulley's cell," he ordered.

"Bit of a tender chick for Pulley, I'm thinking."

"Pulley has her cell under control."

"Do stop snivelling," the turnkey went off, dragging Susannah Holmes down the dim passage.

"Funny one, that," Sam said thoughtfully. "She seemed a nice girl – yet she had the goods on her."

"Women can make fools of us all," Simpson dipped the large quill into the inkpot and carefully recorded an entry in the register, "it'll come out in the wash."

The turnkey pulled Susannah over the yard to the women's section of the jail, unlocked the heavy manacles and pushed her into the dark room. She fell to the floor cowering in a sweat of fear.

"Another one for your fine hostelry, Liz," he announced cheerfully.

The prisoners took only a mild interest in the newcomer and even less in her crying, an unremarkable occurrence in that place. Eventually Liz Pulley went over and poked the girl with her toe.

"Come on, it'll do you no good to blah like that, besides, we'll be wanting to sleep soon and we can't with that racket goin' on."

Susannah, still shaking, made an effort to sit up. Wiping her face, she squinted up at the woman standing over her.

"Good God, it's my little angel!" Liz Pulley dropped to her knees.

"Remember me, you stopped that geezer giving me a pissbawler in the churchyard up by the Maddermarket!"

Susannah nodded, unable to speak.

"Come here, gal, sit on my mattress." Liz Pulley wiped Susannah's face with her shawl.

"I'm so frightened," great sobs racked her frame once more.

Liz held her tightly. "Don't take on so, you looked after Liz and Liz will look after you."

"This gal," she announced to the others in the cell, "broke her brolly over a geezer's head and frightened the bugger away. Saved me from a right drumming, I can tell you!"

"Liz, Liz, I didn't do it. I didn't steal them things."

"Of course you didn't my lovely. No sod in this place ever pinched a farthing. There's more innocents in this place than in the nunnery, I swear."

A few days before Christmas, Bessie came to see Susannah. The yard was teeming with visitors, the site of many tearful reunions. There were lawyers in secret huddles with diverse felons but mostly families and friends who were there to give food and comfort to the gaunt prisoners.

"Susannah, you look so pale and thin, and your lovely hair! What has happened to it?"

"There's only one pipe in the yard for all the prisoners here. We have precious little time to wash and suchlike."

"Susie, are you sure you didn't borrow them things from the Missus just to try on?" Bessie's eyes filled with tears. "I've thought of nothing else these last weeks, my head aches from thinking and worrying."

"I never knew they were in my hope chest!"

"Your brother's in a fearful state, and Sam Rush says it's a real mystery and if he is to become a proper thief taker it's the sort of thing he should solve."

"I wish someone would help, I've no one to speak up for me. They say that I'll be hung if nobody comes forward. Is Harry coming to see me?"

"Your brother has took it real bad, he's going round in a daze they say. But Sam's helping, getting Harry to look into things. I'm not sure what things mind you."

Susannah held her head in her hands and tears dripped to the dirt below.

"Don't cry, Susie, perhaps Sam will find something out. Cook sent these for you." She shoved a pillowcase half full of food into her hands.

Fuller came slouching up with his peculiar gait, drinking from a large earthenware mug. Bessie moved quickly to Susannah, almost sitting on her lap.

"Ladies," he swept off a tattered hat, almost falling over in the process, "my compliments of this festive season to you both."

Bessie gave a little scream and grasped Susannah by the neck, almost throttling her. Henry Cabell strode over, took Fuller by the collar and dragged him away.

"Pay no attention, he can't take his grog but he means no harm."

"Do you know all the criminals here, Susie?" said Bessie.

"I've not met the men before. Some of the females visit them but I never do."

A man wandered up and stared out of the nearest barred opening. Filthy toes peeped out from a split shoe, his trouser bottoms halfway up his thin legs and ragged sleeves showed all his wrists and most of his forearms. Deep sunken eyes, black with fatigue and hollow with hunger gazed dull and lifeless to the bridge. The two girls could smell the man's neglect and they slowly moved away.

Henry Cabell, seeing their discomfort, came over and stood between them and the ragged figure. "There's no need to be affeared of him, the poor man's not had a visitor for two years, he's wanting to see his wife walk across the bridge and bring news of his little ones, but every day disappointment and despair wears away his hopes. I expect one of these days those hopes will go out and he'll go with 'em."

At this intelligence Susannah fished out a bun and offered it to Henry, indicating that he should give it to the ragged man.

"Save it for yourself, miss, old George lives on hopes not buns. You'll need every scrap yourself in this foul place." He walked over to the opening and began a conversation with the filthy figure.

"Who's that?" whispered Bessie.

"I don't know."

"He looks like a murderer to me," Bessie peered nervously over her shoulder. Susannah looked into the pillow case.

"There's a lot of food in here."

"Cook made most of it, the Master gave her a whole five shillings to buy stuff with, and said she was not to let on to anyone."

"Please tell Mrs Choke I didn't steal," pleaded Susannah. Both girls began to cry again.

The bell rang and the yard started to empty. After a final hug, Bessie made her way over the stony ground. She skirted around Henry and shot off across the yard holding on to her hat, coat flapping in all directions.

Henry looked at Susannah and grinned, "I'm not a murderer, miss," he raised his shabby hat and walked off.

Soon it was Christmas Eve. A goodly number of folk from Norwich had climbed the hill to the castle and handed in parcels of food. Woollen socks and scarves were carefully wrapped and left in the care of the turnkey by the great gate. Some parcels contained little texts from the bible, for the good of the felons within the fortress prison.

These were received in the spirit they were given and read out loud. Some were stuck on cell walls and doors as a reminder of Christmas. Many were affected by the kindness of the local citizens.

As the light faded that evening and the cold cloak of darkness settled over the walls, a single candle was lit in the part holding the female prisoners. Suddenly a beautiful voice began to sing.

"Oh come all ye faithful
Joyful and triumphant
Oh come ye, oh come ye to Bethlehem.
Come and behold him
Born the King of Angels
Oh come, let us adore him
Oh come, let us adore him
Oh come, let us adore him
Christ the Lord."

John Euston sat up on his filthy mattress. "Quiet everybody, listen to that!"

The voice was as clear as a bell and the words touched their hearts.

"Good God, I swear that's Liz Pulley!" He went to the bars and peered out.

Candles were being lit in iron-crossed windows all around. A lusty voice from the next cell joined in. Soon another voice in the darkness took up the carol, then another and another. By the last verse it seemed that the whole population of the prison was singing.

John Simpson and Chief Savage stood in a doorway looking out into the yard.

"I'd never have believed it, not even if I lived to a hundred years," Savage said.

The carol ended and an eerie silence descended.

"Give us another Liz, there's a good'un," John Euston yelled.

A chorus of voices joined in from the blackness. Dirty faces crowded round barred windows and a multitude of requests were shouted into the night.

The beautiful notes began again and the prison fell silent. This time Liz Pulley was accompanied by another.

"Christians awake, salute the happy morn
Whereon the Saviour of the world was born
Rise to adore, the mystery of love
Which hosts of angels chanted from above."

The two women sang all four verses to total silence.

As the last verse died away a great babble of voices rose from all sides.

"Why didn't they join in?" Susannah asked.

"The buggers didn't know the bleeding words, did they," Liz retorted.

"You've got a lovely voice, Liz, let's sing another Carol."

"One more then, little Angel, and let's hope this time there's more than just us two who know the words!"

"Hark the Herald Angels sing
Glory to the new born King
Peace on earth and mercy mild
God and sinners reconciled.
Joyful all ye nations rise
Join the triumph of the skies
With the angelic host proclaim
Christ is born in Bethlehem

Each verse was sung to a silent audience but everybody joined in the chorus with full hearts and lusty voices.

Hark the Herald Angels sing
Glory to the new born King."

The sound rolled over the broken spirits within the walls and over the broken bricks of the prison. Citizens hurrying by in Castle Meadow heard the singing and stopped to listen and when they got home to their warm hearths they told their families of the carols sung by the unholy souls in the tall fortress. It was the talk of the prison for a week after. Even the local paper, the Norwich Mercury, reported the unusual occurrence.

In the Governor's office the next day, Reverend Jackson felt humbled because he had had nothing to do with the singing so when he took a Christmas service for prisoners later that day he began,

"Praise to the Lord for he hears all sinners."

On the nineteenth day of March 1784 Sam Rush watched as the cart containing the four prisoners from Norwich Castle swung into the yard at Thetford assizes. He was with James Smythe, both were watchmen who had lately been employed as thief takers in the county. Harry Holmes waited nearby, his face ashen.

"This will be the wench I told you about. There's strong evidence as to her guilt but I can't help thinking something's wrong," Sam said.

Susannah Holmes climbed out of the prison cart and stood blinking in the spring sunshine. Her long hair was hacked short, greasy and unkempt. The pallor of prison emphasised dark rings around her eyes. Sam Rush stepped back as the prisoners, two by two, passed into the Court building. She didn't see the look of pity in his eyes.

"She was a fine wench just four months back," Sam whispered.

"Feelings are a luxury thief takers can't afford. Save your pity for them that loses goods to the thieving bastards," Smythe replied. "Who's the cove she's chained to, I've seen him before."

"John Euston, sometimes he's known as John Hewston, a regular villain. He's been locked up and secured so many times he thinks of himself as a valuable bit of property."

Mr Justice Nares was the Court Judge that day. He was a man who had obviously been much larger than he was now. His face, once full and fleshy, was hollow with recent weight loss and his chin hung with surplus rolls of flesh. Dark rings of sagging skin under his eyes added to the picture of an elderly basset hound in a wig. John Euston was the first prisoner brought up from the holding cell.

"Ah, Mr Euston, we meet again, and so soon," Justice Nares addressed himself dryly to the prisoner.

Euston appeared not to notice the edge of sarcasm. "Your Honour, I am deeply obliged to you for remembering my name."

"You are charged on violent suspicion of having feloniously taken, stolen and carried away two gold rings for the fingers, two gold ear rings and one guinea from the purse of Mary Hazel of Wicklewood in the County of Norfolk. What say you, you blackguard?"

"Upon my honour, your Honour, the sight of Mary Hazel, with her fulsome bosom, encased as it was in fine fabric and golden jewellery, was a powerful draw for any man, particularly a man of limited means. However, Mary Hazel gave me those articles as a token of her esteem."

"Who has laid these charges?" the judge glared around.

"Mary Hazel, your Honour," the court usher stood up from the long bench in front of the judge.

"Well, where is she?" he demanded.

"Dead, my Lord."

Joshua Nares looked up to see John Euston smiling innocently at him.

"Ah, so you've cooked up this cock and bull story. I'm not accepting this poppycock, why would a respectable woman lay such charges if they were not a true reflection of the facts! Answer me that, sir!"

"The passion between us cooled, your Honour. I desired a rest from our discreet liaisons. A woman scorned......"

"Euston, you are a scoundrel of the first order! I see you have been sentenced to death by an earlier court." He scratched furiously at the document in front of him. "I shall order that your execution is respited until further signification of His Majesty's pleasure. Take him down!"

As Susannah passed John Euston in the dark corridor below the court, he winked cheerfully at her. She hardly noticed, shaking as she was from head to toe.

"Susannah Holmes, Your Honour, charged with the theft of a linen gown, one silk cloak, two silk handkerchiefs, one pair of linen sheets and two silver tablespoons, the property of Jebez Taylor, her employer." The Court usher sat down wearily, it was going to be a long day.

"What is your plea, Susannah Holmes?"

"No, no, no, Sir, I didn't, I really didn't." She shook so violently that her words tumbled out in a jumble of uneven sounds.

"Who has laid these charges?"

"The charges are made on the oath of Catherine Eleanor Taylor, wife of Jebez Taylor. She is a woman of business and cannot be here today. Her testimony has been witnessed by a Magistrate in the County of Norfolk, my Lord."

"Are we not to have any witnesses today?" the judge scowled.

"We have the watchman who apprehended the prisoner."

"Well, bring him forward!"

Sam Rush took the oath and stood facing the judge.

"Susannah Holmes worked as a maid at the house of Jebez Taylor. I received word from Mrs Taylor, after the girl was dismissed, that certain items were missing from the house."

"And you arrested her with the goods in her charge, I suppose." The judge looked at him over his glasses.

"They were," Sam nodded. He gave a detailed explanation of what had happened when the prisoner was arrested.

When it came to Susannah's turn to give evidence she could hardly speak. She repeated that she was innocent and had stolen nothing, and that she was sure the goods had been put in her hope chest by mistake.

Mr Justice Nares took a few minutes to scratch some notes on his paper, and then carefully placed the large quill pen in the inkstand.

"Susannah Holmes, we have had a witnessed testimony from a respectable woman of the parish in Surlingham that you stole goods which were found in your possession, the value of which exceeds forty shillings."

Solemnly he placed a black cloth on his wig.

"I sentence you to be hanged by the neck until dead."

Susannah slipped down in a dead faint as somebody in the public part of the court sobbed loudly. Sam Rush stared up at the figure half hidden by an oak post. Two jailers carried the inert prisoner down the steps to the cells below.

In the yard outside Sam Rush found Harry pacing up and down.

"What's the verdict, Sam?"

"She's for the drop, sorry Harry."

"I'm giving up this job Sam, if I was any bleeding good I'd have found out something by now – it's been four months since you took her in."

"Perhaps there was nothing to find out. Susannah might have taken the stuff to spite the old boiler Mrs Taylor."

"You don't know Susannah like I do. She wouldn't take cheese from a church mouse. I'm useless as a parish watchman; I'll go back to sea I reckon."

Just then a well-dressed man emerged from the court. His eyes red from recent tears, he blew his nose loudly into a large white handkerchief.

"Good God, it's Jebez Taylor!" Sam whispered.

Chapter Ten

J ohn Simpson stepped from the wicket gate as the prisoners spilled out of the heavy cart. "How many?"

"Took two, brought back six. This is getting to be a powerfully popular place, no mistaking," the guard grunted.

"Too popular, I'm thinking, and too crowded!"

John Euston and Susannah Holmes were last to emerge from the prison cart.

"What was the verdict this time, Euston?"

"Same as last sessions, no Judge can hang me when the complainant has conveniently died."

"You're a lucky man, Euston."

"I could do with a change of fortune, there's plenty of room for it."

Susannah Holmes, fettered to John Euston stood by listlessly, staring dully into the distance.

"And the girl?"

"Death by hanging. Took it bad, hasn't said a word since Thetford."

The sight of the familiar surroundings of Norwich Castle seemed to bring Susannah Holmes out of her stupor.

"I didn't do it, I'm not a thief," two large tears washed a path down her white face.

"This place is full of people who didn't do it," Simpson answered roughly.

At the door of the female section Susannah held on to the doorframe, unwilling to enter the dark cell. Simpson knocked her hand away from the jamb and shoved her inside; she fell to the bare floor, her face filthy with dirt and tears. Liz Pulley squatted down beside her.

"I'm afraid, Liz, mortal afraid."

"Don't take on so."

"I'm afraid of hanging, Liz, I don't want to die."

They clung together, one distraught and desolate, the other moved by compassion but not having the words to ease her friend's pain. At last, when Susannah's sobs subsided, Liz dried her face on the hem of her camisole.

"Buck up my lovely, you'll never hang. They want young people like you and me in the new lands across the sea. We'll go together, I'll take care of you."

"My brother will find out who put them things in my hope chest, he'll be a good watchman, won't he Liz?"

"One of the best, I'm sure. Never give up hope little angel."

Across the cell, the young girl Mary looked at Madge and raised her eyebrows. The older woman shook her head causing flakes of surplus powder to shower down on her young companion. "Not a bleeding cat in hell's chance I'd say," she whispered fiercely.

Harry Holmes stamped his feet on the hard ground outside the Fox and Hounds in Rockland St. Mary. The first few days of April had turned cold again and everywhere was in the grip of a deep spring frost. It was nearly six o'clock in the morning and soon the coach and four would be arriving to take local passengers to Norwich – some to catch the connection to London.

He was waiting for one such passenger; vigorously he rubbed his hands together and blew into his palms. To get his circulation going, he walked briskly up and down the lane. It was when he was stepping back that a rig drawn by a single horse emerged from the track that led to Surlingham.

The passenger dismounted and paid the driver, who tipped his cap, clicked his tongue and moved the horse off smartly.

"Off to London again, Sir?"

The man moved closer to his trunk lying on the ground and pushed back the brim of his top hat.

"Do I know you, my man?"

Harry unwound the woollen scarf that covered the lower half of his face.

"Harry Holmes, Sir, watchman of this parish."

"Have we met?"

"I'm the brother of Susannah Holmes, your wife reported her as a thief."

"Ah, I was away on business when that unfortunate episode occurred."

"So you were, Sir, but you was back for the trial at Thetford two weeks since."

"Just to observe, nothing more, my man." Jebez Taylor began to look uncomfortable.

"You could have given her a character, Sir, she was in need of someone to speak up for her."

Jebez Taylor took out a large handkerchief and wiped his brow.

"The girl stole a number of items from my house, it wouldn't have been proper to speak for the wench."

"I suppose anyone could have filched them things, Sir."

"How dare you question me, I shall report you to the magistrates!"

"I'm the appointed watchman, it's my job to question people involved in felony."

"The trial's done and dusted man, the girl's sentenced!"

"Sentenced to death! and you was mighty upset at that!"

"She had always been a good girl, I was concerned."

"And I was curious, sir, especially when I see'd that shift and gown held up in court."

The coachman had by now hauled the trunk from between the two men and secured it on top of the coach. Mr Taylor climbed hastily on board.

"Curious, my man, why so?"

"I've met your wife, Sir, she's a touch on the stout side – if you don't mind me saying – for such delicate garments."

Jebez Taylor swallowed hard, dabbed his neck with the linen handkerchief and rapped the roof with his cane.

"Drive on, man," he called to the coachman, "we're late already!"

Harry stared after the coach as it rumbled away, his mouth set in a grim line. When it was out of sight he stalked off down the lane, cursing softly.

The prisoners sat around the walls, glad of the fresh air filtering through the narrow apertures of the old castle. A man had died of typhus the previous night so the Governor had allowed the prisoners, men and women, to mix freely while their quarters were disinfected. A few prisoners, bribed by the promise of extra food, were scrubbing the prisoners' quarters. An air of coal tar and pine water hung languidly in the heavy atmosphere.

John Euston was reading the Norfolk Chronicle given him by John Simpson, the turnkey, and was soon joined by Henry Cabell, who slumped down on the rough ground.

"Eight men in our cell now, one man sneezes and we all get the sweats!"

"Aye, 'tis no wonder men die like flies."

"But not in our cell, thank God. You're right to keep everybody squared up, Henry, that rabble would sit in their own vomit if you let 'em!"

Henry looked around the yard, "I'd be obliged if you'd read some news from the paper, it in't often we know what's happening beyond these walls. Let's go over to the far side, I'm thinking it's fresher by the openings."

John Euston smiled knowingly, "And it's nearer that lass with Liz Pulley, have you spoken to the girl yet?"

"I spoke to her last year, just before Christmas," Henry replied gruffly.

They made their way carefully between little knots of prisoners, ragged creatures exuding the fragrant aroma of the infrequently washed.

John Euston called out, "Liz, I'm about to read to my young friend a few paragraphs from the local news, would you two ladies like to listen in?" He swept off his battered hat in mock elegance.

"Ta, you old shirtlifter, we'll come over this instant!"

Euston cleared his throat. "Now, listen carefully you two young 'uns, and stop gazing at each other like moonstruck calves."

Susannah smiled but Henry made no reply, his senses afire from the smell of her hair, the heady aroma of carbolic soap. She was suddenly aware of the coarseness of her frock, the way it rubbed against her thighs and the rustle of her blouse, she wondered if he could hear it as she shifted position by the stonewall. A faint blush rose to her warm face when she realised the soft fabric brushing against her nipples was making them harden. She worried in case Henry could see their shape.

"Can you dance?" she whispered without knowing why. Perhaps it was to cover her embarrassment.

"I've never danced, never even thought about it," he answered awkwardly, unexpectedly aware of his big feet and heavy boots.

"We had better listen to the news from the paper." She turned away to face John Euston who was noisily smoothing the crumpled newspaper.

Henry looked down in disgust at his filthy boots, with laces made of thin strips of hide.

Euston cleared his throat again and began to read.

'Overcrowded Prisons

During the year of 1775, just before the American Revolution, over 47,000 slaves from the black continent of Africa were being shipped to America.

It is little wonder to this correspondent that the new country no longer wants felons from Great Britain, for it is clear that there is sufficient black labour for all tasks of pioneering and the settling of new fields.

White slavery, for that is what our felons are, is no longer desirable or needed for forced labour.

What, therefore, is to become of our prisons, overflowing as they are with wicked and evil wrongdoers? What of the dangers of disease leaking from these foul and overcrowded places, to creep freely amongst honest citizens? The Government should know that we demand action to prevent noxious airs, infections and distempers being released amongst the populace of our great cities, such as Norwich.'

John Euston looked up from the newspaper. "What do you think of that, Liz?"

"Bleeding cheek, I say, we've got six in our cell now and there's hardly room to turn over and give your arse a good scratch. They're letting in a lower class of prisoner nowadays. If that tart who came in yesterday gives me the pox I'll swing for her, mark my words!"

"Listen, here's another one that's worth looking at," John Euston smoothed out the paper and began reading.

'Newgate Prison

A riot occurred in Newgate Prison on the Wednesday of last week. Two turnkeys were injured and five felons killed. The overcrowding in Newgate is almost unbearable, with six prisoners occupying space intended for just one person. The situation is abjectly nauseous there being neither separation between classes of criminal nor any separation of sexes, leading to scenes of utmost depravity.

We are aware that Newgate is to be rebuilt but we are reliably informed that even when the work is completed it will be insufficient to house all the prisoners currently confined there.

There is a pressing need to build more prisons and an even greater need to begin again the wholesale transportation of undesirables.

Typhus is of great concern to free citizens with overcrowded and unsanitary prisons being the source of many unsavoury infections.'

John Euston looked up to find Henry and Susannah gazing at each other.

"Have you two heard a word I've said?" he demanded.

"I have," Liz butted in, "and it's bleeding miserable. Don't those bastards ever write something cheerful? What about the music halls? Now I like a good show. I had a gentleman who always took me to a show, the funny old bugger always made me sit there with no drawers on."

John Euston tugged Liz's sleeve. "Do you think I should advise young Henry to pay when the turnkeys next arrange an overnight visit for the women to stay in our cell?"

Henry looked up sharply."I wouldn't pay to see anyone," he growled.

Susannah stood up. "And I wouldn't visit anyone who paid to see me," she stalked off as proudly as anyone could in iron fetters.

"Bleeding hell," said Liz, "it must be love!"

That night, on her straw-filled mattress, Susannah thought of Henry again. A wave of heat washed over her as she remembered the tiny strands of chest hair peeping through his shirt. She wondered what it would be like to caress his chest, and to feel the hairs tickle her face if she kissed his skin.

When news of the death of the prisoner leaked out, the citizens of Norwich bombarded the local press with letters demanding to know when the government was going to resume transporting prisoners. Everyone was terrified of typhus, a disease that was seen as epidemic in places. A petition containing thousands of names was collected and handed to the Member of Parliament for Norwich, Sir Harbord Harbord, within a week of the death. He sent it to Evan Nepean, the thoughtful deputy to Lord Sydney, Secretary of State for the Home and Colonial Department.

The government was particularly sensitive to the people of Norwich, second only to London in importance as a city. They were also well aware the notorious Thomas Paine, who had been issuing pamphlets about the rights of the ordinary man, came from Thetford, just thirty miles from Norwich.

Sir Harbord wrote a covering letter

'I have dealings with Norwich Bridewells and the Castle where conditions are truely abominable. Once a man is in prison his awe of the law is lost, what more can it do to him? Thus he practices the grossest of evils upon his fellow felons. First offenders are housed with hardened criminals, boys bed with homosexuals, muggers and murderers prey upon the weak who must submit or learn the evil arts and themselves prey upon others. Prisons pickle men in purgatory and salt them in sin! It is imperative the Government recommence transportation without delay!

The prison here in the old Castle, is disgraceful. The wretches within have one water pump between almost forty creatures, there is no sanitation, cells are left to rot with filth. Something must be done before the streets of Norwich are filled with rioters and rabble rousers.'

In Rockland St Mary, Harry watched the landlord of the Fox and Hounds scrub the steps.

"You waiting for the London coach again, Harry?"

"Aye, I'm taking a passenger to Surlingham."

"That'll be Jebez Taylor, he's a regular right enough."

It wasn't until the little rig was loaded and on the way that the passenger realised who the driver was.

"Where's the regular driver?"

"Busy. I'll have you home safe and sound, don't worry."

They didn't speak anymore until Harry pulled the rig into the entrance to a field.

"Why are you stopping, I'll have the law on you!" The merchant, already suspicious, gripped his money purse.

"I am the law around these parts and I mean to finish our conversation about my sister wasting away in Norwich Castle!"

"There's nothing to discuss, my wife swore on oath a list of things stolen and there's an end to it!"

Harry seized the older man's neckerchief and screwed it tight against his throat. "You filthy goat, you've forced yourself on my sister and given her presents, I swear I'll tell your wife the truth, damn you!"

"You damn fool! My wife already thinks that. She found the shift and gown and a letter I was writing to a friend in London, also named Susannah, my wife thought it was meant for your sister."

"So your wife put those garments in my sister's hope chest?"

"It's possible."

"You should have gone to the magistrate and told the truth."

"I knew nothing of the matter until your sister was committed and my wife will not withdraw her testimony, no matter what. If I did anything in court to embarrass her, my position in her father's business would end!"

"I shall report this to the Magistrates."

"I shall report you for assault."

The two men glared at each other. Harry let him go, noting the dark red mark on the older man's neck with a sinking heart. "You'd let my sister hang just to save your face? You are the lowest of scoundrels."

"Get this rig moving you stupid oaf."

That night Harry related everything that had happened to Sam Rush.

"You shouldn't have threatened him Harry; you could lose your job."

"I've got to do something, Susannah could hang."

At the House of Commons a meeting was held the day before Members of Parliament went off for their Christmas break. The large room was filled with fine furniture and austere oil paintings of past Prime Ministers gazed severely on the dozen or so people assembled there.

Criticism in the press for the Government's failure to take decisive action about the burgeoning prison population had increased. Typhus had broken out in several cities and the source of the infections was blamed on felons spilling from local gaols.

Ever since the Hulks Act of 1776, more and more prisoners had been crammed on rotting ships mostly anchored in London ports and off the south coast of England. These were feared as the root cause of almost any distemper that appeared in the vicinity of embarkation ports or supply centres.

Prime Minister William Pitt the Younger had instructed Lord Sydney, as the Minister responsible, to find a solution.

In the beautifully panelled room several prominent personalities waited for the meeting to begin. Lord Sydney had summoned Lord North who had briefly held the position of Home and Colonial Secretary; Lord Howe, First Lord of the Admiralty, and Sir George Young, another naval man; Pepper Arden the Attorney General and Lord Sydney's own deputy, Evan Nepean, were there. In addition a number of senior civil servants attended, representing government departments that might be involved in transportation.

To set the scene for the discussion that was to follow, Lord Sydney outlined the problems of the prisons, 'bursting at the seams with malign creatures carrying malign and fatal diseases.'

There was no need, every man and woman in England had heard of the most pressing problem of the day. He announced that Prime Minister Pitt was determined that those assembled would finally provide a 'specific solution to this intractable problem.'

Soon there was a lively debate about the merits of various locations for a colony manned by transported convicts. Lord North reminded the meeting that previous transportations to America had provided the Government with income from the fees paid by settlers to obtain indentured labourers and that, once ashore, felons ceased to be a 'burden upon honest citizens'.

He reported that the treasury still suffered from the ruinous costs of war with France and the committee should take heed of 'this calamitous fact when deciding where to send felons.'

Evan Nepean rose to his feet. "A suggestion had been tendered which takes into account the economics of transportation. I refer to the letters from James Mattra."

One of the administration men read a summary of the proposals from James Mario Mattra who had sailed as a midshipman on the Endeavour when Captain Cook discovered Australia.

"Mr Mattra," the man intoned, "was born in America and has worked in administration and diplomatic posts in London, Constantinople and Tenerife. He proposes a colony at Botany Bay in New South Wales to take advantage of the great pines, suitable as masts for ships of the line, and the flax that grows in abundance there and on islands thereabouts. He suggests a free settlement for displaced loyalists from America, peasants from our rural shires and the newly poor. He believes much trade would accrue with China, the Alutions and Japan, and also believes it would be a powerful base from which to deal with threats from Spain, the Dutch and Spanish America. He advocates that such a settlement would be an ideal place where British convicts could be sent and that prisoners, allowed a few acres of their own, would soon provide for themselves. He uses the phrase 'work or starve'!"

The First Lord of the Admiralty, Lord Howe stood up. "I too have seen this man's letters and they are, quite simply, gentlemen, impractical. Can you imagine sending a flotilla of ships, crammed with villains, laced with prostitutes, burdened by a number of dragoons, to an unknown place 16,000 miles away over treacherous seas? Impossible, utterly impossible!"

Sir George Young, soon to become an Admiral, rose. "Captain Cook first mentioned the pines on Norfolk Island and the flax that grows there. He's a man whose judgement is sound. We must not rule out Botany Bay, if only to take advantage of the opportunities for our ships' supplies. The main mast of a seventy four-gun ship must be three feet thick at the base and rise, straight and true, to over one hundred feet. It must be a single tree without a warp or crack. Pine is the only timber that will suffice, grain and resin makes it supple, it bends and absorbs incredible strains of mountainous seas and wind that can blow a man overboard! Presently, such timber can only be got from Riga in Russia. This Country spends £500,000 every year bringing timber and flax from Russia. A ship from there to Portsmouth faces many dangers as well as the uncertain seas. The peace we have with France is uncertain, the Dutch jealously guard their trade routes. We have heard that the French, just two months past, have an agreement with Sweden to establish a naval base at Goteburg where the North Sea and the Baltic meet and where our timber ships must pass within a few miles! Gentlemen, without a safe passage of masts and flax from Riga, our whole way of life is threatened! Without these essential supplies our Navy, the best in the world, is useless. Our ships are already vulnerable on the perilous voyage of 1,700 miles from Riga to Portsmouth but this dangerous French naval base at Goteburg means we must urgently find another source of timber and flax. If that is to be found in the Southern Seas then so be it!"

There was a short silence following this impassioned plea. Several of the committee nodded their agreement.

Lord Sydney rapped the table. "We seemed to have strayed from the problems of the felonious multitude in our prisons to the needs of our Navy! However, if we can kill two birds with one stone then we must do so! Is it the wish of this committee that I recommend we investigate two places in which to establish a base that is to be hewn out of virgin lands by prison labour?"

There was a general nodding of heads and Lord Sydney brought the meeting to a close.

The Christmas Parliamentary recess, which began the next day, ensured that not a thought, nor a spot of ink, was addressed to the subject until the following February.

Chapter Eleven

In Surlingham, the Squire showed the local Magistrate into his drawing room.

"You sent word you wished to consult on a matter of some delicacy I understand?"

The Magistrate nodded miserably and took out two letters from his pocket. "Tis better if you read these, both arrived by hand yesterday."

Turning up the wick of the oil lamp on the big mahogany desk, the Squire read each letter twice. Sighing, he motioned the magistrate to sit down. "What is your opinion of the note from parish watchman, Holmes?"

The Magistrate stroked his sharp chin. "There is more than a ring of truth in that untutored hand. Mrs Taylor is well known for her suspicion of young maids in her household."

"And Jebez Taylor's report of the assault he suffered at the hands of Holmes?"

"It seems a truthful account."

The Squire went to the window and stared out. In a laburnum bush by the window a flock of finches seemed to be having a serious disagreement. Suddenly, they took fright and flew off to a nearby shrub to settle the argument. The Squire returned to his desk.

"Holmes' sister still bides in Norwich Castle awaiting the King's pardon?"

The Magistrate nodded. "I sup with Jebez Taylor two days from now, I could advise him to withdraw his complaint in view of the scandal that's bound to be stirred up if this matter comes to court again."

"Do that, in the meantime I'll write to suggest mercy be shown to Susannah Holmes. I shall also dismiss Harry Holmes from his post, we cannot allow our law enforcers to throttle the likes of Jebez Taylor." The

Squire threw both letters onto the blazing logs, using a long poker to feed them into the flames.

Picking up his top hat the Magistrate paused by the door. "Perhaps I should lend Taylor a scold's bridle for his wife, that woman's tongue causes more trouble than a dozen felons."

It was Liz Pulley who found Susannah sobbing in a corner of the dark cell.

"Whatever's the matter, little angel?"

"Governor Gwynn's just been here."

"Has that old sod been trying it on my lovely?"

"He came to tell me I've got the King's pardon and I'm to be transported for fourteen years." This brought on another bout of bitter tears.

Liz sat back on her heels and folded her arms. "You've got to get yourself sorted out my lovely, it in't no use howling your heart out. Be thankful you'll not be swinging on that gibbet like many poor devils who have bided in this place. You've got to buck up, not let the buggers grind you down. This is your life from now on – face it or be a miserable cow all your life!"

Susannah stared open mouthed at her friend. "You've never spoken an unkind word to me before."

"This rat hole in't a picnic for any of us, we've got to beat the bastards at their own game not lay around like wet rags!"

"Oh Liz."

"Don't 'Oh Liz' me. Get out there in the yard, where there's a bit of sunshine coming through the slits, get a drop of warmth on your clock, it'll do you good!"

Two weeks later, Susannah called out to Liz in the yard. They had not spoken since news of Susannah's reprieve had come through.

"Liz, I've got a letter."

"Whats it say?"

"Here, read it yourself."

Dear Sister,

"I'm so very glad to hear you have been reprieved
but so sorry not to have saved you from the transporting
business. I know you are innocent and I'm sure Mrs
Taylor put those things in your hope chest on account
of her thinking there was something going on between

you and her old man. I tackled Mr Taylor but he won't
do anything because he's afraid the truth about his fancy
woman in London will come out and he'll lose his job.

Susannah, I feel so low about not being able to help you.
I know I've let you down, please forgive me. I'm going
back to sea now I've lost my job as parish watchman.
I'll write again when I've found a berth.
Your loving brother
Harry.

Liz handed the letter back to Susannah. "At least you're not blahing about
the place."

"I'm sorry I've been such a cry baby Liz. I know you're right, this is my
life now and I've got to make the best of it. I just wish my brother wasn't
going away."

"You are lucky to have a brother, there's no sod out there to write to me."

"Liz, let's be friends again, you're the only one in this godforsaken place
worth talking to."

"Aye, let's be friends. Mind you, no more waterworks and a bit more grit!
It's the only way to survive in this place."

Chapter Twelve

John Simpson hurried down Opie Street and into St Andrews Hill. Here, tumbledown cottages were mean and close, populated with poverty, worn with care. Misfortune looked out of windows and hunger lingered in every doorway. Although Norwich was the second richest city in England pockets of penury were to be found everywhere. He bustled past the poorhouse that looked hungrily at the relative opulence of St Andrews Church opposite its shabby windows.

That morning, his wife Rosie had seemed down in the dumps and he was anxious to get home. A few minutes later, he arrived to find both wife and daughter in tears.

"What's the matter?"

Clara burst into a fresh set of tears and ran upstairs.

"Sit down John, I've something to tell you." His wife grasped his hand tightly. "Promise you won't shout and bawl."

He nodded, not trusting himself to speak. She stroked his hand.

"Our daughter's having a baby."

He leapt up, "Good God, who's the father?"

"She won't say, only that they'll wed as soon as he is free."

"You mean the father is already married!" he roared, "I'll soon make her talk."

Rosie dragged him gently back to the settle. "You'll do no such thing, she needs help not hard words. She hardly knows what time of the day it is at the moment."

"We must be told who the bugger is, she can't hide it forever!"

"John what are we to do? Clara's not yet sixteen, what will the neighbours say?

"I don't give a farthing about the bleeding neighbours, I want to know who the father is."

"It's no good John, I've been on at her but she won't tell."

They argued and shouted at each other but she would not let him question Clara. Finally, he got up and paced about the room. "I'm going to the alehouse," he announced, slamming out of the door.

A moment or two later Clara came down the stairs, white faced and trembling.

"When's the child due?"

"Late spring Mum, some time in May."

"So all the nights you said you were working you've been seeing this man?"

Clara ran out of the room without answering.

At the House of Commons, the Transportation Committee had to decide once and for all where to dispatch felons to release the pressure on the overcrowded gaols.

Botany Bay, proposed by Sir George Young, was hotly debated. The cost of sending a colony of felons so far and the dangers of discipline whilst there were subject to prolonged argument. Another proposal was for Das Voltas Bay that lay by the estuary of Orange River on the West coast of Africa. This was said to be a first class staging post sitting on the sea route to the Far East. The surrounding countryside was reported to be as fertile and able to be cultivated enough to provide self-sufficiency for prisoners and displaced American loyalists. A military and naval garrison, once established, would counteract the one commanded by the French at Cape Town.

After much argument, the committee came down in favour of Das Voltas Bay when it was revealed that copper was to be found in nearby mountains. The British Navy had begun to apply a coat of copper to the bottoms of ships to extend tours of service in foreign waters.

Newspapers reported the decision as the 'copper-bottomed' argument.

In gaols throughout the land and on hulks around the coast, prisoners learned of the decision with a mixture of apprehension and excitement. Tales of horrors that might be encountered on the Dark Continent swept through every place of incarceration, terrifying the populace and daily adding to myths and legends of a mysterious land about which so little was known. Norwich Castle was no different, but here transportation was seen by the Turnkeys as an opportunity to rid themselves of troublesome and sickly souls. Between them, Chief Savage and John Simpson had already selected the 'verminous scum' whom they would recommend for the first transports.

John Simpson was himself feeling apprehensive. Despite many rows and threats, their daughter had steadfastly refused to reveal the name of the father of baby growing inside her. In the end she had been despatched to Rosie's cousin in the countryside who was well known as a person who could terminate unwanted pregnancies.

He had managed to arrange a few days leave starting the next day to visit his daughter in Rockland St Mary. He had not set eyes on her since she had been sent to the village. Cousin Emily had sent word that the baby was to be 'got rid of' that weekend. He was grateful to Chief Savage who had not questioned him when given the news of Clara's sudden departure from her duties as maid to his wife. Nor had he objected to Simpson's request for a few days leave.

That evening, when Henry was collecting water for his cell, he hung back a little by the solitary pump, hoping to meet Susannah doing the same task. His luck was in when he heard her struggling in the darkness with the heavy buckets.

"Half a mo miss, I'll carry them for you."

"You always call me miss, my name is Susannah."

The way she said it sent a schism of tenderness down his body. "Susannah, that's a pretty name."

"You've just got out of the dungeons; I heard you tried to escape."

"Got as far as the hanging span – no further," he coloured a little knowing he was regarded as a hero by a few prisoners and a damn fool by others.

"And now get your hide back to the cells, Cabell."

Both turned round in surprise. Chief Savage had been standing in the shadows nearby.

"I was to going to help the girl with the bucket, Chief."

"Move, Cabell, or you'll get a baton across your head."

Henry picked up the full bucket with ill grace and clanked his way noisily over the darkening yard. John Simpson was waiting as usual and unlocked the door. "Where's the second bucket, lad?" Henry cursed. In his anger at being interrupted with Susannah he'd not picked up the other bucket.

"I've left it by the water pump, Mr. Simpson."

"Better get it, quick, I'm not waiting here all night."

Henry turned across the yard hoping Susannah was still by the pump but there was no sign of her. On the way back he heard a slight noise by the wall. Quietly, he lowered the bucket, tiptoed round a buttress and peered into the gloom. The sight that met him hit his heart like a hammer. Susannah was on the ground with the Chief turnkey astride her! He knew women earned money going with guards, but was devastated to find Susannah in such a position. He was about to turn away when she let out a muffled scream. "Henry, help me."

It was all he needed to unleash his rage. Fist, feet, head, it didn't matter; all his pent up passion went into smashing the man he had found with the girl he had grown fond of.

Across the yard, Simpson heard the cries of fury and fear, and rushed over. Henry was kicking the inert turnkey with a cold brutality. Simpson knocked the prisoner out with one blow from his baton. When he opened the shutters on his night lantern he saw Susannah crouched by the wall, whimpering like a puppy.

"Holmes, what's happened here?"

"He tried to ravish me!" She could not stop trembling.

"Cabell?"

"Not Henry, Chief Savage!"

"You're a damned liar."

Simpson blew his whistle and other turnkeys appeared. The unconscious Henry was quickly hauled to the dungeons.

"Get back to your cell, Holmes. I don't want to hear another word from you." He pushed her roughly towards the women's quarters.

"It wasn't Henry Cabell!"

"Beggar off Holmes, I must attend to Chief Savage!"

It was clear the Chief was badly injured and could not be moved without a doctor present. When the prison physician appeared, he promptly arranged for the unconscious turnkey to be taken to hospital.

The following morning, just before he went off duty, John Simpson made his way down the stone steps to the dungeons. Henry lay against the damp walls, legs and hands manacled, flecks of dried blood on his face.

"You damn fool Cabell, if Chief Savage dies nothing will save you from the gallows."

"He attacked the girl, I had to do something!"

Simpson held the lantern to the boy's face. "You are a liar, Cabell."

"Ask the girl, she'll tell you straight."

"If the Chief recovers we shall hear the truth, no doubt he surprised you and the girl, and you turned on him."

"I was with you two minutes afore I found that bastard with the girl! She screamed, I swear."

"I heard no scream, you and the girl are liars. The word of a felon means nothing."

Henry felt his mouth go dry. "Is she alright?"

"I don't know and I don't care. You'll know your fate when the Governor gets back from London. I'm off to see my daughter."

"I'm telling the truth, Mr. Simpson."

"Save your breath, Cabell. If Chief Savage dies you'll swing for it. If he recovers and swears against you, you'll hang. Either way, it makes no difference."

Chapter Thirteen

Two days later, Governor Gwynne returned from London to learn of the assault on his senior prison officer. Savage was seriously ill from his injuries and the doctor wasn't sure if he would recover.

"This is a hell of a mess Doctor, when will we know the worst?"

"Two or three days, I reckon. The man's jaw is broken in two places. I've had to strap his face together."

"Damn Cabell! He's for the gallows for certain, but this will do for me too, the Prison Board will want somebody else in charge of Norwich Castle."

"Wait a few days until we know if Savage will recover. You'll learn the long and short of it from Simpson when he returns anyway."

The Governor nodded grimly. "Cabell's nothing but trouble."

When John and Rosie Simpson arrived in Rockland St Mary he was dispatched to the village inn while she found out if their daughter was well enough to face her father. As he sat down with a jug of beer the turnkey was surprised when Sam Rush appeared.

"What are you doing here?"

"This is my home village, why are you here?" Sam replied.

"I've come to visit my wife's cousin Emily."

"That'll be Emily that's looking after the young girl who's in the pudding club."

The turnkey buried his embarrassment by taking a long draft of beer.

"Is it your girl that's in trouble?" Sam asked kindly.

The turnkey nodded miserably, "You'll say nothing?"

"Everyone in the village knows the long and short of it, but in Norwich not a word!"

The men shook hands and Sam called for two more pints.

"Don't worry, I hear Emily's right handy with a knitting needle. This is not the first young fool she helped out of a pickle."

"Aren't you supposed to do something about such things?" John Simpson whispered.

"There are enough orphans in the poorhouse already. If a young gal's got herself in trouble it's better to stop things working themselves up into a bigger problem. Spare everybody a bit of heartache."

The men shook hands again as a ragged urchin came in the hostelry and peered around. His coat was a hessian sack tied in the middle by a length of string. Someone had thoughtfully cut holes in it for his head and arms. The boy came over to their table and gazed solemnly at them for a moment

"Are you Mr Simpson?"

"I am."

"You're to come double sharp."

The turnkey got up quickly, almost knocking over the table.

"Good luck!" Sam whispered, as his companion followed the little sack on legs out of the door.

The moment he reached Emily's cottage he knew something was wrong. Rosie sat blinking at a small bundle on the table in front or her. Picking up the blood-smeared rags he gently parted the cloth. A tiny face stared blankly back. The lifeless child was completely blue. Carefully placing the bundle back on the table he knelt by his wife.

"Don't take on so Rosie, the poor mite's gone but our Clara can start again. Nobody need know about the baby, maybe this is God's way of giving our girl a new start!"

His wife slipped through his arms in a dead faint. Sweeping her up in his arms he laid her gently on the settle by the cramped window. Cousin Emily was standing by the door to the back parlour, wiping blood from her hands on a cloth, tears streaming down her grey cheeks. Something in her demeanour made his heart pound. Suddenly he knew what was wrong.

"Not my Clara too! Not my lovely daughter!"

"I couldn't save her, John, she passed away just after the mite was born. Her insides must be torn to shreds."

They heard John Simpson's agonised cry all the way down at the inn.

Within minutes it seemed half the village crowded round the cottage when news of the tragedy spread. Sam Rush took John and Rosie to his own cottage while the local doctor was summoned. Sam went off to make a cup of tea, while the turnkey tended his wife.

"John, there's something you must know."

"It'll wait Rosie, get a little colour back into your cheeks my lovely."

"It won't wait, I must tell you while we are alone."

"What is it Rosie? You're trembling like a leaf."

"Before she passed away, Clara told me who the father of the baby is."

His chest constricted and he found it difficult to speak.

"John, the father is Chief Savage!"

He stared at her open mouthed.

"She loved him John! She dare not tell us his name before because she was terrified you would blow your top. She was afraid you'd lose your job if there was trouble between you and Savage."

"The filthy bastard, him a married man of many years." He paced about, fist clenched.

"Now, John, please don't do anything hasty, we have our daughter to bury."

Breathing heavily, he stared at her white face for a long while. Finally he sat down beside her and held her hand. "Aye lass, first things first."

They stayed on in the village until their daughter was buried the next day. The undertaker placed the stillborn infant in her mother's coffin and nobody mentioned the child again, even the vicar said nothing at the burial service. It was as if the baby had never existed. Directly after the burial, Sam Rush took them home in his pony and trap.

When John Simpson sat by the coals in his sitting room that evening thinking of his daughter and Savage together the pain of her death became almost unbearable. Rosie, having gone to bed earlier, wasn't a witness to his bitter tears. Revenge formed a lump in his chest as hard as a flint.

In London, Lord Beauchamp received an envoy from Portsmouth. The sloop sent to Dar Voltas Bay to reconnoitre the area had arrived back in the southern port the previous day. The envoy brought a detailed report of its findings. He read the report several times before sending for Sir George Young. An hour later the naval man arrived in a flurry of excitement.

Lord Beauchamp wasted no time on preliminaries. "We can discount Das Voltas Bay. This report clearly states the whole area is too dry and sterile to be settled. Botany Bay is the only alternative, I'll inform Prime Minister Pitt, you speed up detailed planning. This will be the greatest sea journey ever undertaken in the history of man!"

Sir George swallowed hard, he knew that if anything went wrong, responsibility would be lodged at his door. His promotion to Admiral was threatened.

"Greatest sea journey or greatest disaster?" he asked himself in his carriage back to the Admiralty building. Near the end of the journey a riotous crowd held up his coach and four. Two more prisoners had died at Newgate and a horde was laying siege to Westminster demanding action to rid the country of felons. In a strange way the villainous mob was of comfort to Sir George.

In Norwich Castle two recent prisoners, both elderly, were being questioned by John Euston, Liz Pulley and Susannah Holmes. He was a solicitor with a penchant for gambling and she was his wife. They had lost all they possessed, or rather he had lost everything. They were incarcerated until their debts were met. She clung to her husband, the cause of her troubles. She was a frail bird-like creature; age had dulled the lustre of her eyes and taken the sheen from her parched and wrinkled skin.

He was painfully thin and unusually tall. His eyebrows and cheekbones were sharp and angular, in awful contrast to sunken eyes and hollow cheeks. A pair of lips permanently drawn over teeth seemed to stand out like those of a corpse. The only part of his lined face that showed any life was his eyes. They glittered and shone, constantly on the move.

"Your worship, will you favour us with a legal view of the prospects of young Henry Cabell who recently battered the hated countenance of our Chief turnkey?" John Euston asked mockingly.

"I've heard of the case, if the keeper dies nothing will save the boy."

"Savage was trying to ravish me, Henry stopped him." Susannah shouted.

"It makes no difference, if the officer dies, Cabell will die on the rope."

"If Savage survives?" Euston asked.

"Any witnesses to this supposed attack on a female prisoner?"

"I know what happened, so does Henry." Susannah said fiercely.

"Nobody else?"

She shook her head miserably.

"I can see the body swinging in the gibbet now."

"You're a callous bastard," Susannah shouted.

Chapter Fourteen

Henry lay on the damp straw mattress, arms stretched above him, manacled to the dungeon wall. Footsteps sounded on the stone steps and a face peered into the gloom of the cell.

"Where are you, Cabell?" the man shouted through the grill.

"On my pit, where else?"

"Just making sure Cabell, you're a tricky bugger at the best of times."

The turnkey came in warily, holding a lantern in one hand and a stave in the other. He checked the chains were still attached to the metal loop in the wall.

"You're up before the Governor today, Simpson's with him now, no doubt making sure you'll be stretching your neck on the hanging span afore long."

"Savage was raping the girl, I saw it with my own eyes!"

"She'd have been well paid."

Henry kicked out at the turnkey. The man moved hastily to the door.

"You'll swing for sure Cabell."

In the Governor's office, John Simpson waited while George Gwynne signed and blotted some papers.

"I've been to see Chief Savage. His jaw is broken and he cannot talk, but he will live. His wife feeds him on thin gruel which he sucks through a dry reed."

John Simpson kept his own jaw clenched, the mention of Savage stirred his feelings of hatred.

"I must decide today on a just punishment for Cabell so I need your statement on what happened. The authorities will no doubt have a deal to say about our supervision of prisoners. This is a bad business altogether."

"He should be locked up for a long time."

"Cabell has a sentence of seven years transportation, do you agree we should recommend a doubling of his commitment if the Chief survives?"

"Not Cabell, Chief Savage, he was trying to rape the girl!"

"Good god, are you sure? Was Holmes whoring?"

"She struggled, Cabell stopped him ravishing the wench."

"You witnessed this yourself?"

"I did."

For a moment Governor Gwynne was non-plussed by his turnkey's implacable statement. Laying down his goose quill he viewed Simpson keenly.

"Is there something else?"

"I know where Savage has been getting his sexual favours these last few months and it was not Susannah Holmes. I have a notion that wench is still a maiden."

The Governor slumped down in his chair.

"This is terrible, it reflects even worse on my stewardship of this gaol. The Prison Board will surely demand a change."

John Simpson went to the window and stared down at the felons in the yard below. "When will Chief Savage be well enough to return to his duties?"

"Two or three months, why do you ask?"

"Chief Savage won't lodge a complaint about Cabell once he hears of my evidence so there will be no need to involve the Prison Board. It will be difficult for him to come back here."

Governor Gwynne eyed the turnkey appreciatively. "Go on."

"I hear there is soon to be an opening for a senior man at the Bridewell in Bury St Edmunds. Perhaps with his injuries the Chief needs to be transferred to less arduous duties."

"You make an excellent point Mr Simpson. I'm sure I can persuade Savage to accept a move; Bury St Edmunds is a delightful town." The Governor beamed at Simpson.

"What about Cabell, he must be punished."

"A month in the dungeons should cool his spirit."

"I agree. I will mark the ledger, you inform Cabell of his punishment."

Simpson nodded and turned to leave. Governor Gwynne placed a hand on his arm, "You had better take over the Chief's duties. Not a word of this conversation outside these walls."

Stories of the Chief Turnkey's attack on Susannah Holmes had already circulated and her version was readily believed. In the prison's close community, word of Cabell's sentence soon spread. Susannah was aghast at Henry's punishment.

"He saved me from Savage, Liz, why should he be locked in the dungeons?"

"Don't be a wet ass, Susannah, did you think the Governor would give him a big kiss and shake his hand for breaking the Chief's face? He's a lucky swine to get away with a spell in the hole."

Susannah found the month of Henry's latest confinement passed slowly, enlivened only by odd snippets of information in newspapers about the destination of the next transport. Officially it was called New South Wales but little was known of the land at the bottom of the world.

More prisoners were squeezed into the Castle and the authorities were forced to build a bath house in the yard. A weekly scrub became compulsory for all inmates. This was not well received as the cold water was only changed every tenth prisoner. The bath house was a single room about ten feet square with space for two wooden casks side by side.

In the queue for the weekly scrub, John Euston and Fuller met a prisoner who had arrived a few days earlier. He was a soap maker, wrapped tightly in a long frock coat and canvas leggings. His hat was full of grease owing to a nervous habit of taking it off and constantly ramming it back onto his bony skull.

"You'll be a debtor then," said Fuller noting the man's well-worn clothing.

"Ah the extreme struggle of man against debt! The successful man of business is always fighting the financial foe. A bill of debt beggars belief - it has an extraordinary capacity to run and can outrun the most ingenious engine ever invented; the trouble was I never knew where the brakes were."

"Where was your business?" Euston asked.

"Rampant Horse Street, not one hundred yards from where we stand."

"Funny name for a street," sneered Fuller, a stranger to Norwich.

"Even funnier when you know how it was so named. Most folk believe a great stallion ran wild there after escaping from the horse sale in the market place and rampaged about the thoroughfare."

"But you know differently I suppose," Euston said, cynically.

"I do indeed Sir! In the 1770s, the street was a thoroughfare frequented by ladies of the night. You could not walk ten yards before being accosted by a strumpet, a painted Jezebel!"

Fuller stared at him open mouthed.

"Whores! my friend. Rampant Whores Street! That was what it was known as, the current name is a polite dignifying of the original!"

"You're pulling my pisser," snorted Fuller.

Euston shoved him through the bathhouse door, "You're next, you daft beggar."

They watched him get undressed and plunge into the wooden cask still wearing his greasy hat.

In April, Henry was finally released from the hole. At the first exercise period Euston and Fuller took him to the bathhouse to wash the stink of the dungeons from his clothes and body.

"Better clean yourself thoroughly Henry, young Susannah has been missing you these last weeks." Euston said.

"Has she said so herself?"

"I've been collecting water for the cell every night and she always asks after you. I don't know why, you must be the ugliest cove in the place," Fuller grinned.

That evening, as soon as the buckets were delivered to the cell, Henry went to the bathhouse to fill them with fresh water. He felt strange, as if his blood was simmering deep within his stomach. He opened the door and a candle flared in the darkness.

"Henry, is it you?"

In two strides he was by Susannah's side and grasped her slim waist; she was trembling.

"Mr Simpson told me you were back from the dungeons."

"I thought of you every day." In the darkness he felt his face burning. He had never spoken tenderly to a girl before. He kissed her savagely and she responded. The smooth buttress of Caen stone bit into her back as they kissed deeply again. The bones of her hips pushed against his and the heat in his loins ratcheted up explosively. Hesitating, he slid his hand under her warm jacket and felt the soft rise of her breasts. Suddenly his hand was inside the once white bodice and closed over a hot nipple, swollen and hard. Soon all the buttons of her bodice were undone, her breasts hung warm and pliable, the smooth skin strangely milk-like. Lifting one breast to his lips he sucked hard. She felt the fierce heat of his mouth, her breath coming in shallow gasps, eyelids leaden with lust.

His hand slid down the firm stomach; there was no resistance in the waistband of her full skirt, meagre rations had long since made it too big. The hair in her swollen vulva was amazingly soft and she was hot and moist. She let out a soft scream as he touched her intimately. Suddenly he could wait no longer tore at his heavy belt and let his leggings fall to the ground. Impervious to the hard stone against her back, totally enraptured by hot passion she felt a knot of sensation begin deep within her body. Together they moved in delirious rhythm and cried out as a tide of lust flooded them with unbelievable ecstasy. The potent fusion of pain and pleasure, even in a prison's grim walls, held them locked in love and passion.

Susannah stumbled to her cell across the yard, hot and sticky, perspiration shining warmly on her flushed face. In the corner Liz lay on her mattress, legs carelessly apart, smoking a white clay pipe.

"Why are you so hot and bothered? Anyone would think you been giving some bugger a knee tremble."

Susannah put both hands to her cheeks, her face flushed crimson. Liz leapt up throwing her pipe to the flagstones.

"Well stone me! Someone's picked your cherry at last! Henry Cabell or I'm a Chinaman!"

Susannah began to cry, all the emotions of the last few minutes spilling out in hot tears. Liz held her close, "Don't cry little angel, there's nothing to weep about, every girl has to lose her cherry at some time."

"I love him, Liz, I love him so much it hurts."

"Of course you do and if that swine does the dirty on you, I'll kill him myself."

"Don't tell anyone Liz. Don't let him know I've said anything."

"Of course not, I'll be quiet as the grave."

The next day, when the prisoners were allowed to mix, Liz waited for Henry as he emerged from his cell. She took hold of his neckerchief, a slight figure against his strong frame.

"Listen Henry Cabell, don't go hurting my Susannah. That girl dotes on you, I'll not have any bugger messing her about!"

Henry prised her fingers from his neck. "I love her Liz. I'll take care of her as long as I live. You are her friend, I'll take care of you too."

She pushed him away, "I don't want nobody looking after me, I can take bleeding care of myself!"

Nevertheless, she felt oddly moved by his boyish declaration of friendship and rewarded him with a hearty thump in the chest.

Chapter Fifteen

The Commissioner for the Navy, usually known as the Navy Board, began planning the first great voyage to Botany Bay. The Admiralty advertised for ships suitable to transport 'hardy and seasoned' felons. The task of inspecting the vessels fell to naval officers stationed in various places around the country. Not one ship, neither then nor later, was built specially to carry convicts; existing vessels were to be modified for the incredible sea journey.

Lessons from the previous practice of transporting convicts to America under private contract were learned well. This time Contractors' interest would be restricted to the successful completion of the voyages and to offloading their human cargo on arrival at the new land. The Navy Board asked for tenders at a rate of ten shillings per registered ton per month. Detailed planning was with the Navy Board but overall responsibility for the whole venture was lodged firmly with the Home Office, which had a staff of just thirteen for all of its business. At this stage, their direct involvement was to decide which prisoners to send, where to lodge them on the hulks prior to embarkation, how to transport them from gaols throughout the country and to organise daily rations.

The Home Office also had to liaise with the Treasury, whose payments provided provisions, and for fitting out ships. The wheels of Government, traditionally slow turning and deliberate, were further hampered by the fact that not a single ship had been selected for the momentous journey.

In London, another outbreak of typhoid in Newgate prison sent the population and press into spasms of terror. In three cells intended for sixty five prisoners there lived one hundred and fifty, all women. The obnoxious airs in this sector of Newgate – sweat and overflowing buckets of urine and faeces – forced the Governor to supply every turnkey with a pot of spirits before they would open the cells each morning.

Streets already overcrowded with impoverished people were further burdened with newly-poor home from the American and French Wars. London also teemed with crippled beggars from these same wars so unemployment had risen inexorably. In the wake of these disasters crime had also leapt dramatically and so the Government was daily sledged by newspapers and broadsheets. Former shop girls and maid servants scraped by on pennies stolen, or by joining the army of prostitutes, estimated by the Times Newspaper at 'fifty thousand fallen women.'

In Norwich Castle Henry and Susannah got together at every exercise period. They made love wherever they could squeeze an extra few minutes into the time allowed for collecting water for their cells. Their attachment soon became common knowledge throughout the prison. They asked John Euston to read every scrap of information about the new transportations in newspapers discarded by turnkeys and visitors. They talked endlessly of the new life they would make together in the new lands.

In the middle of July, on his twenty first birthday, Henry received word that Susannah was ill. At the first exercise period he hurried to the women's section to find Liz with Susannah who was vomiting in a corner of the yard. She was deathly white, her face a sheen of perspiration.

"My God Liz, is it the plague?" he whispered.

"You silly sod, she's up the duff! She's with child. Your child!"

Henry's mouth fell open and he stared at Susannah.

"I'm sorry Henry, I didn't know!"

"You're having our baby?"

They fell into each other's arms, laughing and crying.

Liz linked arms with John Euston. "Lets make ourselves scarce you old shirtlifter. Now are you sure I can't cock my leg for you, by way of celebration."

The young couple heard him laughing all the way across the yard.

"Are you sure you don't mind Henry?" she looked at him with such imploring eyes that his heart lurched violently in his chest.

"This is God's boundless gift to us Susannah! We'll work together for the child's sake to make a life beyond the seas! We'll be together where streets are broad, where carriages pass shop windows aglow with lanterns and fine goods. There'll be a time when we're free of chains and unshackled by poverty!"

She was astonished at his outburst, never having heard him string ten words together before. They held each other close, each believing and despairing of the vision he has expressed of their future.

That night Henry shared a pork pie with John Euston.

"You're pleased the lass is with child." Euston said.

"Pleased and worried, this is no place to bring up a young 'un, there's enough distempers in this foul place to kill a horse, let alone an infant."

"I'll help you write a letter to the Governor, asking permission to wed!"

"Would you do that for me John, I'll never ask another favour of you."

"It'll be the best of letters and I've written a few in this place."

A week before Christmas, Henry was taken before the Governor. On receiving the Henry's petition for permission to marry another prisoner, he had consulted prominent members of the legal profession, it was the first time any of them had heard of such a request from a serving felon.

"I understand a new life forms in prisoner Holmes' body and that you are the father."

Henry looked puzzled for a moment. "Susannah's having a baby," he blurted out.

"Quite so, I'll not enquire too deeply how this has come about while both of you are confined in the prison. However, I have your petition before me and have consulted widely on its contents. So you wish to marry the girl?"

"It is my earnest desire Sir."

"You are both incarcerated; you cannot build a home here!"

"We want to give the baby a name, we don't want it to be a bastard child Sir."

The Governor stroked his long chin. "English law regards felons as civilly dead, unable to hold property, to sue, to witness, nor make contracts. It is the latter point that weighs against you. Being unable to make contracts means you are unable to make the solemn and binding contract of marriage. Your petition, therefore, must fail. I cannot make any arrangement for you to be married to Holmes."

"They can't want the child to be a bastard Sir. Is there no chance they'll change their minds?"

"Not a cat in hell's chance, Cabell."

All prisoners were manacled when called before the Governor. Outside, the turnkey unlocked the chains binding his hands and feet. Henry, hardened by injustice, felled the man when he thought he was laughing at him. He spent the next two months chained to the wall in the deep dungeons.

When Henry was released from the dungeons he was thin and weak, dysentery and sickness having drained him of strength. Within hours of being 'topside' he was isolated, the prison doctor fearing that he might be infectious.

"It's either gaol fever or worse, Governor."

"Let's pray to God it's not Typhus, it'll run through the prisoners like water if it is."

"Not only through the felons, Governor, Prison staff too."

The Governor instinctively clamped a nosegay to his face. "God help us."

Henry was placed in a small room behind the cells. As soon as word had spread of his isolation Susannah approached John Simpson in the yard.

"I want to nurse Henry Mr. Simpson. I can keep him cool when his fever's raging." The turnkey eyed her carefully, "It might be typhus - you don't want to catch that."

"I want to look after him, he'd be my husband if they let us wed."

"What about the baby that grows within you? You'll not want to risk losing that!"

"Nothing will matter if I lose Henry."

"You're a damn fool Holmes. A baby's life is more precious than both of you put together."

She began to weep copiously.

"Alright, look after him if you must, but don't say I didn't warn you."

He watched her shamble as quickly as she could to the isolation room, ankle irons ringing out at every step. John Euston and Liz had been listening nearby.

"You're a toff Mr Simpson." Liz called out.

"I've not done the girl any favours believe me," he growled.

The two prisoners went over to the room where Henry lay. It was used as a storeroom when it was not needed to house infectious felons. They peered in through the half open door. Susannah squatted beside Henry, washing his face from a bucket of water.

Liz stepped back holding a rag to her face. "See his eyes? They're like pissholes in the snow."

Euston nodded grimly, "I'm thinking the authorities should prepare a pauper's grave for the lad, there's a smell of death about this place."

That night at his cottage in Colegate, Simpson told his wife about Susannah nursing Henry.

"Sounds like something powerful is called for if that boy is to be helped." Rosie looked thoughtful. "You're thinking of the girl too if I'm not mistaken."

"Aye lass, I am, she's heavy with Cabell's child."

"I'll see what I can do John" she took her only book from a shelf. It was titled "Medicinal Herbs," and was well thumbed. She spent most of the evening weighing, boiling and straining herbs in a series of pots.

The next morning she gave him an earthenware jar, brimful with a sticky brew.

"What's in it Rosie?"

"Mainly jalap with aconite and herb-robert for inflammation. I've added dash of southern wood and agrimony."

"Will it work?"

She shrugged, "Here, take this endive tea too. Get the girl to make him swallow it whenever he can – it's good for cooling fevers."

At the gaol Susannah burst into tears when he gave her the medicines. Her face was haggard and drawn. He guessed she had had little sleep since the previous day.

"Remember you have a child growing inside that needs you in good health." He spoke tenderly remembering his own daughter's death in childbirth.

Newspapers continued their campaign to restart transportation as soon as possible. More and more articles, inspired by Government leaks, appeared indicating that arrangements for the ridding the country of prisoners and noxious bridewells were well underway. However, the destination chosen seemed to be cloaked in equal measures of mystery and confusion. The Government was indeed considering places other than Botany Bay. The enormity of a journey across 16,000 miles of treacherous seas weighed heavily on those planning the expedition. Destinations such as Madagascar, Tristan de Cunha and the Coffee Coast near Cape Town were under careful consideration.

The destination of the transports was of no concern to Susannah Holmes. Her only thoughts were of Henry's survival. She had John Simpson's instructions about administering the medicines to the father of her child to the letter. Liz brought food and water to the room where she cared for

Henry. For two days he had babbled and sweated on her lap, face drained of colour. On the morning of the third day, at a time when all the prisoners were in the yard, Susannah staggered out into the cold air, weeping bitterly.

Liz and John Euston hurried over, clamping rags to their faces.

"He's gone, Liz, my Henry's gone!"

John Euston's shoulders sagged. He had grown fond of the rugged young giant. Liz comforted Susannah while Euston went cautiously into the dark room. A moment later he was back at the door.

"Dry your eyes Susannah, Henry sleeps, he's not dead!"

Liz ran into the storeroom and dropped to her knees. Carefully she peeled back Henry's eyelids.

"Well I'll be buggered! Henry's fever has broken. He sleeps like a baby!"

The news spread like wildfire in the yard. Even those that had fallen foul of Henry's temper were pleased. Prison fever and typhus were the most feared of distempers, so anyone recovering was a great boost to those living in close proximity. Outside, Liz found Susannah leaning against the walls of the storeroom.

"Cheer up, girl, Henry's going to be alright."

"Liz, I don't feel well."

Liz caught her as Susannah collapsed against the rough flints. "You need to get a bit of kip, little angel, you're worn out."

Susannah, a surprised look on her face, stared at a puddle of liquid forming at her feet.

"Christ, her waters have broken, get a kettle on someone, we need hot water!" John Euston ran out of the storeroom, then back again in a complete panic. Liz was little better but soon had Susannah lodged in a sparsely furnished room in the Governors' quarters. Liz and another prisoner, Ann Turner, were allowed to stay. Liz's contribution to the impending birth was that plenty of hot water was required. She had once lodged with a woman specialising in aborting unwanted babies and so swore by the efficiency of this essential. Ann Turner, raised on a farm, had seen many a lamb born so was more experienced.

Liz lit a fire in the iron grate, using logs supplied by the Governor. "Get your clothes off Susannah and lay on that mattress, it won't matter if it gets messed up, it's the Governor's!"

"Stop buzzing about like a blue-arsed fly, Liz, and bring more candles, I can hardly see my bleeding hand in front of my face!" Ann Turner ran her hands down her grubby skirt as a contribution to a clean birth.

In the early hours of the next morning, the 17ᵗʰ day of February 1786, John Simpson, standing in the freezing cold below the chamber, heard the lusty cries of the first baby ever born in the Castle Prison. He went up the steep flight of stairs and rapped on the door.

"Bugger off, we're busy" Liz shouted.

"How's the girl?" Simpson shouted back.

The door opened a fraction and Liz peered out, her face as white as the frost on the ground.

"She fine and the baby's healthy, its got a huge diddle though!"

"You silly sod, that's the cord, come back here and help me tie it off!" Ann Turner bawled from the depths of the room.

The turnkey went down into the frosty yard. A clear moon and bright stars added to the pristine scene. He felt strangely light-hearted in the sharp freshness.

"A pure new life in this evil place, truly it's a miracle."

He had stayed over his usual duty hours, anxious to know if Susannah Holmes and the baby would survive. He made his way home to tell his wife the news of the birth and to prepare for the journey to visit his daughter's grave.

Later that day, when returning to duty, John Simpson found himself regarded as something of a hero for bringing in herbal medicines to break Henry Cabell's fever. He went directly to the first floor chamber and knocked at the door. "Everything decent in there?" he called. There was no answer so he pushed open the door and peered in.

"Put the wood in the hole, Mr Simpson, it's perishing in here!" The three women sat in a semi circle around the embers in the grate. A lone candle flared in the hearth. A glistening dewdrop stretched on Ann Turner's sharp nose. She rubbed it off with the back of her hand.

Ann Turner was in her mid twenties and was no stranger to prison. Her auburn hair that gleamed like burnished gold when she had arrived in the prison was now dull and lifeless.

She had been fined five shillings for beating out a man's eye who had failed to pay her fee. At her trial she had unfortunately declared that the fine was good value and she would gladly pay another five shillings to knock out his other eye. On hearing this, the judge had obliged her with a spell in prison instead of the fine. Later she had relieved the Chaplain of his purse containing five pounds so had been sentenced to death. A few weeks earlier this had been reduced to seven years transportation.

"Cat got your tongue, Mr Simpson?" Ann Turner disposed of another dewdrop. From his comprehensive cloak the turnkey produced two bundles, each wrapped in white cloth. He handed them to Susannah.

"Here lass, these are for your baby, they're a gift from my wife."

She unwrapped the first bundle, inside was a tiny knitted coat with a row of white buttons gleaming against the rich wool.

"Oh Mr Simpson, this is beautiful!" She held the tiny coat up to the fitful light, eyes moist with tears.

"My daughter was having a baby but she died. My wife made the coat for her nipper." He turned away as a lump came into his throat as it always did when he talked of his daughter. He unwrapped the second bundle. It contained a dozen white squares. "My wife made them from worn sheets." He turned to go. Liz and Ann each took an arm stopping him from leaving the room.

"You a good 'un, you are." Ann squeezed her breast against his arm.

"Fancy a tumble on the mattress, it's a cold morning but we'll soon get your blood rattling."

"You're a wicked pair of strumpets, I'll have to go," he smiled. "I'd better have a quick peep at the new inmate. Boy or girl?"

"Boy" they chorused.

"How's Henry?" Susannah whispered as she showed him the infant's pink face. "Sleeping like a log last time I saw him."

"Mr Simpson, you have been so kind, thank you."

"Don't thank me, thank my wife- she made the medicines and the clothes."

The women grinned as they heard him stumbling down the stairs. "He's not a bad un if you squint your eyes a bit!" Liz announced.

As soon as Henry was well enough, he was allowed to visit Susannah and the baby. Susannah lay on the straw mattress suckling the small pink infant. Dropping to his knees, Henry stared at the child.

"What shall we call him, Susannah?"

"He shall be named Henry like his father and his father's father."

"My dad would have liked that."

"It's a fine name."

"I'll always love you Susannah."

"I know."

Liz Pulley came over, her arm folded across her ample bosom. "Right, bugger off now, Susannah needs some shut eye."

In the yard, Henry badgered John Euston to write another appeal, this time to the Prison Board, for permission to marry Susannah.

"Tell them about the baby; tell them we want him properly christened."

The older man crafted another petition and enclosed a letter from Reverend Jackson supporting the request. Within a week, the reply was delivered by to prison. Governor Gwynn himself handed the letter to Henry.

"I'll take it to Susannah; she has a better eye for words than me." Henry told the official. The Governor and Rev Jackson watched him go, holding the official-looking missive in front of him as if fearful it might explode.

Henry found Susannah sitting by the door of the washhouse. It was the first day that her two companions had allowed her to leave her mattress. They sat in the dirt nearby showing off the baby to a succession of prisoners.

"Susannah, I've got a reply to the petition."

"What does it say?"

"You read it, my guts are too tight to hold it still."

She broke the wax seal and carefully extracted the thick paper. "I'll read it out loud Henry, then we'll both know at the same time." It was addressed to 'Prisoner Cabell, Norwich Castle'.

'The Prison Board are familiar with the term of your petition, having been fully acquainted with this matter when consulted by Governor Gwynne on occasion of your first petition. Prisoners are not allowed to enter into any contract, marital nor material. Therefore your petition to marry another prisoner is refused.'
Prison Board
Castle Fortress
Norwich

"Don't worry, Henry, we'll find a way, they'll not beat us." She held his hand to her chest, rocking him like a baby.

Liz stared at the couple, the letter clearly visible in Susannah's hand. "Bastards," she muttered.

Chapter Sixteen

A month after the baby was born, news of a riot aboard a hulk moored in Dartford Harbour made the headlines. John Euston read out the first few lines from a front page story in the Norwich Mercury.

'Eight prisoners were killed and thirty six injured, most as a result of musket fire, although four turnkeys were badly beaten by a wild mob of felons.'

The uproar of this scandal and subsequent terror of the local populace led to an upsurge of newspaper diatribes on the inefficiency of the Government. The Times was particularly scathing, making a great deal of the fact that nobody in Parliament seemed to know to where the prisoners were being sent to. Throughout spring and summer, intense pressures were brought to bear on William Pitt's Government, particularly by MPs whose constituencies included hulks crammed with prisoners, ready to restart transportation.

In June 1786, the Times leader named the destination as 'Botany Bay, New South Wales'. The Government had dismissed all other destinations after an exhaustive study. William Pitt finally gave the go ahead for the prison fleet to set sail for Botany Bay. Oddly, the decision was not conveyed to the Admiralty until 31 August 1786.

The Navy Board chartered five ships; The *Alexander, Friendship, Charlotte, Seaborough* and *Lady Penrhyn*; plus three other vessels to be used as store ships; the *Borrowdale, Golden Grove* and *Fishburn*. It quickly became clear that that these vessels were not enough so a sixth transport, the *Prince of Wales* was contracted. To these nine vessels two more were added- the warships HMS *Sirius* and HMS *Supply*. Eleven vessels to undertake the greatest sea journey ever attempted.

The merchantmen were all reasonably new three masted ships, except the *Friendship*. She was a brig with two masts. The largest transport was the *Alexander* with a length of 114 feet and 31 feet across the beam.

In Norwich Castle, Susannah received a letter from her brother Harry.

'*Dear Sister,*

I have seen such things in far off places you will not believe. The foreign man is so different from us, sometimes brown like a nut and sometimes black and shiny as a burnished fireplace.

I often think of you dear sister and will visit as soon as I can. Sailors never know where they are headed. I might even come into Yarmouth or Lowestoft one of these days. I have been paid off from this ship but don't worry I will soon find another. I hope you are well.'

Your loving brother.

Harry

Susannah was glad that there was no forwarding address. She did not want to tell him that she had a baby out of wedlock.

A story widely reported in the press came as a devastating blow to Henry and Susannah. Unknown sources were quoted as indicating that only young females would be selected from gaols throughout the country, there being 'sufficient male blackguards in the hulks around London and the South Coast to fill the first fleet many times over'.

Henry sought an interview with Governor Gwynne but he was unable to shed any light on the matter and dismissed the reports as 'wild rumours'.

Liz Pulley told Susannah to start thinking of herself and the baby without Henry. "Henry might not get transported for years. You and the little one will need someone to take care of you."

"I'll wait for Henry no matter how long it takes."

"Listen, little angel, there's no rhyme nor reason that says Henry will be sent to the same place as you. They say the land in the South Seas is ten times as big as this Country and there won't be regular stagecoach trips between places, you can bet on that!"

"I don't care, I'll always love Henry."

"Love is like a new frock. Lovely at first but soon it gets worn and dirty. At some time you have to throw it out and find another that suits you better."

Henry, in his own hand, wrote to Jacob Preston, local Member of Parliament, imploring him to allow them to wed so that they would not be torn apart. John Euston, at Henry's request, had written three months earlier to the same man but had received a reply indicating he had no jurisdiction in such matters and could not help. This time Henry wrote of *'a faultless child and unprotected mother, likely to travel alone to unknown lands'*.

Jacob Preston was touched by the sincerity of the poorly written letter that begged with passion for the three of them to remain together. Subsequently, he wrote to Lord Suffield, M.P. for Yarmouth.

'Cabell's attachment to the woman Holmes is so strong that rather than be separated from her, he is desirous of being transported to the same place."

Lord Suffield, who was on good terms with Lord Sydney the Home Secretary, wrote to him on their behalf.

'I understand these two never were confederate in any crime or misdemeanour but that of child making. I should hope there might be less objection to their being united by way of transportation'.

Henry and Susannah, knowing nothing of these letters between parliamentarians, waited in desperate hope within the walls of Norwich Castle.

On October 12 1786, one day after his 48th birthday, a letter was delivered to Captain Arthur Phillip at his farm in Lyndhurst, Hampshire. The letter bore the seal of King George the third. It was official confirmation that he was to be Governor of a territory called New South Wales, and in charge of the eleven ships that would make the hazardous journey.

He knew why he had been appointed. A dozen years earlier, he had received permission to join the Portuguese Navy who were at war with their Spanish neighbours. During his service he had delivered four hundred Portuguese convicts across the tumultuous Atlantic to Brazil. It was this impressive feat- he didn't lose one convict- that caused the Navy Authorities to select him for the risk of taking British felons to Botany Bay.

He was anxious to get back to sea. For two years he had been on half pay, waiting for a seagoing commission to come up. His last command had been the sixty four gun ship HMS *Europe*. He had no family, having parted with his wife many years earlier during another enforced period on half pay.

After receiving the letter, he left detailed instructions with his senior farm hand and booked a seat for the next day's coach to London. He knew meticulous planning was essential for a successful voyage with hardened criminals on board. He was acutely aware that taking a fleet to a destination nearly 16,000 miles away would require all of his powers of organisation and tenacity in dealing with shore-based administrators.

In the Governor's quarters overlooking the yard in Norwich Castle, John Simpson read the letter again. "This is going to cause a deal of trouble, Governor."

"There is nothing to be done, the die is cast."

"Are we not to be rid of at least one male prisoner to Botany Bay? There's enough villains here that we'd be glad to see the back of, I'm sure."

"The letter states that only three female prisoners, Liz Pulley, Ann Turner and Susannah Holmes are to be transported."

"I hoped we'd be rid of one of the more troublesome criminals, like Cabell. Surely it cannot be just, breaking up families; Holmes will have problems surviving, burdened with a small child!"

"In the eyes of the law there is no family, just a young woman with a baby. The authorities need to balance the first fleet to Botany Bay- they appear to be short of young women."

"We should give the news after lock-up. Cabell will have a few hours before morning to get over his disappointment."

"More trouble, I suppose, from that young man." The Governors peered glumly into the yard below.

"Aye, the lad's trouble right enough, but I can't help feeling its wrong to separate those two. His affection for Holmes seems true enough."

That evening, John Simpson and Governor Gwynne, accompanied by another turnkey went to Henry Cabell's cell. There were eight prisoners in the cramped room.

"We've received orders about who is to go on the first fleet to New South Wales." The Governor announced shortly.

"Who are the lucky ones?" Euston asked sarcastically.

"No men are going, just three women from this prison, Liz Pulley, Ann Turner and Susannah Holmes."

Henry gave vent to a loud cry, somewhere between anger and despair. The other prisoners moved back as far as they could.

"Stand still, Cabell!" Simpson grabbed Henry holding his wooden baton against the prisoner's throat. "Remember you've still to hear from Jacob Preston after your last appeal. Any trouble and nobody will support your petition."

John Euston stepped forward and threw an arm round his young friend. "Mr Simpson's right Henry, you'll need all the help you can get."

The three officials backed carefully out of the door. In the yard, Governor Gwynne mopped his brow.

"That went better than I thought it might."

"Lets wait until tomorrow, Cabell can be like a volcano, erupting when you least expect it."

In Liz Pulley's cell, the three men were careful to stay by the door. "We've received word from the Home Office about the first transportations to New South Wales."

Liz and Susannah instinctively grasped each other.

"Liz Pulley, Susannah Holmes and Ann Turner are all to proceed on the first transport."

"And my Henry?" Susannah whispered.

"There are no other prisoners from Norwich on the first transport."

The whole prison heard her anguished scream.

The next day, word of the transportation passed from lip to lip. Henry and Susannah were left by themselves in a quiet corner of the yard.

"Henry, I'm not going without you, I care nought for anyone else."

"Fret not lass, we've not yet had a reply to my petition. John Euston reckons the long delay is a good sign."

"Surely there's none so callous as to separate a child from its father."

"We'll ask Mr Simpson to put in a word for us. His wife's been sending in milk for the nipper, maybe she can add a line or two."

From the doorway to the washhouse Euston and Fuller were keeping a wary eye on Henry.

"Common sense and the Government are often strangers. We must keep Henry hoping otherwise there will be big trouble. The lad fears the girl will forget him and he'll never see her or the child again."

Chapter Seventeen

John Simpson made his way up Castle Hill carrying a carpet bag, his breath steaming in the early morning light. The prison cart was by the gates, two sullen horses stared balefully as if he was the cause of their having to rise so early.

The women prisoners waited inside the big double gates, each carrying a ragged bundle of possessions. Susannah's eyes were red from weeping. Every day during the last week she and Henry had asked if a reply had been sent to their petition. Every day they had been disappointed. Susannah had vowed not to leave without Henry but the turnkey on duty that morning had made sure he carried the baby out through the gates first. She had followed.

The baby lay in a wooden box swaddled in virtually every garment it possessed. The box had come from the fruit market and smelled of apples. The women were all cross locked, a heavy chain linking hands and feet making movement difficult. Tucking the boxed baby under his arm, Simpson led the strange procession through the gates to the waiting cart.

"I want no trouble from any of you, it's a long journey to Plymouth where you are to be lodged on a hulk."

"Any chance of getting these chains and cuffs removed? My bleeding wrists are red raw already."

"Hold your tongue, Pulley. The chains will come off when I'm satisfied you'll be no trouble."

"Where's Plymouth, Mr Simpson?" Ann Turner asked.

"It's on the south western tip of England, the bit that points towards America. It'll take quite a few days to get there."

Thank you for helping to keep me safe.

- Every year, **over 10,000** animals are thrown away like rubbish

- Our National Cruelty Line receives **1.3 million calls a year**

- RSPCA inspectors investigate more than **150,000 complaints** of cruelty and neglect a year

Call our Cruelty Line on 0300 1234 999 to report cruelty or an animal in distress.

Thank you for helping to keep me safe.

- Every year, **over 10,000** animals are thrown away like rubbish

- Our National Cruelty Line receives **1.3 million calls a year**

- RSPCA inspectors investigate more than **150,000 complaints** of cruelty and neglect a year

Call our Cruelty Line on 0300 1234 999 to report cruelty or an animal in distress.

A charity registered in England & Wales. Charity no. 219099.

The cart rumbled through the cobbled streets leaving the walled city by St Stephen's Gate, disgorging Simpson and the women by the inn just beyond the gates. The hostelry, aptly named the Coach and Horses, was a passenger pick up point for the coach to London.

Governor Gwynne, anxious that the reputation of Norwich Gaol did not suffer from the appearance of ragged convicts when they arrived at the hulk, had issued the three women with fresh clothing. It was apparel donated by well off citizens and fitted where it touched. The comparatively new clothes were supplemented by the prisoners own collections of shawls, capes, and woollen wear that suffered from the lack of washing facilities at Norwich Castle.

John Simpson shepherded the prisoners to a back room away from the disapproving stares of the other passengers, pointedly covering their faces with nosegays.

Threatening each with dire consequences if they moved an inch, the turnkey went to discover whether the coach was on time. As soon as he left the room, Liz Pulley stood up to stare out of the window.

"You're not thinking of scarpering are you, Liz?" Ann Turner whispered.

"What, bound hard and fast to you two? No, I was just enjoying being in a hostelry again, there's nothing like the smell of stale beer."

"Do you think we'll get a chance to scarper?"

"We'll keep an eye open but Mr Simpson's a wily old cove."

"I can't escape, Henry may be on the next transport," Susannah said.

"Listen, little angel, there's a good chance he won't. Nobody knows who's being sent where," Liz said.

"You'll probably never see him again and that's a fact!" Ann Turner added.

At this Susannah began to sob so Liz put her arm around her shoulders.

"Don't fret so, you got to keep your pecker up for the child's sake. He don't want his mother snivelling all the time. Besides, Ann is right, you've got to think about getting another to look after you. Henry might lie rotting in Norwich for years."

"No one is going to change my mind Liz, I'm waiting for Henry and that's that."

"Suit yourself, but you're a bloody fool girl."

The coach arrived and the team of four were swiftly replaced with fresh horses. Passengers and possessions piled in according to their tickets. The prisoners were booked for the outside but John Simpson made Susannah take his inside seat with the baby on her lap, much to the displeasure of a rotund gentleman and his wife. John Simpson sat on the back outside with the other two prisoners, well wrapped in a heavy cape reinforced with a long woollen comforter.

The coachman, having imbibed a tot or two of hot brandy and water, mounted his box, cracked the whip and away they went down the London road. Soon the horses were smoking hard and it was a job for the driver to see ahead through the rising mist. At every hamlet and village he announced the arrival of the coach by way of a few challenging notes on his key bugle as if he were a Captain of Horse bugling his men into battle.

After Thetford, the next town of any size was Bury St. Edmunds, where the coachman pulled his steaming horses into the yard of The White Hart – an animal rare in nature but common in the world of inns. The coachman jumped down, jammed his whip in the box and handed the ostler the reins having pocketed the leather stay that buckled all four straps together. The stableman unhitched the horses and began the job of rubbing down, having first covered each with sacks to prevent them cooling too quickly.

Inviting everybody to 'get down and stretch your legs' the driver stretched his in the direction of the fire within and the added comfort of hot brandy and water. Liz and Ann Turner, having made the painful descent from the 'back outside' stamped their feet on the hard ground, restricted as they were by the weighty fetters. Susannah took the opportunity to change the baby's sodden clothes.

"Any chance of a noggin of ale Mr Simpson?" Liz asked.

"Do you have money?" he demanded, eyeing the fire flickering an invitation through the misted windows. Liz looked at Ann who shook her head.

"We'll have a piss instead!" Liz announced.

The turnkey led the prisoners to the rear of the inn and waited while they relieved themselves behind the barn. After securing them to a post in the barn and Susannah to the Coach he went in search of a pot of ale.

When it was time to resume the journey the passengers struggled out of the inn, reluctant to leave the warming fire and spirits. The coachman was last to appear and smelled strongly of several medicinal brandies. He climbed laboriously up to his box, feet and hands missing a number of vital holds on the way. It took a while to buckle the four reins in the leather stay but eventually the coach roared off, a sight more flamboyantly than before, the coachman's face a beacon of red. As if they sensed the drivers hands were not as steady as before, the horses strained at the harness, jingled the reins and generally danced down the dirt road rather than pull steadily as they had on the first part of the journey.

John Simpson, Liz and Ann Turner, on the top outside, were forced to hang on as the coach swayed and surged and found every pothole in the track. After an hour of this jostling ride, the 'top back' passengers were beginning to feel as if they were on a lively ocean running ahead of a gale. Fortunately, the carriage turned off the main thoroughfare towards Long Melford where they were to change the horses again. The team of four, sweating and steaming, crested a rise and began their run down a slope to the inn below. The driver got out his key bugle with a flourish and sounded a series of sharp notes to forewarn the ostler to prepare fresh horses in the yard below. Despite the remarkably wide street, the coachman, anxious to show his mastery of driving four in hand, misjudged the stopping distance and the whole party inside was thrown in a heap when the coach slammed into a broad oak post.

The post, one of several, served its purpose of preventing damage to the inn but had also smashed the front nearside wheel to pieces. The horses tossed their heads and rolled their eyes at the coachman who had tumbled off his seat as the carriage pitched forward and sideways onto the front axle.

Miraculously none of the outside passengers had been thrown off but Liz Pulley and Ann Turner were not slow at giving their opinion of the driver's skills when they stepped down. Ann Turner also threw up neatly into the rotund passenger's top hat that, conveniently, had landed upside down. After he had freed himself from the clutches of the coach door, the owner of the hat vented his anger at the unfortunate Ann Turner.

Liz Pulley rapped him on the chest with her metal cuffs. "You silly bugger, she's bilious! Do you think she's spewing her guts up for fun?"

The passenger and his wife retreated to the safety of the inn, muttering deprecations quiet enough for Liz not to hear. Inside, in a perspiration of profanity and heat, the gentleman let it be known that he was going to sue everyone in sight 'for every last farthing'.

Susannah and the baby had escaped unscathed, the wooden fruit box being a particularly handy container in which to come a cropper.

John Simpson took his prisoners to the yard at the back where a series of rooms had been fashioned by putting in an extra floor in the capacious barn. The rooms were for less well off travellers. Simpson had reserved the largest room for the three convicts when it had become clear that the wheel and axle could not be repaired immediately. He left them bolted to a stanchion while he arranged for food to be brought.

The smashed wheel was quickly replaced but the damaged axle proved more difficult and it seemed they would be held up. The other passengers had been taken in a pony and cart to Sudbury where they had secured seats on another London bound coach.

John Simpson stared morosely out of the window of the Bull Inn. Long Melford seemed to be a prosperous town; the main street was remarkably wide and crowded at the moment with hundreds of sheep being herded along by three boys with long staves. Prosperous looking houses vied for space with shops on either side of the broad thoroughfare and he could just make out an imposing looking church at one end.

An old man stood beside the turnkey, his back so bent that his chin was almost resting on the knob of his walking stick.

"Fine sight at this time of the year," the old man waved his stick at the flock of sheep.

"Looks like a town of some importance," Simpson replied.

"Wealthiest town hereabouts, plenty of money in sheep – this lot's due to end on any number of Christmas plates, but not before the wool merchants have had their cut!"

"That's a fine church up the hill, I expect that's worth a look?"

"You'll be wondering what to do with those three whores you have in chains I expect."

"You've heard of the prisoners then?"

"The whole town's heard of 'em!" the old man snorted.

"Not one of them is convicted of whoring, but I can't keep them chained to the inn all the time.I thought I'd walk them about a bit."

"Show 'em Melford Hall up here a ways, Sir Hyde Parker and his family, the new owners have only just moved in. I 'spect they'll view the whores with as much curiosity as the whores will view them!"

"And the church?" Simpson reminded him.

"Built by the wool merchants, it's as big as a cathedral, some say."

The turnkey thanked him and turned to go back to his quarters at the rear of the inn. "You'll be bringing the women to the inn?" the old man enquired anxiously.

"They'll have to eat, I expect."

"You'll be allowing them to earn a crust now they're here?" the little man rubbed his hands vigorously; his thin hooked nose, already red from the sharp air, seemed to glow.

"I've not given it a thought."

"There will be a shilling or two in it for yourself I 'spect!"

John Simpson tipped his hat at the old man and went back thoughtfully to his rooms; he had heard stories of turnkeys hiring out women when they were escorted between prisons.

When he unlocked the prisoners' room Liz Pulley and Ann Turner were crouched over the fire and Susannah Holmes was feeding the baby under cover of a shawl.

"We are stuck here for a time," he announced, "so I'll be relieving you of the restraining chains but I want no trouble from any of you scallywags – any shenanigans and you'll be locked up double quick!"

Liz Pulley grinned and held out her hands. "We'll be as good as angels, Mr Simpson."

"Butter won't melt," Ann Turner winked at Liz.

The turnkey looked enquiringly at Susannah, "I hope Henry's in no trouble, Mr Simpson." She hadn't listened to a word of what had been said.

John Simpson wanted to look around the village, so he had no choice but to take the women with him after issuing another stern warning about their behaviour. It was the first chance for Liz and Susannah to experience normal life for over three years, and although Ann Turner had spent less time in the Castle she too was anxious to see the sights.

It was a fine town with many timbered houses of almost two hundred years old, mingled with thatched cottages and a few new houses built in the modern style called 'Georgian'. But the shops were what interested the prisoners more and the little village had a surprising variety: cobbler, saddlemaker, blacksmith, haberdasher and corn merchant, plus the usual baker, greengrocer and butcher. But it was the drapers to which the three women made a beeline to stare longingly through the square panes.

"Please Mr Simpson, lets 'ave a look inside," Liz pleaded.

"You're supposed to be exercising your limbs not my patience!"

"None of us have enough clothes for a sea journey, Mr Simpson, can't we have just a quick look?" Susannah pleaded.

"I got only one pair of bloomers, and the tie ribbons gone on them- you can check if you want to," Ann Turner began to lift up her voluminous skirts.

Hurriedly he pushed them into the shop before they had a chance to embarrass him further, "Just a quick look mind, and show the shopkeeper you have money!"

Soon they were trying on dresses, bodices and other items that John Simpson did not recognise. He insisted on remaining in the shop with the women so was left holding the baby. Liz Pulley and Ann Turner made sure he was entertained and embarrassed by leaving the curtains to the changing area agape at opportune moments.

The shop keeper was in a quandary whether to admonish the women for their antics but the prospect of sales eased her dilemma and she contented herself with standing between the turnkey and the open curtains, spreading her shawl and muttering imprecations such as 'dear me' and 'whatever next' interspersed with 'suits you, dear' and 'looks lovely, ducks'.

This lively tableau was spiced up when a dried up woman came in, saw what was going on and immediately began beating John Simpson about the head with a walking stick declaring he was a 'filthy swine' and 'ought to be ashamed of himself!'

The turnkey took this all stoically, declaring at intervals, "Duty, madam, duty," and refused to move.

The woman, who it transpired was the vicar's wife, finally retired to a chair in the corner to rest where she vinegared her temples and watered her head as she tried to ferment herself into a passion again. Liz Pulley, sensing a lull in the entertainment, extended a stockingless leg out of the curtain far enough to reveal the bottom of her bloomers ribboned at the knee and invited the turnkey to 'feel the cloth'.

At this the vicar's wife let out a scandalised shriek, rushed out of the shop and was last seen running helter skelter down the High Street with the hem of her skirts in her hand.

The three women finally purchased several items, mostly 'nearly new from gentry' as sworn by the relieved shopkeeper.

Liz Pulley bought a dress for two shillings which she said might be her wedding dress in the new lands should she decide to let just one man 'pump me bellows'.

The prisoners declared it the best day they had had 'forever'. John Simpson was inclined to agree with them, having been reduced to wiping tears from his eyes at the old lady's expression of horror and the shopkeeper's efforts to extract herself from the cleft stick of income versus propriety.

John Simpson, relieved of the baby by Susannah, was seized on either side by the two other women and steered up and down several side alleys in such a harmonious and congenial fashion as to lead one bystander to declare rather ironically that the three of them were 'as thick as thieves'.

The little party had lost their way when they came upon the little man they had met at the inn who was almost bent double. He stood by the entrance to a field, nose glowing and chin on walking stick.

"Which way to The Bull Inn?" John Simpson asked.

"Up here a ways," he waved his stick vaguely in the direction they were heading, "you'll come to a track on the left – don't take it. After that there's another road on the left but don't take that. Then there's a road on the right – leave that alone."

"Which one do we take?"

"None, go straight on, just past the Dog and Duck!"

They left the old man slapping his thighs and collapsing in the hedge, highly entertained by his own hilarity.

Just before the Bull Inn they encountered the vicar's wife in conference with a small group of women. Seeing them she pointed her stick like a gun and began shouting at the top of her voice, "Jezebels, trollops, hussies!"

They were glad to reach the Inn where two farmers promptly swept off their hats and thus elegantly ushered them into the stone-flagged hall. Directly in front of the wide entrance, massive moulded oak beams dominated the area where the visitors arranged their accommodation. The hall was festooned with notices of good beds, strong ales, clean stabling and so on.

To the right was a large commodious room, already full to over-flowing with country men with ruddy faces and ostlers of a similar hue. The room, about forty feet wide, had a large fireplace, itself some ten feet in width, which accommodated several fat behinds steaming damp out of their breeches. The back wall was a collection of variously coloured bricks that seemed to have been placed haphazardly along its length. A mortuary of stuffed animal heads with pained expressions lined the fireplace wall and stared longingly at the leaded windows opposite. In the great cross beam over the fireplace the image of a bull etched in the grain glared morosely at a strange carving on one of the ceiling beams; this depicted a mysterious wild man, an image popular a hundred years earlier to ward off evil spirits.

The room was a noisy babble of chatter, mainly of farmers, merchants and serving wenches bearing trays of beer and spirits.

"Mr Simpson, can we eat here tonight, I'm starving?" Ann Turner squealed.

"We'll be eating together in the rooms at the back of the inn," he growled.

"Oh, Mr Simpson, let's have one little drink here tonight, we've been as good as gold, 'aven't we?" Liz pleaded.

"Good! You've scandalised at least two women of this parish, one of 'em the vicar's wife!"

Susannah emerged at the turnkey's side "Liz and Ann meant no harm, Mr Simpson, its years since they had the chance of a bit of fun, you can't blame them for having a laugh."

"And we'll be stuck in that black hulk soon enough," Liz added.

The mood of the little knot of people suddenly changed and they began to press in towards the turnkey growling imprecations such as 'poor creatures', 'chained like dogs', 'let's give 'em a send off', and 'how would he like to be locked up!'

Finally, the beleagured turnkey held up his hands and silence gradually settled in the packed room.

"Alright, I'll allow the women one drink after they've filled their bellies with a good meal. One drink only mind!"

A roar went up and John Simpson had his back slapped vigorously. As he led the prisoners through to the rooms at the rear Liz turned back to the crowd and with an enormous wink declared, "One drink only mind!"

The resultant roar could be heard at the other end of the long high street. The landlord, a big man with a black beard, watched as two serving girls pushed their way through the throng. "It's going to be a good night," he declared, rubbing his hands together, "tap another barrel, George!"

The boy thus designated opened a flap in the floor behind the counter and disappeared into the cellar below.

He was right, it turned out to be one of the most uproarious nights The Bull had enjoyed for many a month. When the guard and the prisoners had eaten, Susannah asked to be left with the baby, as she wanted to write to Henry. The turnkey locked her in the room and, after delivering a fulsome lecture to Liz and Ann on the theme that they must 'behave themselves' and 'no vulgar antics', accompanied the two women to the public bar where he was determined to 'watch you buggers all night'.

He didn't stand a chance. As soon as they appeared all three were presented with a foaming flagon of ale and the women dragged off to 'give the room a tune'.

Liz obliged with a bawdy song about a farmer, his wife, a farmhand and a large carrot. Ann Turner accompanied the ditty with much wobbling of her bosom and flashes of her neat ankles.

John Simpson, presented with a fresh jug of ale as soon as he had emptied one, was unable to get near the two prisoners. After the third flagon he found himself enjoying the hilarious show that Liz and Ann were putting on for the locals. Late into the evening he vaguely recollected Ann dancing on a long table and, being mighty proud of the new bloomers she had purchased that afternoon, displaying them in all their glory to the whole room, whilst Liz romped to a lewd version of a popular music hall refrain.

Both women spent a lot of time wriggling their bottoms on numerous laps and generously helping various men to finish off their ale. Ann Turner earned the undying admiration of the room by dipping a breast in warm brandy and water ('only the best, my dears') and allowing the men to suck the liquid dripping from her large nipple. She cuddled customers like an overgrown children and charged them sixpence for the privilege. Liz too seemed to be accumulating an extraordinary pile of coins, but Simpson was unable to fathom how she managed it, occupied as he was trying to hold still the table that seemed determined to out spin the stuffed animal heads around the room.

Finally his watchful companions helped him to the safe harbour of his room away from the danger of drowning in beer.

The next morning, he was awoken by strong sunlight searing his eyeballs that, when they focussed, after several attempts, turned out to be the flame of a bedside candle.

After sluicing himself under the pump in the yard, retching in the hedge and walking up and down the lane a few times, the turnkey made his way to the prisoners' quarters.

Liz lay snoring in a tumble of covers on the bed, garlanded with numerous labels from the inn proclaiming 'strong ale', 'pickles', 'finest preserves', and so on.

Susannah sat in a chair by the window, her face streaked with tears. There was no sign of Ann Turner.

"Where's Turner?" he demanded of Susannah.

"I haven't seen her since she left last night."

"You could have yelled through to me when you woke this morning."

"I'm not her keeper, you are!"

Cursing, the turnkey made Susannah sit on Liz's bed and chained them together and to a large trunk.

"Where's Turner gone, damn you?" he shook Liz awake.

She stared vacantly, her face a yellowy hue. "I don't know," she croaked.

"Damn, damn, damn. This means trouble." He slammed out of the door. Liz sank back on the mattress, closed her eyes and said goodbye by breaking wind vehemently.

Ten minutes later, the turnkey was no nearer to finding the missing prisoner. The 'pot boy' and serving girls couldn't remember when they had last seen her. The landlord could only recall Liz and Anne being carried around the inn by drunken revellers and out to the barn at the back where he supposed that they were put to bed.

"If the prisoner has got away you'll never get any more trade from Norwich prison, I'll see to that."

"I didn't force grog down your throat!"

The two men glared at each other until the potboy came to the rescue by suggesting that they mount a search of the village. The local watchman was roused and soon two groups of men went from house to house each side of the main thoroughfare. Gardens and sheds were searched but there was no sign of Ann Turner.

Two hours later the searchers were back at the Bull Inn. Simpson questioned the other two prisoners again.

"You had no drink last night Holmes, you must know what happened to Turner!"

"I woke when they came banging in here and dumped Liz on the mattress, but I didn't know Ann wasn't with them. There was no way I'd have got out of bed in my night clothes with that lot milling about!"

"What about you, Pulley, can't you remember what happened?"

"I'd had a drop too much, the ale here is heavy enough to sink a ship. Not like the piss we get in Norwich."

"Has Turner talked of escape?" he demanded.

"Never a word, Simpson. On my honour," replied Liz.

"Honour? You don't know the meaning of the word!"

The turnkey stomped off down the stairs again. The landlord found him staring out of the latticed windows, his face a dull grey.

"You'd better get some grub inside you, a man can't think on an empty stomach."

"I had a skinful last night, it's my fault the girl got away."

"What will happen now?"

"I'll report the matter when I get to London and when I reach Plymouth."

"And when you get back to Norwich?"

"I'll be lucky to keep my position when the facts are known."

The coach driver came in to report that the coach had been repaired and Simpson and the prisoners should be ready to resume their journey within the hour.

"I'd better have some grub for the other two, and a drop of warm milk for the child."

"I'll send it up in half an hour."

The meal was brought by the potboy who winked at Liz as if they were on the most intimate of terms. She favoured him with a pained expression as he backed away grinning, out of the door.

"I can't take ale no more Mr Simpson. I blame prison, living like a nun is no good for me."

"You've never lived like a nun, Pulley," he growled.

From the yard below came the sound of the horses being hitched to the coach. Simpson led the two women down, still chained together. Liz had claimed Turner's bundle of possessions, announcing "She int likely to come back for 'em, is she?"

There was a slight delay after a strap snapped when the lead horse reared. A fat farmer, vaguely familiar from the previous night's festivities, sidled up to Liz.

"I got a few shillings that are looking for a new home," he whispered, ignoring the turnkey.

"The shop's shut for repairs." She didn't bother looking at him, being wholly engaged in contemplating a blackened sausage she had saved from the meal.

"Three shillings, not a penny more," he announced.

Poking him in the chest with the sausage she said "Hard luck my old tub of lard, this mare's wrecked and heading for the knacker's yard. Now piss off."

A sudden commotion from the stables caught Simpson's attention. A grinning ostler came out of the stable and beckoned him over. The turnkey took the precaution of dragging his prisoners with him. At the door they all stared into the dim space. From a pile of straw, the head of Ann Turner slowly emerged, a pale imitation of the raucous frolicking creature of the previous evening, looking in imminent danger of an appointment with her maker.

"Turner, you bastard, we've been looking all over for you." Simpson's shout woke a medium-sized pig that was chained to the befuddled prisoner's ankle cuffs. The ostler was so convulsed with the sight of the two of them that he felt the need to summon the innkeeper and most of the remaining household. The porker, being content with the arrangement, promptly went back to sleep, snoring loudly despite frantic attempts by Simpson to free it from Ann Turner who was wailing and groaning in equal measure.

The landlord, assisted by the pot boy duly separated the two creatures and carried the pig into the yard where it curled up to sleep again having had as much to drink the previous evening as the fragile prisoner.

Ann Turner was led into the sunlight by the relieved turnkey. She studied him through half closed eyes and had to prise open one optic for better viewing.

"Crumbs Mr Simpson, you look like a walking corpse. I've seen livelier faces twitching on the gallows!"

He pushed her roughly to the top outside and secured her to a metal stay. A crowd gathered to watch the departure of the prisoners. Some of the new friends Liz and Ann had made the previous evening were there, plus several women including the vicar's wife they had met in the draper's shop. The coachman, sporting a new muffler, cracked his whip and they moved off.

The vicar's wife waved a brolly in their direction. "Be gone, harlots of the night!"

Some of the women thought this an admirable turn of phrase and clapped politely. Another, emboldened beyond her usual demeanour shouted "Delilahs!" and immediately retreated into the folds of her coat, turning a bright pink.

Liz dusted off her hands daintily and stuck her head out of the coach, beckoning to the vicar's wife. "Madam, your husband is not as fat as he looks when he is out of his vestments!"

Being a good mimic she delivered this is in beautifully modulated tones, and gave a regal wave to the knot of men by the inn. They responded with a loud cheer and much waving of hats as the coachman whipped his team into a trot.

Chapter Eighteen

S ome of the merchant ships destined to house prisoners were berthed in the naval dockyard at Deptford on the Thames, a short coach ride from the Houses of Parliament. The Navy board had issued a new book of regulations for transporting felons to New South Wales. The regulations were primarily for the benefit of contractors and masters of the merchant men but also served a purpose for all officers and naval men due to sail with the fleet.

The regulations stipulated convicts' quarters were to be properly cleaned, regularly fumigated and adequately ventilated. All bottom boards from the lower decks had to be taken, twice weekly, to the deck, scraped and washed in sea water, and dried before being replaced in the prisoners' quarters.

The prisoners were to be provided with decent clothing, bedding and medicine, and given regular fresh air and exercise on deck whenever possible. A space six feet deep and seven feet wide was allowed for every four prisoners. The head height was such that prisoners had to slide into the allocated space.

Bulkheads were built to contain convicts in manageable groups. Loopholes for muskets were made should it be necessary to quell riots or disable troublemakers. Deck hatches were specially strengthened so they could be doubly secured.

As a check that instructions were carried out to the letter, ships' masters had to maintain duplicate logs, one of which was to be handed to Captain Phillips, the Governor of the new territory, at Botany Bay. The log books were for recording daily the position of each ship, speed and direction, and details of the weather; but in addition, occurrences of note such as births, deaths, sickness and offences committed by prisoners or seamen were noted. Details of daily expenditure were to be recorded regarding food and water for the felons, as well as the number and duration of the occasions that they were allowed on deck or if they were not allowed, the reasons why.

Even ships Surgeons had to maintain a daily record in duplicate of prisoners' sickness and medicines used. They also had to record how often prisoners were allowed on deck, presumably as a check on the master's logs. The surgeons were to specify when fumigations and scrapings of convicts' quarters took place. One of the duplicate diaries was also to be placed in the safe keeping of the Colonial Governor when the ships reached New South Wales.

Contractors had to deposit a bond of £1,000 per ship which was only returned if the Governor certified 'the true and just delivery of prisoners, provisions and stores belonging to the Government and that the master and surgeons properly carried out their duties at all times'.

Logs and surgeons' diaries were to be lodged with the Governor in a safe and secure place and be open to Government officials as required by the Crown.

Lieutenant John Shortland, Naval Agent for the first fleet, had spent the day inspecting transports being fitted out to accommodate felons and guards for the journey to New South Wales. He was an experienced Agent, having worked on many transports to America but knew a sea voyage of 16,000 miles with around fifteen hundred prisoners, guards and crew would present far more difficulties than the usual journey across the Atlantic. His job was to supervise preparation of the ships. Later he would be required to accompany the fleet on its historic voyage to ensure Government orders were carried out to the letter.

Lieutenant Shortland was a diligent man who carried out his duties with uncommon zeal. His thoughtful approach was to prove immensely beneficial for the prisoners, guards and crew on the epic journey to the unknown land discovered by Captain Cook.

The two ships he had inspected that day were the *Charlotte* and *Prince of Wales*. The latter was almost new, having been built that year at a shipyard on the Thames. The *Charlotte* too was Thames-built three years previously and had seen service along both Portuguese and Russian routes.

In his lodgings that evening, he dipped his goose quill into the glass inkpot and wrote his daily report on the progress made in refitting the two vessels. At the end he added an unusual rider.

———————

'*Sirs,*

I am concerned that such cramped and confined quartering of felons over so long a voyage may lead to depraved propensities being visited, one upon another, with unmentionable consequences. I recommend, in the strongest possible terms, the desirability of separating, at the very least, young boys from seasoned felons hardened to the rigours of prison dangers.'

It was to prove a chilling prophecy of one of the dangers ignored by the planners.

Far away to the east, the coach containing the prison party from Norwich lurched its way down the old Roman Road until it reached the busy town of Chelmsford, where it turned towards London on the ancient highway known as the Great Eastern Road.

The prisoners, and John Simpson, on the top outside, were cold and wet. A biting wind from the North Sea cut into clothing, numbing limbs and conversation alike.

The coachman, encased in a heavy greatcoat stiff with dirt, was also swaddled in a voluminous cape as a rebuff against the stinging rain. The wind sent cold pellets into the ears and eyes however much the exposed passengers huddled into their coats or sought comfort in the proximity of their fellow sufferers.

After a time, rain swept plains were populated with buildings, sparsely at first, then the distance between hamlets and villages shortened until finally there was no more open country and they entered the edge of the great City of London.

Six hours and several changes of horse later, the coach drew up at a hostelry in Whitechapel. A creaking sign announced it as 'The Rook and Tower' and showed a suitably villainous looking blackbird perched on a turret.

The coachman, immobile behind the steaming horses for the last fifty miles, lurched off the cross seat and tumbled down to the muddy yard having thrown the reins at the ostler and banged his tickler into its box.

Passengers and prisoners straggled into the inn and made their way to the merry welcome of a log fire. A podgy potboy heaped a few more logs on the flames, stifling the heat, much to the dismay of the new arrivals. He quickly blew the fire up with bellows, huffing and puffing to keep pace with the pumping. Soon the logs glowed a bright red and warmed the grateful travellers.

A buxom girl with a bright smile and pretty ankles produced a steaming pot of soup with a number of medium sized potatoes jostling just under the surface. Soon heavy wet capes and coats were piled in a heap in the corner and everybody tucked into bowls of hot soup mopped up and fortified with chunks of fresh bread.

That night, the party from Norwich, locked in a room above the stables – Liz and Ann secured to the iron bedstead by way of a long chain – lay huddled together for warmth.

"Are we near to the hulks yet?" Susannah asked.

"We in't even halfway yet, and if that bleeder Simpson thinks I'm sitting on top of that coach tomorrow in filthy weather he's got another think coming. For all I care he can piss up his hind leg and play with the steam," Liz snorted.

At ten o'clock the next morning, the bar of the Rook and Tower was already crowded. The three prisoners sat close together concealing their chained wrists from inquisitive eyes. John Simpson had removed the ankle chains earlier so they drew less attention in the crowded inn.

The throng of customers was vastly different to those they had met in The Bull at Long Melford. This was an altogether more rough and ready crowd sharply versed in the art of looking after 'number one.' Torn tights, leather waistcoats and tattered jackets were the order of the day together with scuffed and worn boots. Poverty stared out of every pocket but nevertheless ale and proximity created a convivial atmosphere so there were lots of cheerful greetings thrown across the packed room.

Suddenly a shout from the far side announced that the coach was coming and the company turned as one to the windows to see what bits of humanity would be discharged into their avaricious care.

Two young girls in faded frocks and pert hats had been talking to the only two top hats in the room. When the crowd turned to the door, one of the girls deftly relieved the taller of the two men of a gold pocket watch and passed it to her companion who slipped it into her long skirt. The girls looked around to see Liz and Ann staring at them not four feet away. Liz shook her head fiercely and raised her manacled hands from under the table; Ann did the same. Shocked, the two young girls ran out of the inn and disappeared into the crowd outside.

A sharp-eyed customer saw the fetters and called out "prisoners at the bar!" This provoked several ribald comments, all of which the three women bore stoically until one of the 'top hats' discovered his pocket watch missing.

Suddenly the atmosphere changed and there were several calls for the watchman to be fetched.

John Simpson who had been standing guard between the door and the prisoners rapped a heavy key on a table and called for silence. The packed bar quietened, more out of curiosity than anything else.

"These women are in my care and I've been watching 'em like a hawk, there in't no way any of 'em can move. It in't possible they can lean across and steal a man's fob."

"Where's my gold watch then?" demanded the taller top hat.

"More to the point, Mister, where are the two young mares you were buying ale for?" The podgy potboy piped up and folded his arms as if that answered the case for the defence.

The two men looked at each other, swore, and forced their way through the people by the door and into the road. They ran down the thoroughfare peering into every alley and shouting 'Watchman! Constable!" in such an agitated manner that the spectators from the 'Rook and Tower', spilling out of the bar, began to cheer every shout.

Simpson and the potboy, jammed together by the crowd at the door, shook hands at their joint triumph. The potboy refused the turnkey's offer of a drink, preferring to take the coin instead. Freeing himself from the jostle of bodies, the turnkey returned to the corner seat where he had left the prisoners. Only Susannah Holmes and the baby were there. For a moment he was too outraged to speak.

"Those crafty hatlots, where have they gone? Speak up Holmes or I swear I'll have that baby put in a home!"

Susannah gripped the child so hard that it began to whimper. "They just went off when I was changing my boy, I don't know where."

He slammed his fist on the table in front of him, prompting the baby to cry in earnest. From the far end of the room, Simpson heard the familiar rattle of heavy chains. In a few strides, he was across the room and threw back the heavy curtains to reveal Pulley and Turner standing on the broad windowsill.

"Get off there you villains, I'll clamp you tighter."

"Whatever's the matter you miserable sod? We were just watching the fun from here." Liz stepped down by way of a handy chair.

Some of the crowd had filtered back into the bar and were enjoying this new sensation. The turnkey, caught between anger and doubt, took several deep breaths. Before he could speak the potboy came across.

"If they'd wanted to get away, sir, they would have slipped out the back door," he whispered.

"If I hadn't heard the chain rattle I'd have been running down that backstreet myself searching for the buggers, seeing how the door stands open."

The turnkey looked suspiciously from the potboy to his prisoners suspecting a conspiracy. All three had such an air of innocence that he was forced to give up the notion. Nevertheless, he bolted Liz and Ann together with a chain he kept handy.

The landlord brought the matter to a conclusion by announcing the Staines coach as raring to go. Liz finished fished out a copper from a fold near her bosom and pressed the warm coin into the potboy's hand warning him not to spend it on a loose woman.

Without wasting any more time the turnkey secured his prisoners on the top outside of the waiting coach watched by the Rook's customers. Soon they were waved off by the potboy who blew effusive kisses at Liz perched on the back, and finally mystified everyone by licking the halfpenny he had been given, sticking it on his forehead and favouring her with the most stupendous wink.

The streets were packed with people, handcarts, hansom cabs and heavy carts plus a fair smattering of dogs, cats and individual horsemen. Progress was slow so the passengers had plenty of opportunity to observe their surroundings.

In the main it was a dreary journey through narrow, dismal streets filled with ragged creatures and dirty urchins whose primary purpose seemed to be to walk down the middle of the highway in order to slow up the traffic or to dart in front of horses causing a great deal of shouting and whip waving from angry drivers.

The coach made its way down Cheapside and past St Paul's Cathedral where a solemn patrol of black robed ministers walked two by two behind a purple clad figure in a tall hat, all holding immense candles like swords pointing to heaven.

At the top end of Newgate Street the newly reconstructed Newgate Prison sat, a grim place with high walls and snaking queues waiting to visit with sundry parcels about their persons. This caused the coachman to call over his shoulder in a jovial fashion, "Anybody need to be dropped off here?" accompanied by a ferocious wink at John Simpson.

Soon they encountered the aromas of Smithfield market; it was a bloody place and so were the people who worked there, smeared as they were with the debris of an open air slaughterhouse. The rancid smell of blood, fat, bones and guts caused a frantic flurry of nosegays to be applied by those fortunate enough to possess them.

After Smithfield, rigs, coaches, and carts seemed to move more quickly and they soon left the place behind. About an hour later, they passed a great park that appeared to be full of well dressed ladies parading with parasols shading them from the non-existent sun, and men in tall hats riding horses who frequently stopped to raise their hats and talk to the elegant females.

"Toffs mucking about in Hyde Park," the coachman called it.

Later they stopped for a pot of grog and a pie at Hammersmith, after which the prisoners dozed until they reached Staines, where they were to pick up another coach.

That night, John Simpson kept his prisoners chained together and did not allow them near the public. The next morning, the little group from Norwich set off early for the West Country. They had another two hundred and fifty miles to travel. It was to prove an arduous journey as a succession of coaches took them towards the infamous hulks lying off the port of Plymouth.

By an odd coincidence, Captain Phillips had also bedded that night at the inn in Staines. He was travelling in the opposite direction to meet officials from the Navy Board and to carry out one of many inspections of the fleet.

At the meeting by the Tower of London he was introduced to John Shortland, the Naval Agent, and was delighted to find that their ideas for the fleet to the new lands were similar. Both had details of all the vessels selected and guards who would accompany the fleet and subsequently provide a force for order in New South Wales. A military presence was also considered a wise precaution against the possibility of other nations attempting to take over the newly discovered land.

Captain Phillips and John Shortland devoted a great deal of time checking that all requirements of the huge venture were being met and compiled a long list of missing stores. John Shortland had spent twenty-five years in the transportation service and had been at sea for eight years prior to that when he had reached the rank of lieutenant, so was particularly useful in determining what was required.

Captain Phillips fired off the first of many letters to the Navy Board containing a list of the essential supplies that the two men reckoned to be missing from the original requisitions. Many lives, including those of felons, crew and guards on that first great voyage would be saved by the diligence of these two officers.

The second day out from Staines proved to be a fortunate one for the prisoners perched on the coach outside. An old man and his wife had been unable to take up their seats at the Black Horse in Salisbury owing to their luggage being deposited in a ditch when the carter lost a wheel on a narrow track through Wishford Wood. This meant that John Simpson and the three women had the coach to themselves so they took over the inside seats.

Winds and rain sweeping over Salisbury Plain had made the previous twenty-four hours hard going for those exposed to the elements. However, now the four from Norwich prison were ensconced in the inside seats they could, for the first time since the journey started, talk together while travelling. Liz Pulley and Ann Turner also amused themselves by waving regally at bystanders as the coach passed through the numerous hamlets and small villages.

The following day, despite two more passengers joining the stagecoach, they were again allotted inside seats until it reached the old town of Exeter.

After the pandemonium at Long Melford, John Simpson had been careful to take his meals with the prisoners in their rooms. Although Liz and Ann had subsequently assured him that they would be as 'pure as nuns in a convent' he had made certain that they kept their word by shackling them to their beds every night and not leaving their sides during the day.

By Exeter, his attitude had softened and, realising this was the last time the women would know any kind of freedom for many years, decided to allow them to eat in the public bar of the hostelry. They had almost sixty miles or so to go before they reached Plymouth and, barring accidents, would get there around late afternoon the following day.

That evening the turnkey, as had become his habit, rapped on the wall between their rooms to let the women know that he was on his way.

"Now, listen carefully you buggers, this is your last evening afore the hulks so we're eating downstairs tonight. I want no behaviour like Long Melford!"

Liz was beside him in an instant, eyes lit up with delight. "Mr Simpson, we'll make sure you don't misbehave."

"Not me – you!" roared the turnkey.

The three women fell about laughing and immediately got out their 'parlour paint' to prepare for the evening ahead. The turnkey issued several dire warnings – to which the women paid scant regard – and he eventually retired to make arrangements with the landlord.

When he led the three women into the bar there were several whistles and someone sent over a jug of ale, but the turnkey had chosen well and they were boxed in a corner booth shielded from the crowded room by stout oak boards. This didn't stop Liz Pulley leaning sideways out of the cubicle to reply to a number of ribald comments and requests from the patrons who, in the main, appeared to be a sea faring crowd. Despite interruptions, the meal proceeded well and the atmosphere remained jovial.

Liz struck up a conversation with an elderly cove in the next booth. He had spent some time by the fire and his face was a mottled red from the considerable heat of the blazing coals.

As is the way of elderly gentlemen, the older they get the higher their waistline. This old man's belt circled him somewhere near his armpits and necessitated about a dozen buttons down the front of his trousers.

"Eh," Liz called out so that the whole bar could hear, "Listen, my little wizened person, I reckon if your belt gets any higher, you'll be needing to undo your flies to carry out any conversation at all!"

The crowd roared their approval and even the old man joined in.

"I reckon," he gasped, "I've lost the lead from my old pencil, but it don't matter cos I got no one to write to anyway!"

Ann Turner stood on the wooden seat to declare that she knew of an address to where the old man could correspond.

This all met with the general approval of the customers and the landlord sent over a jug of ale 'on the house'.

The serving girl, when clearing away their plates asked Susannah if she could hold the baby awhile; the child lay sound asleep in his box. Despite her misgivings about waking the baby, there was something about the girl's manner that made Susannah agree.

The girl fetched a chair, sat next to the booth and carefully lifted the child from its makeshift crib. Susannah was relieved to see her cuddling the baby in the most gentle of manners but startled to observe tears coursing down the girl's cheeks. Liz, who was nearest, put a hand on the young girl.

"Are you alright, lass?"

"I had a child," she said simply.

After a few minutes the girl went off, wiping her face on her apron, having returned the baby to the box, still asleep. When she had gone the landlord came over to clean their table.

"That was my girl," he said. "Had a baby a week ago – the mite died not two days since."

"The poor little mare!" exclaimed Ann Turner.

"It's for the best, we never knew who the father was. I reckon he was a matelot, probably copped by a press gang or buggered off himself, either way we've seen neither hide nor hair of him, not never!"

Much to the disappointment of the customers, as soon as the meal was finished Simpson led the prisoners back to their rooms but was unable to prevent Liz and Ann planting fulsome kisses on several locals "to wish them and England goodbye."

In the clinch with the first old man Liz achieved the twin objectives of making him happy and relieving him of a guinea from his trouser pocket.

The next morning they were seen off by Agnes, the landlord's daughter, who had the pleasure of holding the baby for a few minutes while the prisoners were boarded and their luggage stowed in the deep boot.

The road down through South Devon was full of twists and sharp upturns that needed the aid of the driver's whip to negotiate. They caught glimpses of the English Channel and could smell sea air. Ann Turner declared it was "old seaweed, heavily salted and served cold."

At the new bridge between Kingsteignton and Newton Abbot they passed a curious gaggle of prisoners, chained together and guarded by a contingent of Welsh Guards with bright red jackets and light coloured trousers. They wore tall black hats with thin white plumes pinned to the peaks.

There were about thirty prisoners with stout chains securing each row of three men. The column moved slowly, every man's movements heavily hampered by the weight of chains, handcuffs and ankle manacles.

Soldiers, bearing muskets across shoulders in the 'sloop' position, marched alongside under the command of an officer on a white horse.

John Simpson leaned out of the window and called to the officer to ask him where they had come from.

"We're from Bristol Bridewell and are heading for Plymouth. Altogether 'tis a three or four day journey if we get no trouble from this rabble." He tipped his cap and wheeled the horse towards the rear of the straggle of men.

The Norwich prisoners, who had been subdued since leaving Exeter, viewed the column of chained men with sinking hearts. The unexpected appearance of the batch of felons reminded each what lay ahead.

Silence descended on the coach as it creaked and groaned over the winding road and the passengers reflected on the fate that awaited them. Nobody realised the disaster that lay ahead for Susannah.

It was November 5th, Guy Fawkes day, 1786.

Chapter Nineteen

Preparation of the first fleet had become a nightmare. Contractors were responsible for ordering food, clothing, nails, tools, bedding, medicines and hundreds more items. Officials and officers were charged with checking that supplies were delivered and supplied in the correct quality and volume.

Management of the very means of transport – ships, innumerable spares, arms, marines, and so on lay with the Government and ships' officers. Getting it all ready, in place, in shipshape order, together with felons, crews and guards was a massive undertaking.

In London, Captain Phillips had moved his belongings to the warship *Sirius* at Deptford and had been welcomed aboard by his second in command, Captain John Hunter. It was a sturdy three masted vessel and, at 520 tons, was the biggest of the fleet.

In taking up his post, Phillips became Commodore of the Fleet and a suitable flag was run up the main mast. As soon as this was done, the *Sirius* officially became flagship of the First Fleet.

In the Commodore's cramped cabin, Phillips, Hunter, the Reverend Richard Johnson and John White, Surgeon General, were awaiting the arrival of Evan Nepean, deputy to Lord Sydney. Phillips had already acquainted his colleagues with details of his latest reports to the Naval Board expressing dissatisfaction with the chief contractor, Duncan Campbell.

Evan Nepean was a man who understood that every voyage, short and long, required a great deal of planning and attention to detail.

He knew this was to be a hazardous and exceptional journey and had agreed to the meeting so that he could acquaint himself at first hand with the difficulties.

When he arrived, Phillips introduced him to the others then lost no time in explaining his fears.

"Mr Nepean, Sir, it would aid this expedition if you would discuss my complaints with Master Campbell. I ask for the supplies to be assembled here in London so that they may be counted and checked but Campbell sends some to Plymouth, some to Portsmouth and little enough to our store here at Deptford. I wonder if some supplies are sent to Portsmouth to be counted and weighed then returned here to London to be counted and weighed again. I quite understand that Campbell is unwilling to supply the victuals until just before the fleet sails but why do we wait for essential items such as musket balls and paper cartridges? There is no reason why fresh clothing for the prisoners should not be here now, inspected and checked by our own men; we have enough difficulties verifying prisoners' and mariners, rations; we cannot be expected to count every nail, tool and rope at the last moment as well."

Evan Nepean nodded and continued making notes. "I have a number of these complaints already but I note them again. Is there anything new you want to record?" John White, Surgeon General, coughed politely, "If I may make a point about the voyage it is to emphasise an equal concern about Duncan Campbell. In my view the man is a charlatan, a crimper of the first order and not fit to shoulder the responsibility he carries for this fleet. Scurvy can kill half the crew on a long voyage but there are no anti-scorbutics ordered for the whole fleet. It is scandalous that we should have to demand the inclusion of such vital supplies. It is essential we have the items Captain Cook relied upon for his great voyage – we must have portable soup with plenty of meat rendered into a cake by boiling together with malt and sauerkraut. Green vegetables and fresh meat at every port is essential too."

"Wait, gentlemen, wait," Nepean held up his hand. "You must detail every supply you fear is lacking and send it to me, I will consult with the Navy Board on your behalf."

"I am concerned about the distribution of the prisoners," Captain Hunter spoke at last. "I foresee a great deal of trouble from that quarter."

"Fear not," Evan Nepean replied, "even now a good number of female prisoners from every gaol in the land are being conveyed to hulks in preparation of their embarkation to this fleet."

"You misunderstand me, Sir, I was referring to the allocation of female felons when they board the fleet – that is when trouble begins for officers and seamen. Women are damned difficult to control and keep contained from the crews!"

"When we know precisely how many females are to be embarked we will allocate them to the vessels with security in the forefront of our plans. Most women will be embarked upon one ship to minimise riotous behaviour." Nepean said.

The Surgeon General banged the table and made everyone jump, "The clap, gentlemen, what about the clap!"

"The clap, Mr White?" Reverend Johnson ventured.

"Syphilis and gonorrhoea sir, twin scourges of sea faring men throughout the world! The clap follows Jack Tar just as surely as a ship follows tides and currents of oceans. Into this vile venereal potion we are adding hussies harbouring God knows what poxes!"

Reverend Johnson gazed at the low ceiling as if expecting to find an answer there. Failing, he studied his elegant cuffs and scratched his head.

"It will be rampant, gentlemen!" the Chief Surgeon burst out again, "we'll be poxed to the eyeballs in no time at all, by God!" He banged the table again, as if enjoying the prospect.

"Not by God," murmured the clergyman, "decidedly not by God!"

Evan Nepean covered his mouth with his hand, concealing a smile. "What do you propose to counter this calamity, Mr White?"

"Inspections, Sir!" he boomed, "every female must be examined and those displaying the symptoms must be sent back to their prisons and dosed there. The pox is not a welcome shipmate, Sir, not a welcome shipmate at all!"

"I'll leave that matter in your hands, Mr White, all females to be examined for the pox then!" Evan Nepean said smoothly. "Now we must inspect the goods in a warehouse at Deptford, I have a parliamentary meeting in two hours."

They left the chief surgeon behind, suddenly chastened by the problems of intimately examining almost two hundred women on board hulks and ships not equipped for such examinations.

In Devon, the coach stopped with a jerk and the driver jumped down. "Five minutes stop afore we run down into Plymouth," he shouted.

John Simpson and the three prisoners were the only passengers so they eased stiff limbs down the step to take advantage of the break. The child lay sleeping in his box crib. The port of Plymouth lay in a fold of the ground below them. Row upon row of red tiled and thatched roofs faced the sea like ranks of an army waiting for an invasion. The harbour was busy, small and large sailed vessels moved gracefully through the blue waters. Outside the harbour waves heaved and crashed on rocky shores and minute coves. Serried ranks of ships with sails furled lined the harbour walls. The four from Norwich gazed down at the scene before them.

"Looks like Yarmouth to me," Liz declared. "I went there once with a friend.Sailors are lusty bedfellows and no mistake!" She looked dreamily into the distance.

"Henry worked on the ships out of Lowestoft. He said they caught hundreds of fish in the North Sea," Susannah said wistfully.

Liz took hold of the turnkey's arm and steered him a little apart from the others. She looked earnestly into his eyes.

"What are the chances of me getting wed, Mr Simpson?"

"Well, I don't know, Liz, I've never thought of you as the marrying type."

"Not good enough, you mean," she said bitterly.

"It'll need a strong man to keep you in order, Liz."

"I'll have to learn to cook, I suppose," she said morosely.

"It will be a fine chance for you to start afresh and you'll have plenty of suitors."

"You really think so, Mr Simpson? You're not pulling my pisser are you?"

"Will you be happy with one man?"

"Oh gawd, this marrying business is so complicated!"

The driver cracked his whip. "All aboard me hearties."

Plymouth was a good five miles away but the run was easy, downhill all the way. When the coach stopped by the entrance to the harbour, it was nearly three o'clock.John Simpson took the precaution of chaining the three women together before going off to find out where prisoners embarked for the hulk.

When he returned ten minutes later they were sitting on the low harbour wall, munching pies.

"Where did you get those?" he demanded.

"Coachman," Ann Turner answered shortly.

"Lovely man, not as suspicious as some I could mention," Liz added through a mouthful of pastry and meat.

"Dozy sod!" John Simpson muttered, "Never mind, the Navy's got a log cabin by the harbour from where boats go out to the hulk. You three are to be lodged aboard the 'Dunkirk'.

The coachman, watching from the box, jumped down and went to Liz. "Left your scarf in the coach, my dear," he announced.

She cupped his ruddy face and gave him a resounding kiss while Ann Turner hugged him from behind. "You are a gent of the first order!"

The coachman winked. "No bother at all, my dears," he beamed.

The little knot of prisoners, the boxed baby and the turnkey made their way in single file down the dockside.

"Get anything?" Liz whispered.

"A shilling," Ann replied.

"Sixpence each then!"

They came to a ramshackle wooden hut by the water's edge where a bored-looking dragoon leaned on his musket by the door.

"Three more for the *Dunkirk*," he called into a dark interior.

A red tunic bearing sergeant's stripes and supporting a chubby face emerged to squint at the prisoners.

"Ah, yes, three from Norwich, you're expected," he grunted, thumbing through a dog- eared list of names, "Sit on that wall a minute."

Simpson unlocked the chain binding the women together so they could do as they were told. All three scanned the water for the ship that was to be their prison. It was surprisingly close.

The black mass of the hulk loomed before them, sitting sullenly in the sea, itself a prisoner, festooned as it was by huge chains bolted to the bed of the bay by unseen anchors. The menacing shape, stripped of masts and rigging, wallowed to the slap of water, stayed by chains, each link half the size of a man.

Susannah Holmes swallowed hard at the sight, picked up her baby as he began to cry and nuzzled its mouth against her breast under cover of her cape.

A calamity was about to befall them both.

The baby's cries alerted the sergeant to the fact there was an infant with prisoner Holmes. He had taken it for granted that the box she carried contained her few possessions. He peered again at his list.

"There's no baby here," he announced.

John Simpson looked up sharply, "Let me see."

Wrenching the sheaf of papers from the man's hands he drew his finger down the list until he came to the section headed: 'Castle, Norwich.

Prisoners – three.' The women were listed but there was no mention of the baby!

The sergeant grabbed the papers back, "No baby on the list, no passage across to the hulk!" His jaw jutted out stubbornly.

A furious row broke out. Simpson, Liz Pulley and Ann Turner argued fiercely with the sergeant and the dragoon. Slowly the two soldiers were forced back by the weight of the argument until they were compelled to take refuge in the hut. The turnkey and the prisoners continued to shout into the hut, but the sergeant filled the doorframe with his bulk.

Liz Pulley poked him on the chest. "You are a bloody fool," she shouted, "I wouldn't even piss on you if I found you in the gutter!"

The violent argument was abruptly ended by Susannah who was at the edge of the dock. "If anyone tries to take my baby I am going to jump in here with him!" She held the boy over the water, her face awash with tears. They all knew that she meant every word.

"Hold hard, young woman, don't be daft now," The tone of the sergeant's voice suddenly softened.

"You had better row us to the hulk and let the Captain know what's going on." John Simpson too was shaken by the determination in Susannah Holmes' manner.

Ten minutes later, a longboat made its way across the harbour, rowed by two dragoons with the sergeant clutching the rudder and a sheaf of papers.

At the black hulk, the sergeant scrambled up a wide rope net after commanding the dragoons to 'watch 'em close'. There was no need; the prisoners and turnkey were equally determined to watch him closely.

It was an hour before Captain Broadley disturbed his afternoon nap to see the sergeant and another twenty minutes before the solder was able to convince the Captain that the girl was serious in threatening to throw herself and the baby into the harbour.

While this went on, John Simpson and the prisoners sat in the longboat bobbing up and down with the waves. The dragoons had fastened the craft to the rope net but this did little to lessen the effect of the waves surging against the hulk.

Ann Turner vomited over the side, her face an awful shade of green. Liz held on tightly, heeding the dragoon's advice to stare at a fixed point on the shoreline. Both Simpson and Susannah were badly affected but it was the baby's cries that distressed them most. The mite was screaming, his face was bright red. Everybody's nerves were frayed and John Simpson hollered his frustration at the deck above. The occasional face appeared over the rail but only to tell him to 'pipe down you great lummick!'

Eventually, Captain Broadley leaned over the side to peer down at the occupants of the long boat. "Turnkey, have you got papers for the child?"

"No papers exist, the Castle gaol at Norwich is not within any parish boundary. Local clergy will not accept the registration of any child born outside their parish so it is impossible to record a birth in the prison," John Simpson croaked, his throat already sore from shouting.

"I'll take the prisoners but I don't want the child. I have no orders for the child!"

"We're not going anywhere without Susannah and her baby!" Liz Pulley yelled back. Susannah stood up, held the baby over the side and began to scream at the top of her voice. Ann Turner was sick again.

The Captain withdrew to confer with the sergeant, a few minutes later, he peered over the side again. "Alright, come aboard, one at a time!" He ordered.

Ann Turner was first up the rope net, assisted by one of the dragoons. John Simpson helped steady the boat which was rising six or seven feet in the afternoon swell. Liz Pulley insisted that the dragoon cover her completely in the climb up, like a spider taking a fly across its web.

When it was Susannah's turn, she was unable to climb with the baby. John Simpson took the child from her, intertwining his free arm in the netting and bracing the boat against the hull with his legs. She climbed gingerly up the rope net with the dragoon straddled about her. Progress was slow as Susannah frequently stopped to check the baby who was held by John Simpson.

Captain Broadly leaned over to call down to the turnkey. "The sergeant will come down with a basket for the child, we'll haul it up once it's fastened."

The soldier eventually appeared with a straw basket but when he jumped down into the longboat, the basket was suddenly whisked away by unseen hands.

"Hey, what about the baby?" Simpson yelled.

"Your problem, turnkey, I've got no orders for a child!" Captain Broadley shouted back.

Pandemonium broke out on the deck above. Susannah's agonised scream carried clearly across the harbour, causing citizens to stop and stare at the hulk. Liz and Ann fought with the marines shouting all the obscenities they knew. Susannah launched herself at Captain Broadley kicking and scratching. Other mariners appeared from nowhere to help contain the three women. Two of them dragged Susannah over the deck to force her down the hold. Her screams tore at Simpson's heart in the longboat below.

"Blast your treacherous eyes, damn you to hell." The turnkey was more furious than he could ever remember. Susannah's cries reminded him of the desperation he had felt when his daughter died in childbirth.

The sergeant was unrepentant. "I told you, no papers, no berth aboard *Dunkirk*. Captain Broadley's a stickler for paperwork."

Simpson, seething with anger and exhausted by the bitter battle, could do nothing as the marines rowed him and the baby back to the shore.

Chapter Twenty

John Simpson spent a restless night despite being exhausted from the long journey to Plymouth and the hours spent arguing with the mariners and Captain Broadley.

After the longboat had reached the harbour wall, he had made his way to the nearest inn where the landlord's wife took charge of the baby when she heard what had happened.

Word soon spread about the plight of the baby separated from its mother by the Master of the hulk in Plymouth Sound. A small gathering in the inn seemed to favour him depositing the baby in a local orphanage until he had got the question settled. A thin man insisted that his wife would look after the child for 'five shillings a week, four weeks in advance' and wagered that no one could make a better offer.

Later, a matelot from the hulk came in and joined in the talk of the Captain tricking the prison guard into taking a baby back. He said the child's mother had tried to throw herself over the side and one of the other women prisoners had kneed the Captain 'amidships' for which she had been sentenced to 'the hole'.

Having finished his breakfast, Simpson made his way to the knot of people around the sailor. "What's the Captain's name?"

"Broadley, some say he goes to bed with the rulebook under his head in place of a pillow."

"Tell Captain Broadley he's not heard the last of this, rule book or not. No mother should be separated from a suckling child!"

The landlord's wife came in holding little Henry, wanting to know what Simpson was going to do.

"I shall take the child to London, to the Home Secretary himself and demand he issues papers so that the child is given back to its mother, where it belongs."

Several offered the turnkey a drink and the landlord's wife kissed him heartily then retired, blushing, when the others cheered her impetuosity.

The turnkey asked the sailor to tell Susannah of his intentions and assure her that he would not abandon the child. At this, he was offered more drinks but declined, indicating that he needed to make arrangements for the journey.

The turnkey caught the first coach out of Plymouth the following day, he was cheered off by a little group of people who had heard of his mission. The innkeeper's wife handed young Henry over 'cleaned and fed, all barnacles removed', together with a parcel of food for him and the child. She had packed a jug of milk, but warned him that the baby would have difficulty in keeping it down, as he was used to milk from the breast. He had received detailed instructions about how often to feed the child and a young woman insisted on telling him how to wrap the baby's napkin, making him practise on her own child until she was satisfied that he was reasonably competent in the task.

As the coach and four trotted out of Plymouth to make the long climb towards the east, John Simpson began to realise the enormity of his task. How could he possibly hope to find, let alone persuade, the Home Secretary to issue papers for the baby? He could see himself wandering about London before being forced to return to Norwich with the child.

A collection was organised by the landlord around his customers and other curious folk and had yielded the princely sum of two guineas. He pressed the money into the turnkey's hand as his wife passed the baby over

A kindly couple of passengers cradled the baby for a while and soon he was snoring loudly, catching up on the slumber he had missed the previous night. He slept solidly until the coach reached the inn in Exeter. It was the same hostelry where he and the prisoners had stayed two days previously.

This was to be a stop of one hour, for a meal and a change of horses, so the passengers were ushered into the back room where food was served. The first person he saw was the landlord who recognised him immediately. The turnkey explained what had happened and that he was on his way to London, hoping to get papers so that the child could be taken back to Plymouth.

The landlord went off, muttering. Agnes, his daughter, came to look after little Henry for a while. Simpson declined, preferring not to do anything which might wake the infant. It wasn't long before there was a cry from the makeshift cot to let everyone know that he was hungry.

Agnes was out of the kitchen before the first cry had finished and hovered by the box. "Shall I pick him up, Mister?"

"I've got to look after the child, I might as well start now. You can warm up this milk though."

She sniffed the contents of the jug and pulled a face before disappearing back to the kitchen. A few minutes later she returned with a warmed bottle of milk.

Try as he might, the turnkey could not get little Henry to take the milk. Soon he was yelling at the top of his voice and the landlord asked him to take the child further away 'so folk can enjoy their meal in peace'.

"Trouble is, the little mite's not yet weaned," he explained.

Agnes almost wrestled the screaming child from his grasp. "I've got milk," she announced.

By the time he had extricated himself from the corner seat, she had taken the boy into a small room nearby where he was astonished to find her breast-feeding little Henry.

"I've got milk," she repeated. "Plenty of it, spills out all the time it does."

He backed out of the door and bumped into the landlord. Both men looked at Agnes with the child and shut the door on the scene.

"Blast, I smell trouble," the landlord muttered.

Thirty minutes later, Agnes emerged with the baby who had been fed, washed, changed and now fast asleep.

"You can't take the bairn all the way to London. Leave him here until you get back, I'll care for him." He realised that she was close to tears.

"I cannot," the turnkey said kindly, "If I'm to persuade the Minister to issue paperwork for the boy he must be there in my arms. I've got to pull at the man's heartstrings, don't you see?"

Agnes blinked back the tears. "You'll make the mite ill, he can't take cow's milk, he might die!"

"I can't leave him here my little woman. If I fail to get papers for the child, I shall have to take him on to Norwich to his father."

Agnes pushed the child into the turnkey's arms and ran off sobbing.

"Coach leaves in five minutes," the driver shouted.

John Simpson placed the sleeping child back in his box and went out into the yard. The other passengers soon joined him and waited while the ostler led the team of four in a semi-circle to the entrance. Swaddled in an enormous greatcoat, the driver emerged from the inn to inspect the harness. As he did so, a tremendous row broke out in the inn. Suddenly, the door was thrown open and Agnes stepped out in a long coat with a jaunty bonnet perched on her head.

"I'm going and you can't stop me," she yelled over her shoulder.

Her face was the picture of determination. The astonished turnkey stared at the landlord who stood red-faced, arms akimbo, looking equally amazed. Agnes, arms crossed, plonked herself in the seat next to the gaoler, her bottom lip jutting out.

"You need me!" She said, staring ahead. Looking down at the box between them, she repeated, much more softly, "The baby needs me!"

The coachman cracked his whip and the team of four pulled onto the highway.

As if on cue, little Henry woke up and began kicking. Agnes picked him up, whereupon he broke into the most enormous smile.

"Quite right, my dear," the woman in the seat opposite said primly, favouring John Simpson with a ferocious look.

"Good on you," her husband nodded vigorously.

The turnkey was quite certain that neither had the faintest idea what was going on.

"I've got money for my ticket and accommodation," Agnes said tartly.

"Lord Almighty!" was all the turnkey could manage before slumping back in his seat.

The woman opposite sniffed contemptuously and stared archly out of the window, as if determined that she would never again look at the turnkey.

Convicts from all over the country were being housed in the Hulks moored off the South Coast and London ports. Felons arriving on the Thames were divested of all clothing and given prison garb. Most, having lain in overcrowded and unsanitary gaols, were infested with lice and other pests. The guards had no means of determining which of the prisoners were so the order went out to change all clothes.

Usually, prisoners clothing was slashed to render it unwearable but the Captain, or the Mate designated to deal with the felons, were not above keeping any outfit deemed of particularly good quality. Many a young blade, caught in some criminal endeavour and sentenced to transportation would lose their silk shirt and breeches only to see an officer sporting them the next day.

New prisoners were taken aboard, told to strip and then put into a barber's chair. It didn't matter if they were adorned with flowing locks or matted hair, it was soon scattered on the deck to be sold to wig makers. Particularly verminous looking creatures also had their armpits and pubic hair shaved, an altogether more delicate operation.

The next stop was a soak in a cold bath and a scrub with the hard soap that was issued to the Navy at the time. If a man was judged to be unclean after this, he was doused again in cold water. Failure to scrub clean after a second bath was considered insubordination, the penalty for which was to be scrubbed down by two matelots armed with stiff deck brooms.

Male prisoners were clothed in white woollen frock coats and trousers, some with grey or yellow jackets, all with broad black arrows with crude red numbers on back and front to indicate that they were 'government property'.

Commodore Phillips and Captain Hunter were aboard the hulk *Justica*, moored between Barking Reach and Gallions Reach. Duncan Campbell, Chief Contractor to the fleet, owned the vessel. Phillips and Hunter were there to inspect the prisoners and discuss with the Ship's Master any difficulties that he was having. Although they had no jurisdiction over the hulks, the information they gleaned would, they reckoned, be useful when felons were transferred into their care, and would also be helpful in their battles with Campbell.

For over six years, Duncan Campbell had been a transportation contractor when prisoners were sent to America. When transportation was stopped after 1775, Parliament had passed a temporary bill – which was destined to be renewed yearly – to punish any male '*lawfully convicted of great or petty larceny, or any other crime punishable by transportation by being kept to hard labour by raising sand, soil and gravel, and cleansing the River Thames, for the benefit of navigation*'. Supervision of prisoners lay with Justices of Middlesex. They had appointed Duncan Campbell to oversee the project and to provide food, shelter and clothing and virtually left him to his own devices.

Thus Captains Phillips and Hunter were dealing with a man who possessed many high- ranking contacts in the transportation system and who had had, for many years, full rein over how he dealt with prisoners in his care.

———

Convicts at work in London were a notable sight and the idea of giving them hard labour was popular. For some years prisoners had been cleansing the river and converting shelving banks into quays, yards and docks for the Royal Arsenal at Woolwich. All were heavily shackled, some were chained both at waist and neck, depending on the severity of their crime. Men wielding heavy cutlasses to deter escapers and discourage idleness guarded them.

The two naval men watched from the upper deck as prisoners came aboard the hulk from their day's labour. All were in filthy condition, their clothing in tatters. Despite having strips of cloth wound around fetters many bled from ankles that were rubbed raw by the sharp metal edges.

Two seamen pumped water from the river over the men as they came aboard. Most went below still caked in mud but with the added encumbrance of being wet and cold.

"I would not treat my dog as badly," Captain Phillips stated bluntly for the benefit of the Captain of the hulk.

"It's the only way to treat scum, once below they'll cheat and rob each other like jackals."

The two Officers said nothing but later, aboard the *Sirius*, Phillips wrote again to Evan Nepean.

'*My Dear Sir*
We must have a complete set of warm clothing to issue to
every prisoner together with extra clothing to issue during
the journey to the new lands. The clothing we have seen
on hulk prisoners is inadequate for a voyage that will pass
through freezing seas and chilling winds. I consider it
imperative that the contractor, Duncan Campbell, provides
such clothing without further delay so my officers may
ascertain the fitness of garments for the inclement weathers
that we shall surely encounter.'
Commodore Arthur Phillips

Earlier that day, the Commodore had learned that out of the three hundred and sixty prisoners on a hulk in the Thames, eighty one had died of gaol fever in the first three months and that death generally claimed one in three hulk prisoners before they finished their sentence. He was determined that no such calamities would befall his fleet.

Knowing that speed was essential, John Simpson had booked on the 'through coach', which, as far as possible, stopped only to change horses and give passengers time to snatch a meal or refresh themselves. However, when they reached the hamlet of Basingstoke in Hampshire, they had to stay overnight because passengers had to transfer to another operator's coach which began its part of the journey early the following morning.

John Simpson stumbled out of the coach, stiff from the jolting journey. He had not managed to work out how to approach the task of persuading a Minister of the Crown to allow little Henry to travel with his mother. Agnes had slept soundly when she wasn't feeding the baby. It seemed to the turnkey that the baby was in danger of drowning whilst with the innkeeper's daughter. He stamped around trying to get some circulation in his numb feet while Agnes took the baby into the 'Masked Highwayman', a low-slung inn nestling in a fold of ground on the edge of Basingstoke.

A boy took the turnkey's bag and walked ahead, jangling a broad leather belt hung with keys which were spaced evenly around his waist. Agnes followed with the baby and when the boy flung open a dim chamber, Simpson was surprised when she followed him into the room. Taking the candle, she bade the boy goodnight and closed the door firmly when he left.

"I told them you were my father. Anyway, they had only one room," she said defiantly, flinging her coat and bonnet on a bed.

The baby began to grizzle, so she sat on the covers fumbling to open her bodice. The turnkey hastened to the door to arrange a meal for them. Downstairs, the potboy, a well-built individual with a round face, fetched him a pint of ale.

After a second jug, John Simpson stood by the roaring grate where the fire crackled greedily consuming dry logs and bucket of coals tipped atop by the bulky potboy. He beckoned the boy over from the hall where he was pulling faces at himself in a pane of glass.

"Now my friendly firkin of fat, what's to be eaten in this commodious establishment?"

The boy peered at him with one eye closed as if he was a beast from another land. "Lamb and spuds," he announced, "we're strong on lamb and spuds in the Highwayman."

"Then that is what we will have, two portions of your best lamb and potatoes to be served when the long clock strikes eight bells!"

The boy backed out of the door, slightly alarmed. The turnkey chuckled to himself, having no idea why he was suddenly feeling so cheerful, perhaps the ale was stronger than he had realised.

He and Agnes relished the lamb and finished with apple pie, washed down with grog. She told him of her life in Exeter, having helped out in her father's inn ever since her mother had 'gone off with a Jack Tar' two years previously. She completely ignored his question about the father of her own baby, preferring to talk about how lovely little Henry was.

When they retired to bed, he waited outside while she undressed and got under the covers. When it was his turn, he slipped swiftly under the sheets and lay there listening to her pitch about in the darkness. He knew she was awake and was not surprised when she called softly to him.

"Henry's a beautiful baby, I'd like one like him."

The turnkey swallowed hard and was surprised when his reply was about two octaves higher than usual, "You would?"

"I'd prefer a baby made by you, not him."

"Him?" squeaked the turnkey.

"Father!" she said shortly.

He was trying to work out if she meant the father of her baby or her own father when he fell into a deep sleep. He woke the next morning to find she was already up and dressed. Little Henry was having his morning feed.

The coach made rapid progress and rolled into Westminster late in the afternoon. Booking two rooms at the coaching inn, John Simpson left Henry with Agnes and went off towards Parliament.

At the doors to that great debating chamber, he asked every well-dressed man who went in or came out if they knew the Home Secretary, Lord Sydney. A number just shook their heads and walked past, most didn't bother to reply.

After two hours, the number of people leaving the building had dwindled to almost none when John Simpson decided to ask a parliamentary watchman standing by the great double doors. When he had explained who he was and why he was there, the man became more sympathetic.

"You've come all the way from Plymouth? How long did it take, I hear it's hundreds of miles away."

"Lord Sydney, can you point him out to me?" The turnkey reminded him.

"There he is!" The watchman suddenly pointed to a man getting into a hansom cab on the far side of the square. By the time the turnkey had run across, the hansom had disappeared down a side street. Wearily, he made his way back to the inn, determined to return the next day.

At the Inn, the barman asked if he had had any luck when he ordered a pot of ale. Clearly Agnes had told him why they were there. "Takes guts to do what you're doing, have one on me." The barman slid the jug across the table.

Gratefully, he slaked his thirst then made his way to the rooms above. Agnes lay fully-dressed on her bed, curled up with the baby. He woke her gently and recounted the events at Parliament.

"Tomorrow." He said. "I'll go again in the morning but for now we had better get some victuals inside us."

Word had spread about their purpose and one or two people brought drinks over then asked questions about the baby and his mother. All agreed with the landlord's opinion that it was 'a crying shame to treat a child like a bleeding unwanted puppy!'

Towards the end of the meal, a customer who had bought them a drink earlier came over with another man. He asked Simpson to repeat his story once more for the benefit of the newcomer who he introduced as a friend named George.

"So you want to talk to Lord Sydney and get papers for the baby? Well, I know where he lives."

"You do! Show me, I'll go right away."

"You'll do better tomorrow, tonight the noble Lord is likely to be out, attending an official function."

George explained that he was a reporter with the London Chronicle and often did Parliamentary stories for the Evening Post as well, so was familiar with where to find Government Ministers. After more discussion, he promised to pick up the turnkey the next morning and take him to Lord Sydney's home.

"Bring the baby!" He said firmly.

"I intend to," John Simpson replied.

At the entrance to their rooms, Agnes placed a hand on his arm. "Do you want me to come to you after I've got the baby to sleep?" She asked shyly.

The turnkey felt a little bolt of lightning strike his nether regions, "It's the nicest thing anyone has asked me for a long time, Agnes, but I'm tired, dead tired."

"Goodnight then," she went quickly into her chamber.

The next morning, the Reporter and John Simpson, clutching the sleeping child, made their way to a street near the Houses of Parliament. It was a beautiful tree-lined avenue, flanked on either side by imposing residences. Almost all the houses had three storeys which were supported by a basement with windows under the level of the pavement. The residence of Lord Sydney had the benefit of wide steps which lead to double doors set between two imposing columns.

George warned him not to be put off by Lord Sydney's butler, who had the reputation of setting himself against anyone he considered unsuitable to meet his Lordship.

"Are you coming with me?" The turnkey asked, hoping for some moral support.

"No, the butler knows me too well, I'll stand across the street until you come out then you can tell me what was said and who's there."

"I thank you for the trouble you're taking, I'd never have found this place without your help."

"No need to thank me, this will be a good story, whatever happens. Now remember, don't <u>ask</u> to see Lord Sydney, just act as if he will <u>want</u> to see you. Take no truck from Mr High and Mighty Butler!"

John Simpson squared his shoulders, marched up the steps and rapped the gleaming brass knocker firmly. George backed off to stand in the gutter on the other side of the street.

Chapter Twenty One

In the dusty exercise yard at Norwich Prison, Henry Cabell slumped against the cold stones of the Castle. He held the letter that Susannah had penned at Long Melford, most of which held expressions of her devotion to him. She had also included a brief description of Liz and Ann carousing with the local farmers at the Bull Inn.

Henry's enraged reaction to this and his suspicions that Susannah too was having a good time had angered John Euston and the two had had a bitter row. Euston told him he did not deserve Susannah.

There were few in that place who dared to speak plainly to Henry but Euston had. "You are an ignorant man in many ways, Henry. Violence and fists are the tools of those with no words or reason. You will want help soon, perhaps another petition, maybe asking the Governor or Parson to add a few words. Yet you lumber about beating those who get in your way, turning those who might help you against you. Within days of Susannah and your son leaving this vile place you doubt the lass."

Henry sat alone a long time, fighting the demons within. His friend's angry words rang around his head. Other prisoners, seeing him crouched against the flints clutching his head, knew the signs and kept well clear. Eventually, he stood up and went to seek John Euston. Henry found him scrubbing a vest in a bucket by the washhouse.

"A man can't help black thoughts in this hell hole." He said angrily.

"You must help it if you want to see your son and Susannah again."

"I'm blocked at every turn, what can I do?"

"It's a poisonous place right enough, evil leaks from every crevice. But you've got to work hard to get into the Governor's good books if you want to be on the next transport."

"I know you are right John but anger is a black dog inside me sometimes. Its my master although I know it should not be. Now shake my hand, a man is nothing without friends."

Governor Gwynne, peering out of his window overlooking the yard, overheard the exchange. Softly he closed the opening and shook his head. "Euston's right lad, you'll never get my help again. You are too much trouble and cannot to be relied upon," he muttered quietly to himself.

On the hulk, Susannah was inconsolable; she and Ann Turner were billeted in the middle deck amongst a hundred or so other women prisoners. Liz Pulley, after doubling up Captain Broadley with the swift application of a well-aimed knee had been dragged down to the bowels of the vessel, kicking and cursing for all her worth. Banished to the 'black hole,' a space in the bilges six feet by six feet, swarming with cockroaches and seasoned with foul smelling bilge water, she was soon to find herself inspected by two large rats, their bright eyes gleaming in the dark hold.

Prisoners went mad in the black hole, some even died not having seen the light of day for weeks on end.

After two days, Susannah was allowed to exercise on the deck clamped in short chains as a precaution against her declared intention of 'doing myself in'.

Susannah's demeanour improved when she heard that John Simpson was taking care of young Henry. She couldn't believe that the turnkey would take the baby to the Home Secretary or that he would succeed in his quest to obtain the necessary papers. She felt the best that she could hope for would be for the baby to end up with his father in Norwich Castle. Nevertheless, she frequently emptied her laden breasts of milk to prevent them from running dry. She initially kept the milk in empty bottles but abandoned this when another woman stole the stored liquid for her own child. Susannah received no sympathy from the other prisoners as the saying 'waste not, want not' was well understood where food was scarce. It wasn't long before she was glad to squirt the surplus liquid into the hungry mouths of assorted children.

Susannah and Ann Turner soon discovered that if Norwich Castle was a school for criminals then the *Dunkirk* was a university of comprehensive evil.

There was virtually no work to occupy the prisoners – only occasionally were men required for tasks on the foreshore – thus prisoners spent their days in idleness, planning escapes and recounting felonies so that others might profit from their experiences.

Some men undressed to go to bed but others preferred the protection of stockings and breeches as a rebuff against the depraved, thus many went for weeks without washing.

Some prisoners were appointed 'boatswain's mates' to organise distribution of food to six or seven others. They also had to keep deck lights burning and pass information about other prisoners. Rarely did they inform on fellow captives, it was too dangerous, but they did alert Officers to the needs of themselves and others.

Officers only went amongst the felons in a real emergency but the guards never ventured below after lock down. Below decks was closely confined and far too perilous, so prisoners were left to themselves for hours on end to gamble, thieve, whore and hammer out coins. A skilled coiner could hammer out sixpences from a half-crown and make an extra shilling in the process.

Even women there for minor crimes became experts in sin and hardened in villainy. But mostly they languished idly, engaged mainly in gambling, or profane talk about crime. Another favoured subject was inventing preposterous and ingenious methods to escape slow death on the hulks.

Susannah and Ann felt this aura of evil around them and were fearful, as were most newcomers to the hulks. Susannah spent most of her time on deck staring across to the harbour, hoping to see the friendly turnkey and her child.

Handicrafts flourished aboard, men and women used makeshift tools and stolen materials to conjure improbable baubles which were sold, subject to a hefty commission for a mariner, at nearby towns and villages.

Susannah, initially heartened by the news that Simpson had taken charge of her child, sank slowly into a mood of deep despair as the days passed. She had begun to swear and curse with the worst of the female felons, neglecting both her appearance and her usual fastidious attention to cleanliness.

Ann Turner took it upon herself to bully her into washing every day but had been alarmed on the second morning to find Susannah staring into the murky waters of Plymouth Sound perched on the edge of the ship. She had pulled the girl weeping from the gunwale and been rewarded with an earful of obscenities.

There were about three hundred prisoners on the *Dunkirk*, a third of whom were women. They were kept in different decks and exercised at different times but were not always separated. Some of the women were adept at finding their way to the men's quarters and, more often, into the sailor's billets. A number of male prisoners imprisoned on the *Dunkirk* for some years knew every corner and curve of the ship. This hardened gang of felons seemed to be able to wander freely wherever they wanted.

Ann Turner was of the opinion that they had the guards in their pockets. On the fourth day of their imprisonment on the hulk, Susannah and Ann were to witness an escape engineered, for a fee, by a group of experienced felons.

A prisoner named Cornelius Jeckyll had received a letter from his wife telling him that she was going to 'do a bunk' up north and take their two children. It was to the gang of felons that he turned for help to escape.

The gang congregated at one end of the deck looking for a victim. Without warning, the leader cracked a bystander on the back of the head with a wooden stave. Immediately, the deck was awash with men brawling and shouting.

Susannah and Ann, along with other female prisoners who were swabbing the women's deck ran for the cover to escape the vicious fighting below.

In the confusion, Cornelius Jeckyll and another man were quickly concealed in water casks which were waiting to go ashore to be refilled. As soon as they were hidden, the brawl stopped, leaving several bodies sprawled about with broken heads and bloody faces.

Ann and Susannah saw all this from their vantage point but said nothing, frightened for their own safety.

It was a full day before the authorities discovered that two prisoners had escaped. All details of the escapees were routinely passed to watchmen and other authorities between the hulk and the felons' home city, and the second man was soon recaptured. After serving time in the black hole and having the comfort of being flogged for his audacity, the other prisoners treated him as a hero.

A few days after the escape, Cornelius Jeckyll was apprehended at a hamlet called Cheddar at the foot of the Mendip Hills, just south of Bristol. When he was brought back to the *Dunkirk*, Captain Broadley, incensed by the loud cheers of the prisoners, ordered him to be publicly flogged.

The flogger was a corporal in the marines, seemingly as wide as he was tall, with a bull-like neck. Wielding the lash was a task he relished; it was the only time any prisoner saw him grin.

Prisoners watched the floggings in a state of fascinated repulsion. The corporal, being experienced, drew blood after four or five lashes to give

Cornelius a red shirt. The prisoner said not a word, only once imploring the corporal to 'flog fair' and keep the whip from his neck and face. Thirty lashes later he was led past a white- faced Susannah and Ann, blood squelching from his shoes at every painful step, his back beefsteak raw. A sailor, as was the usual practise, tossed a bucket of sea water over the man's lacerated wounds, managing at the same time to soak the two horrified women with blood and gore.

"Good God Ann, I think I shall die if I don't see my Henry and baby again!" The two friends clung together in fear and trepidation.

Standing on the steps of the Minister, John Simpson looked across the road to the reporter who indicated that he should knock again. He did so and the door opened almost before he had finished.

A tall spare man, dressed in the most extraordinary velvet vest and britches inspected him from under a pair of huge eyebrows similar to his own.

"John Simpson of Norwich to see Lord Sydney," he heard himself say as he stepped past the startled butler.

The man hurried after him, "Do you have an appointment, Sir?"

John Simpson thrust Henry into his arms and took off his heavy coat. "No, but tell Lord Sydney I'm here on urgent business and," he leaned confidentially towards the butler, "tell him it's about this baby!"

"Lord Sydney has never been to Norwich."

"The baby's mother has been to London," he winked elaborately at the startled butler, exchanged his coat for the child, and sat down on one of the chairs lining the hall. The velveteened servant almost fled up the wide staircase. The turnkey heard the sounds of a fiercely whispered conversation on the landing and felt himself being viewed over the balcony above. He continued to stare ahead while sitting straight-backed in the heavy chair. Doors opened and closed on the landing above and more whispered conversations took place until eventually the butler came down to usher him into a sitting room, closely followed by a man well-dressed in tight trousers, dark jacket and a high collar that made his face rather red.

"I am Evan Nepean, deputy to the Home Secretary. On what matter do you wish to consult Lord Sydney?"

John Simpson placed the baby on the polished table, carefully unwrapping the woollen muffler to reveal his face to the politician.

"This baby was born in the Castle gaol in Norwich. The birth of the child cannot be registered in a parish because the Castle boundaries are outside any parish. Yet when his young mother is sent to Plymouth to be transported to new lands across the seas, the captain refuses to take the child because he has no papers! He tears the baby from its mother's breast and commands me to take it back to Norwich. The cruellest blackguard in the filthiest backstreet would not act so, and yet an officer of this country's navy does! It is an outrage Sir, an outrage and quite possibly a death sentence on this child, innocent of any crime or misdemeanour!"

"And the child has no connection with Lord Sydney?"

"Lord Sydney holds the child's life in his hands – and the boy's mother's life too. She threatens to kill herself if the child is taken from her!" Simpson replied angrily.

"And you are?" Evan Nepean said smoothly.

"John Simpson, turnkey of Norwich gaol, assigned to deliver three female prisoners to the hulk *Dunkirk* at Plymouth."

"Do you act under orders, Mr Simpson, or are you here by your own initiative?"

"I'm here under the orders of my own heart, to see a nursing baby re-united with its mother."

Evan Nepean stroked his long face and studied the turnkey carefully. "Wait here," he commanded and went swiftly out of the room.

Within a few minutes, he returned with Lord Sydney and the butler. The Home Secretary peered carefully at the baby then studied himself in a wall mirror. "Nothing to do with me," he snorted, glaring at the butler who shuffled uncomfortably from one foot to the other.

He looked up, as if spotting the turnkey for the first time, "What are you here for, man?"

"Papers, Sir, papers for the baby," Simpson answered stubbornly.

Evan Nepean had been staring out of the window at the street below. "The new colony will be needing babies. We expect babies, it's one of the reasons we are sending mainly young felons to New South Wales."

He took Lord Sydney by the arm and pointed at the reporter waiting on the opposite pavement.

"It is a very humanitarian purpose you have set yourself, Mr Simpson. I am sure we, as members of the government, can be equally good hearted, don't you agree My Lord?"

Lord Sydney looked at the reporter outside and then at his deputy. "A very noble journey Mr Simpson, I commend you for your efforts."

The turnkey wiped his brow, not knowing what to say. The butler was sent to bring writing paper printed with the imposing crest of the House of Commons.

John Simpson quickly recovered. "Would it be possible to include the name of the baby's father on the papers, Sir? He has petitioned for permission to accompany the baby and its mother. He languishes in Norwich Gaol."

Lord Sydney and his deputy looked again at the reporter stamping his feet across the road.

"He's young and strong?" demanded Evan Nepean.

"Ideal as a settler in new lands, you have my word," the turnkey answered eagerly.

Ten minutes later, John Simpson was standing on the portico holding little Henry and the precious papers in his hands. In the Minister's imposing residence, Lord Sydney and Evan Nepean smiled as the reporter joined the turnkey to walk down the street together.

Later, having spent some time in George's company, giving him full details of Henry Cabell and Susannah Holmes and having recounted at least three times the events in Lord Sydney's drawing room, Simpson arrived back at his lodgings.

When staff and customers heard the news, he was treated like a hero coming home from war. People shook his hand and slapped his back and he soon found several pots of ale awaiting his attention. Time and time again he was told what a good fellow he was for daring to confront a Minister of the Crown in his own home.

After a time, Simpson realised he had not sighted Agnes since his return to the inn. He found her red-eyed on the bed when he took the baby to her chamber.

"What's the matter, Agnes, does something ail you?" She shook her head and turned away. "I got papers for the baby, and papers for the child's father too!"

She sat up, drying her face with a handkerchief that was already sodden. Henry was bawling for all he was worth, so she opened her blouse and guided the nipple into the child's eager mouth.

"You'll be taking Henry away, now I'm no more use."

"You can come to Norwich with me, I've to deliver the papers to the prison so the child's father can be transported to New South Wales."

She shook her head sadly, "I've got to go back, if I stay longer I shall love Henry too much."

They sat in silence for a while, disturbed only by the baby slurping noisily at the girl's breast. Suddenly the door was flung open and the Landlord came in holding a broadsheet.

"You're in the papers on the front page!"

The caption said, 'Baby Torn from Mother's Breast' and a sub-heading trumpeted 'Humane Turnkey Saves Child'.

There followed a long article detailing the callous Captain's refusal to take the baby on board the hulk, along with his mother and John Simpson's subsequent dash to London to confront Lord Sydney with the 'crying infant in his arms.'

When they eventually went downstairs the regulars of the tavern treated them royally. Agnes remained in the background, happy to cuddle the child and hold him up periodically to be toasted.

At the coach offices in The Strand the next morning, John Simpson said goodbye to Agnes. Earlier she had handed him three stone bottles filled to the brim with breast milk that she had been saving for the baby.

He promised to let her know what happened and thanked her for accompanying him to London. Finally, she stood on tiptoe and kissed him warmly on the cheek.

"Is your marriage a happy one?" She whispered earnestly.

"It is," he nodded.

"Thought so," she stepped smartly on the box and disappeared into the coach.

Before leaving on the 'Anglian Express', the turnkey bought a copy of the London Chronicle. George, the reporter, had also written an article about his exploits for this paper; it was headed '*Humane Turnkey*' and finished by praising Lord Sydney for addressing himself to the happiness of '*unfortunate creatures unable to help themselves.*'

In his chambers in the House of Commons, Evan Nepean read the articles concerning John Simpson's journey of mercy. The tone of these reports, although emphasising the heroic deeds of the '*Humane Turnkey*', also contained favourable commentary of Lord Sydney's compassionate treatment of '*even the lowest creatures*'.

In a parliamentary debate that afternoon, Lord Sydney talked grandly about *'universal acceptance of our noble heritage of justice for every citizen in our land, especially those pinioned by poverty and stayed by ignorance'*. These words were widely reported throughout the Country and thus his stock rose upon the efforts of a determined gaoler from Norwich.

John Simpson's actions towards the harsh treatment meted out to prisoner Holmes, and her plight, had not gone unnoticed in other quarters.

Lady Cadogan was genuinely touched by the story of a young prisoner being forcibly separated from her child. The report in the London Chronicle had also chronicled Henry Cabell's resolute attempts to obtain permission to marry Susannah Holmes and that those efforts had been thwarted by the authorities. Being well known for charitable work, Lady Cadogan set about starting a fund for Susannah, Henry and the baby.

Another interested reader of the reports was Commodore Phillips who was spending a few days in his Hampshire home. He penned another letter to Evan Nepean, asking him to consult Lord Sydney on how he should regard prisoners transported to New South Wales. *'Should I'*, he wrote, *'regard them as convicts or colonists?'*

Later Lord Sydney was to reply that convicts should be contained as secure as any gaol until the fleet reached its destination whereupon they would, perforce, become colonists. This was to influence many of Commodore Phillip's actions over the next few years.

Chapter Twenty Two

John Simpson looked out of the coach as it entered the ancient St Stephens Gates of Norwich. He was glad to see the familiar sights of women selling flowers and vegetables by the side of the narrow road, itself bedecked with poles of washing hung from windows. In Castle Meadow, he stared up at the Norman fortress on its great mound but decided to go straight home. After the long journey north he did not feel like making the lengthy explanation sure to be needed by Governor Gwynne.

At his home in Colegate, his wife was astonished when he arrived with Henry yelling in his arms, but he stifled her questions with a brusque "Tea for me, mother's milk for young Henry, and my boots off in front of the grate, then I'll tell you everything."

Some time later, with the baby asleep on the couch, his big hand wrapped around a hot mug of tea, John Simpson related the events of the previous few days.

"You've seen the Houses of Parliament?" Rosie asked, open-mouthed.

"Aye, and I've sat my backside in one of Lord Sydney's chairs in his great house! The hall was as big and this and the front room put together!"

Her face was a picture when he produced two London papers with his name prominent in both. She went from one to the other, drinking in every word.

"It's a fine thing you've done, John, I'm proud of you."

The turnkey didn't reply, he was fast asleep in his chair.

The following morning, John Simpson presented himself, little Henry and the official paperwork to Governor Gwynne, who raised his eyebrows at the sight of the baby in his makeshift cot. He waited while his employer studied the instructions from Lord Sydney and the newspaper reports.

The Governor was particularly animated by the press reports. "This is excellent news, nobody will question the management of this gaol in the light of your exploits on behalf of prisoner Holmes. I doubt whether Cabell is worthy of your efforts, but at least we will be rid of a troublesome prisoner. The Castle is proud of you, and if I'm not mistaken, the citizens of Norwich will praise your actions too!"

He opened the door and yelled "Fetch Cabell!" to the guard outside. A few minutes later, Henry stumbled up the steps to the Governor's rooms wondering why he was not cuffed and chained. The Chief Turnkey and George Gwynne stood facing him, arms folded, looking serious. John Simpson was the first to speak.

"Henry Cabell, I've two things for you. The first is a paper signed by Lord Sydney, to say you can join Susannah Holmes on the hulk at Plymouth and the other is a boy that can shite through the eye of a needle." The two men stood aside to reveal the baby in his wooden crib.

Henry was dumbfounded.

"Mr Simpson took it upon himself to go to the Home Secretary's own house to get papers when the child was refused a berth on board the hulk. Now, as a result of Chief Simpson's fine work you will be allowed to accompany prisoner Holmes to New South Wales!"

Henry, his throat a knot of emotion, gripped the turnkey's hands, eyes moist with tears, still unable to utter a word.

The Governor stepped forward and laid a hand on his arm. "Take your son, Cabell, and this jug of mother's milk, and prepare yourself to travel. First thing tomorrow you're off to the *Dunkirk* in Plymouth Sound."

Henry lifted the child from his box and backed out of the door still unable to fully comprehend what had happened. The two officers watched from the window as Henry skipped across the yard, unhampered it seemed by his heavy iron ankle fetters.

"You've done a fine job for Cabell and for this gaol Mr Simpson. I shall borrow these London papers for a while – I'm sure the Norwich newspapers will be glad to know of your deeds in the metropolis. Get off home, you'll need some rest. You can take Cabell and his son to London and on to Plymouth by the noonday coach tomorrow!"

Before leaving, the turnkey made his way to Cabell's cell to find John Euston trying to calm his emotional cellmate.

"Did you really go to the Home Secretary's own house to get papers for us?" Henry asked.

"I was so incensed by the Captain's refusal to take the child, I'd have sat in the Ministers' hall for a week!"

"Why was the nipper refused?" John Euston asked.

"No papers!" Simpson answered shortly. "Now, Cabell, I'll have plenty of time to tell you the long and short of it - I'm taking you to Plymouth tomorrow. Now I'm off to find a wet nurse for that boy of yours."

That night the Norfolk Chronicle reported:-
'The laws of England, distinguished by the spirit
of humanity that framed them, forbid so cruel an act as that
of separating an infant from its mother's breast.It cannot
be but a pleasing circumstance for every Englishman to know,
that, thoughMinisters, must, on most occasions, be difficult
to access for the general public.

> *However, when delay would materially affect the happiness
> of even the meanest subject in the kingdom, the Minister
> himself not only attends to complaints properly addressed, but
> promptly and effectually affords relief'.*

The article went on to give details of John Simpson's – '*the distinguished Norwich turnkey*' – determination to right the wrong of separating an unweaned child from its mother and how he had bearded the Home Secretary in his own home to obtain the papers needed.

In London, Lady Cadogan's appeal for a public subscription for the '*unfortunate creatures*' was already attracting funds. It was to raise the substantial sum of twenty pounds - a labourer would have had to work nearly two years to earn such an amount.

Commodore Phillip spent more and more time with John Shortland who was proving an invaluable ally. The Naval Agent's extensive knowledge of the needs of prisoners and guards on the American runs enabled them to block flagrant and not so obvious breaches of the supply agreement, as practised by Duncan Campbell, the fleet's Chief Contractor.

The two men met to inspect a gang of prisoners working on a new dock opposite Greenwich, guarded by troopers commanded by a Captain who seemed to be in charge of everything except his temper. Each prisoner had a fourteen-pound iron riveted to his right ankle, as a practical discouragement to swimmers.

The men's thin clothing, unsuited to heavy work, was black with mud. A barge dredged up foul-smelling silt with heavy buckets dragged along the bottom of the river. Felons on the barge heaped the mud in large baskets. It took two men to haul the baskets along the quayside on flat platforms equipped with small wheels at each corner. These were emptied by teams of four behind the newly constructed quayside consisting of stout posts hammered into the river and buttressed by equally thick planks attached horizontally. It was back-breaking work and the men could only work two hours on, one hour off.

As the two officials watched, a party of four guards and three convicts arrived in a boat from the nearest hulk. The prisoners struggled with the body of a man who had died the previous night. On the quayside, they threw the near-naked corpse in a wheelbarrow. The strange procession moved slowly up the foreshore and on to the wet marshes beyond. The gang working on the dock paid no heed when the grim cargo passed. The corpse was buried in the marsh with little ceremony.

John Shortland, observing Commodore Phillip's look of disgust, suggested they return to their nearby carriage. The Commodore, taking a last look at the desolate scene, had learned little of practical use that day, but quietly resolved to treat prisoners under his command with humanity. He said little to John Shortland, only that the prisoners were treated worse than dogs.

That night the Commodore began a list of 'rules and punishments for convicts' that he would issue to Captains and Commanders of Marines on each ship in the fleet. These rules were to supplement the 'laws of England' until they reached New South Wales.

Chapter Twenty Three

The story of the turnkey's efforts spread like wildfire amongst the convicts in Norwich Castle. The whole prison population, led by John Euston, gave him three cheers when he appeared to take Cabell and the child to Plymouth. A delighted Henry shook hands with practically everyone in the yard, including turnkeys, several of whom had felt the force of his fists at various times over the previous few years.

He heartily thanked John Euston for his friendship and promised to write of his progress in the New Lands. He assured his friend that he was determined to make the best of transportation for his family.

The coach travelled the same route as John Simpson's earlier journey. At the Bull Inn in Long Melford, some customers in the bar had read of the turnkey's adventures and he was treated as something of a celebrity, and had to recount all that had befallen, Susannah, the baby and himself on the journey to Plymouth and at Lord Sydney's house.

The journey went swiftly and, on the fourth night, they came to the Inn at Exeter. Agnes offered to feed the baby almost as soon as they arrived. The breast milk they had brought with them, bartered by the turnkey's wife for herbal remedies from two young mothers, had run out, so they gladly handed the child to her.

John Simpson ordered a meal for himself and Henry Cabell in the public bar. He remembered how the three women prisoners had enjoyed an evening in the company of folk other than convicts, faced as they were, with bleak times ahead. The meal passed well with Henry excited about meeting Susannah the next day, and Agnes sitting with them, nursing the baby as if he was her own.

When it was time for bed, Simpson secured Henry to the bedstead by means of a chain and padlock.

"No need for the irons, Mr Simpson, I want to get aboard the hulk. I can't do that without you and the papers."

"I know, lad, but you being locked up means I can sleep easy."

The Turnkey went off to get the baby from Agnes who insisted on giving it a last minute feed. He found her in a nursing chair on a darkened part of the landing, the baby asleep at her breast. Agnes eased the child away, dabbing at its mouth with a white cloth, in no hurry to put her breast back.

"I'll come to your room to change the baby's napkin," she said softly.

"Sharing with the prisoner," he said, smiling weakly.

"My room is at the end of the corridor," she whispered, "facing the front of the inn."

He followed her there and didn't emerge until morning.

The coach to Plymouth was half full, so the turnkey bolted Henry to an inside seat and took the baby to say goodbye to Agnes and her father. She had served breakfast in silence, favouring him with the occasional smile.

In the kitchen, he was shocked to catch a glimpse of the landlord touching his own daughter with a strange familiarity as she bent to put a log on the grate. Confused, he stepped back into the corridor, and the words she had spoken with such vehemence in London came back to him. "Father," she had said when he asked who it was she did not want a baby with.

Outside, the coachman cracked his whip to signal the start of the run to Plymouth. The landlord, one arm round his daughter's shoulder, waved them off. For the rest of the journey, the turnkey was haunted by Agnes' resigned expression as she watched the coach depart.

Hours later, when the team began to rumble over the cobbled streets of Plymouth, Simpson turned his thoughts to Captain Broadley, Master of the *Dunkirk*. Only days earlier they had been hurling insults at each other, and he wondered if Henry Cabell would suffer because of the row.

The turnkey and his prisoner made their way to the hut housing the soldiers ferrying convicts to the nearby hulk; the sergeant recognised Simpson immediately.

"You're back then," he grumbled.

"I am, and with papers."

"You were a lot of bleeding trouble last time!"

"So was yon Captain Broadley."

Taking the papers, the sergeant held them against his list, following each name with a grubby finger. He got to the end, grunted irritably and started again. At last he looked up from his laborious search and squinted angrily at Simpson.

"These names are not on my list!" he shouted. Henry started forward menacingly but the turnkey held him back.

"Those papers are signed by Lord Sydney, the Home Secretary himself!"

The sergeant ran his fingers over the impressive wax seals of the Minister and stroked his chin.

"Corporal!" he called one of the two men lounging in the hut. "Put these two on the list; I'll get the boat and we'll row 'em across to see if these papers are genuine!"

The corporal emerged rubbing his eyes, "Name?"

"Henry Cabell."

"HENRY KABLE." The man added the name with painstaking gravity to the list.

Henry was to be favoured with this new surname for the rest of his life.

On board the *Dunkirk*, someone had set fire to a straw mattress in the women's quarters so all female prisoners were making the most of an unexpected period on deck. Liz Pulley had been released from the black hole a few days earlier, but was still defiant of authority. Kneeing Captain Broadley the minute she had come aboard had raised her in the other prisoners' eyes, so she had been greeted well when she emerged from the punishment cell. She was billeted with Susannah and Ann – all three shared a space six feet in width by four feet in height.

"If that Captain Broadley don't give us a better billet, I'll knee the bugger in the foreshore again – see how he likes being cramped up and bent double!" Liz had declared. "Every time I slide myself in that space I feel like a bleeding drawer in a chest."

On the day John Simpson and Henry arrived from Norwich, a prisoner named Elizabeth Hayward came over when she saw Liz emerge from the hold. Ann and Susannah had befriended the girl when one of the seasoned convicts had attempted to bully her into giving away a scarf.

"Are you the one who decked the Captain?"

"It's not the first time I've done that to a matelot!" Liz grinned. "How old are you lass?"

"Thirteen years."

Elizabeth Hayward was small for her age and possessed only what she wore – a long thin frock, undervest, pantaloons and a pair of holed stockings – plus the woollen scarf she kept round her neck. It was her prized possession.

Most of the prisoners bound for Botany Bay were young as decreed by the Beauchamp Committee who wanted '*young able convicts for the new colony*'. Almost nine out of ten prisoners were aged thirty five or less although there were a few older female felons.

They were interrupted by a flurry of movement from the bridge when three officers bustled down the gangway. The ship's bosun cleared knots of women out of the way as the Captain and First Mate strode towards the rail.

Over the side of the ship, the red face of the dragoon sergeant appeared, holding a roll of papers. The papers were sent up by way of a basket. Captain Broadley and the first mate studied the documents and peered over the side at the boat below. The two men conferred again before the first mate stood on a raised hatchway and shouted.

"Susannah Holmes, step forward!"

Warily, Susannah approached the officers just as a bulky figure appeared on the deck from the boat. As the figure straightened up he caught sight of her approaching.

"Susannah!" Henry shouted at the top of his voice. Swiftly he unbuttoned his jacket to reveal the baby fastened to his chest.

The first mate was brushed aside by Henry and the young couple met in a whirl of laughing, crying and hugging. A circle of prisoners magically appeared to surround them and prevented the officer lashing out at Henry. Ann and Liz danced about in a mad jig of joy.

"My little angel 'as got her baby back!" Liz shouted over and over again.

All the women aboard knew that the Captain had parted Susannah from her child and many were enraged by the callous act, and most assumed she would never set eyes on the boy again.

The touching reunion was a rare moment of joy for the women convicts and a version of 'Auld Lang Syne' began around Susannah, Henry and their baby. In the boat, below John Simpson heard the roars of approval and sank back, beaming with relief.

The sergeant scrambled back into the little boat and cast off from the hulk. "It's the papers what's done it," he grunted. "The Captain's a powerful one for paperwork – especially if there's a wax seal attached!"

In the Captain's cabin, the First Mate took the list given him by the sergeant and copied the two new names onto his record of prisoners. Henry would only see his name in writing again when he reached Jackson Cove in New South Wales and by then it would be too late to change it from the new spelling of Kable.

Even Captain Broadley, writing the next day to Lord Sydney, did not get the name right.

Plymouth DockNovember 16th 1786
> Sir
> I beg to acquaint you that I yesterday afternoon received
> on board His Majesty's Ship Dunkirk (in obedience with
> Lord Sydney's commands) a male child, said to be the son
> of Susannah Holmes, a woman under my Custody, and at
> the same time Henry Cabal, a convict from the gaol at
> Norwich was delivered to me.
> I am very respectfully Sir your most obedient and humble servant
> Henry Broadley.

When John Simpson returned to Norwich, he was officially appointed Senior Turnkey and given two and sixpence extra on his weekly wage. News of Henry and the baby being reunited with Susannah reached the little church in Surlingham, Norfolk on the day that Bessie married Tom, the young gardener. Sam Rush, Parish Watchman and County Thieftaker, gave the young housemaid in marriage.

Henry and Susannah could hardly believe their luck at being together again. They clung to each other surrounded by, it seemed, the entire contingent of female felons. Their happy reunion triggered many emotions in the watching crowd; mostly a shared joy but envy and anger were also present. There were other children, other husbands, brothers and sisters left behind. A good number of the prisoners had petitioned for permission to take a loved one along with them to the new lands; very few were successful.

When the throng of women finally dispersed, Henry and Susannah found a quiet space to be alone. "I thought I would never see you again, Henry, if you had stayed in Norwich Castle you would have been locked up for only three more years. By coming to the new lands I heard your seven year sentence begins anew!"

"I care nought for that, my life is linked to yours, I'll work all my days to make my son's life better than ours!"

She clung to him, feeling his strength, "No less than me Henry, no less than me."

There was no provision on the *Dunkirk* for couples and Henry was quartered on the lowest level of the men's section, mostly seeing Susannah and the baby from afar during exercise periods. To prevent problems, the authorities kept the sexes separate on board ship. The mens' allotted time on deck ended before female prisoners were allowed out.

Henry soon realized that men left behind to scrub decks after exercise were still there when the women appeared, so he volunteered for this duty. A bribe to one of the guards gave him a little time to meet Susannah. These fleeting moments became precious to both of them.

Chapter Twenty Four

The *Dunkirk* could accommodate three hundred and fifty prisoners and over the next few weeks it was to become almost full. New prisoners were allocated space on the lowest level where unruly convicts were kept, thus allowing the worst behaved to prey upon new arrivals before they had time to learn the ropes.

If a man earned the good opinion of the guards and officers, he would be moved to the middle deck, and then to the upper deck which had larger portholes for freer ventilation of air and was much drier, being further removed from the sea. It was a crude but effective method of inducing good behaviour.

The women were on two levels in the forward hold next to the crew's quarters. There were stout planks separating the two sections but these were no barrier to a determined few. Some women were adept at breaking into the crew's sections.

If caught, the women were sent to the lower deck or, for the persistent offenders, to the black hole. Usually any sailor discovered with a woman, found himself before the Captain who prescribed the cat-of-nine-tails as a remedy against debauchery.

A number of officers were open to bribes to ease prisoners' burdens or to allow extra rations. A few took money or favours from the women, but failed to deliver promises. No matter what punishments were issued, the *Dunkirk*, like all hulks, remained a hotbed of crime.

As one ship's officer wrote in the daily log – *'the prisoners are perversely obstinate to the cat o nine tails and return to thieving like dogs to their vomit.'*

Henry, by dint of hard work, quickly found himself on the most favoured

---

deck where talk was marginally less desolate than at the deepest level. Even here tales of evil, crime and debauchery were regular subjects for late night discussion.

Christmas in Plymouth in the year 1786 was murderously cold below decks, the only source of warmth were smuggled candles and heat from the bodies of fellow prisoners. Thick flakes of snow fell for two days, covering the ship like icing on a cake. The man who had escaped a month or so earlier, Cornelius Jeckyll, died on Christmas Eve. In moments, convicts anxious to ransack his few possessions began to fight.

When the scavengers were that certain everything had been looted one shouted through the hatch that Cornelius had died.

Nothing was done until Christmas morning when the body was hauled up on deck, washed in full view of the assembled prisoners, and placed in a makeshift coffin. From there it was taken to the quay where it was transferred to a wheelbarrow, to be transported to the dead house, a ramshackle building up a nearby side street. Here it lay for four days until it was claimed by local surgeons under the provisions of the Anatomy Act which allowed them to refine their skills of dissection.

Refitting transport ships and provisioning of the whole fleet proceeded slowly. Commodore Phillip and Lieutenant Shortland worked together almost every day to get the flotilla ready for the epic voyage.

Commodore Phillip's zeal in getting the organisation right was intensified when the first convicts were transferred on January 6th 1787 to his care, from the Woolwich hulks. Male convicts were put aboard the *Alexander* and females found themselves on the *Lady Penrhyn*.

Alerted by Captain Duncan Sinclair of the *Alexander*, Commodore Phillip went to inspect the prisoners on both ships. The women in particular were in an atrocious state, ill clothed, slovenly and full of lice.

The first men aboard the *Alexander* were little better so the two Captains, together with Shortland and Phillip jointly signed a letter to Evan Nepean. The first batches of prisoners to board transports were from hulks owned by Duncan Campbell so a deal of the criticism was aimed at him. As the flow of felons from gaols, bridewells and other hulks flooded onto the transports over the next two months, fleets' surgeons and masters voiced similar complaints about the state of the prisoners

Discipline and security on the transports was a matter for the Marines, and was much stricter than most had experienced on the hulks. Rations for felons were based on an allowance issued in the Royal Navy, convicts receiving a third less than enlisted men.

Each mess of six were allocated a specified amount. Individuals received a daily ration amounting to five ounces of bread, seven ounces of meat, four ounces of flour, half ounce of butter and half ounce of rice. In addition they were allowed two pints of pease weekly.

Unscrupulous stewards cheated prisoners out of their rations whenever they could. A steward found using false weights on board one transport was sentenced to fifty lashes as a reward for his industry. The prisoners made the man's life such a misery afterwards that he was dismissed from the service.

Despite such practices, almost all prisoners were fed better than they had been, the hulks being notorious for scant rations and a good number of gaols worse.

In Portsmouth, where the *Prince of Wales* and *Scarborough* lay at anchor, convicts were lined up in a large shed to be examined by the ships' surgeons, before being rowed out to the vessels.

Any found fevered or suffering grievously from wounds were sent back to their previous place of incarceration. In the huge shed it was impossible to examine every one closely - particularly women in front of male prisoners. The stench of stale clothes, sweating bodies, uncombed hair and feet that hadn't seen a splash of water for weeks was almost unbearable.

On embarkation, the prisoners were given a number and allocated to a mess of six. Each was issued with bedding, eating utensils, mattress, pillow and one blanket.Eating implements consisted of two bowls and one spoon.

In Plymouth, rumours flooded the hulk *Dunkirk*, but nobody knew for certain when prisoners were to be embarked upon the sailing ships.

Henry struck up a friendship with the corporal of his watch, enabling him to spend a few minutes each day with Susannah and the baby. Initially made a 'mess captain' – one of those who had to distribute daily rations for six convicts – Henry was appointed a 'deck captain' early in February, holding responsibility for resolving squabbles for all men quartered on his deck.

As February came to an end, the *Dunkirk* housed over three hundred prisoners, two thirds of whom were waiting to embark on the first fleet.

In the close dark below decks, fever flourished, and two more convicts suffered its fatal effects. On his deck, Henry had his hands full protecting the weak and young from ill-tempered attacks provoked by tension and hunger. There were some in the prison service who believed a low diet fatigued the body, diminished evil activities and thoughts of escape.

Despite the confusion and terror of life aboard the overcrowded hulk, Susannah and Henry drew closer together. Their stolen moments, aided and abetted by Ann Turner and Liz Pulley, seemed even more precious for their brevity. Long hours spent apart were made bearable by the intensity of their feelings when snatching moments in each other's company.

They also received unexpected good news about Lady Cadogan's public subscription appeal for Susannah and her baby. She wrote to Susannah, via Captain Broadley, to enquire on what she wanted the money spent, suggesting *'clothes for Susannah and her child and tools of husbandry for the baby's Father'* as useful gifts for those beginning again in a new land.

Susannah replied asking Lady Cadogan to arrange for clothing and tools to be purchased and boxed securely for the journey. She also requested some money be sent to her at Plymouth *'to relieve us of immediate poverty and buy items essential for such a long and arduous journey.'*

The clothes, tools and 'books of useful instruction' were boxed and sent to the ship *Alexander* and marked for the young couples' attention. The box was to be the centre of an extraordinary court case when the fleet reached New South Wales.

On 4th March 1787 three ships, sailing in convoy, entered Plymouth Sound. Almost immediately rumours began to circulate these were vessels of the first fleet.

The ships were the *Charlotte*, *Friendship* and *Hyena*. HMS *Hyena*, it soon became apparent, was full of marines who were to be used as guards on board the other ships, but both merchantmen had been converted to carry convicts.

Fever had claimed another life and the hospital deck was full to overflowing with the sick. Gunpowder was exploded between decks to kill vermin and holds were sweetened by oil of tar and lime.

It soon became clear that orders had finally been received for the dispersal of prisoners. Twenty five women were to be transported by road to London to be embarked on a ship in Woolwich docks – the *Alexander*. In the confusion of preparing the women for the journey to London, Henry managed to spend a few moments with Susannah to find she was close to panic.

"What ails you Susannah, we are starting soon for the new lands, anything is better than this hulk full of diseases!"

"Henry, the men are to be embarked on one ship and the women on another! We shall lose each other again, I feel it in my heart."

Liz Pulley, carrying the baby, joined them. "'Tis true, I had to let that fat matelot feel my tits before he told me the men are to board the *Charlotte* and women the *Friendship*."

Chapter Twenty Five

By late February 1787 gaols, bridewells and hulks feeding the flow of felons to the first fleet had almost completed their mission.

The Portsmouth Gazette reported 'a party of prisoners, two hundred and ten strong, ironed together and to the wagons in which they travelled, reached the harbour to be embarked on ships bound for Botany Bay.'

The prisoners, guarded by a Company of light horse, were unable to reach the ships immediately owing to a gale whipping up heavy seas. They had to doss down for five days in a wooden warehouse with no bedding. Most of the convicts, mainly men, were in a pitiful state, cold, hungry and dressed in rags.

Eventually, the *Scarborough*, a two decked, three masted vessel, was crammed with these prisoners. The height between decks was less than four and a half feet.

The *Prince of Wales*, the other transport in Portsmouth harbour, was slightly smaller but contained only fifty prisoners – all except one, were female. The extra space in this vessel was for animals; the authorities knew that when the fleet reached the Cape of Good Hope a substantial number of cattle would be needed for breeding stock and food in the new lands.

A few days later, two ships that had embarked prisoners in Woolwich docks entered Portsmouth harbour. The *Alexander*, the largest of the transports, had two hundred and eleven male prisoners and the *Lady Penrhyn* one hundred and one female prisoners.

A few days before the ships left Woolwich, Commodore Phillip, accompanied by John Shortland and Captain John Hunter, made an inspection of the prisoners on board the *Lady Penrhyn*. The Commodore was appalled by their condition and sent one of his most vitriolic letters to

Evan Nepean. Cleverly, he placed the blame on the local judiciary for the womens' plight.

'The situation in which Magistrates send women on board the *Lady Penrhyn* stamps them with infamy – tho' almost naked, and so very filthy that nothing but clothing could have prevented them from perishing, and which could not be done in time to prevent a fever, which is still on board that ship, and where there are so many venereal complaints that must spread in spite of every precaution I may take thereafter.'

Within a few days the Commodore was writing again, this time to complain bitterly that 'despite several entreaties the women's clothing has still not arrived.' In another blast at the ordnance office he pointed out that ammunition for small arms was lacking. 'What', he wrote, 'is the use of pistols and muskets without ball and powder?'

In Plymouth, Captain Broadley gathered prisoners on the hulk to announce what the prisoners had known for some days – that 'those bound for Botany Bay had to pack their belongings and prepare to board the transports at first light on the morrow!'

Immediately after the meeting all the talk was of women being transported on the *Charlotte*.

Later, Henry and Susannah snatched a few minutes together in the lea of some large crates.

"I'm frightened, Henry."

"I'm afraid too, afraid I'll lose you on the voyage."

"It's to be women only on the ship."

"There'll be crew and marines too!"

"I want no one else, Henry."

He stared morosely into the sea. "I heard tell the marines will be staying when we reach Botany Bay and many a man will be looking for a wife. The marines earn a wage, I'll have to slave for a master!" he said desperately.

"You're my man Henry."

They clung to each other for some minutes, no words were necessary. At last Henry broke the silence.

"No one can blame you for choosing another – I can only promise love."

"We're clamped by fetters Henry, and some might consider us nothing more than slaves, and yet we meet, we talk, we have a son born out of love. We are not free yet we have freedom."

They were interrupted by a young girl, generally regarded as a copper short of a shilling, who wandered into their tight space and dropped to her knees. Her mother had died the previous night. She began to pray.

"Dear God, instead of letting people die and having to make new ones, why don't you keep the ones you've got, it would save a lot of trouble."

Susannah hugged the girl, Henry gave her an apple he had been saving.

The next morning all male prisoners were assembled on the main deck. Women prisoners had been moved off the ship earlier in the dimness of the small hours. A drummer played a long roll that was the signal for everyone to be quiet.

"These men for the *Friendship!*" the bosun shouted and began to reel of a list of names. Seventy six names were called out; Henry's was one of the first.

A flotilla of small boats ferried men to the ship rolling gently in the cold sea, stayed by huge chains fore and aft. As the vessel loomed menacingly out of the morning mist the men grew silent, fear creeping into their bones with the cold drizzle.

Henry squeezed his eyes against the grey light, hoping to catch sight of Susannah and the baby on the *Charlotte*. He knew it was a hopeless task, the ship was too far away for any detail to be seen, besides he told himself, she was almost certainly locked in the hold.

His thoughts went back to the previous evening when they had spent an hour together. The crew had turned a blind eye to a certain amount of fraternisation between the prisoners, knowing full well the hardships of a long sea journey; an arrangement Captain Broadley and the officers concurred with by keeping out of the way, merely posting extra sentries around the harbour to pick up any convict, or Jack Tar, bold enough to try to escape.

Henry and Susannah had shared out the remaining money from the few pounds they had received from Lady Cadogan. They had often talked about the day a local dignitary, a relation of Lady Cadogan, had brought the bag of coins to them on the *Dunkirk*.

"I could feel from the weight it was more than I had ever seen in my life before," Susannah told him, not for the first time.

They had reminisced again about their good fortune and went through, for perhaps the tenth time, the list of clothing and tools stored on the *Alexander* for their use in the new lands.

"We must be just about the luckiest couple on board the whole fleet," Henry declared.

They made a solemn pledge to love each other in Botany Bay just as much as in England and had managed to make love in their secret place amongst the scattered crates and boxes.

Henry remembered all this as the jolly boat pitched and dipped in the sullen sea. Soon the prisoners were clambering up the rope nets to their new quarters. As they came aboard each were given a cursory examination by the ship's surgeon, Thomas Arndell.

When all seventy six were assembled, the Master, Francis Walton, addressed them.

"You are now in the hands of the authorities appointed by the Government to transport you to a land called New South Wales. There you will work to build a new Colony for England. As in our American Colony, opportunities will abound for those prepared to toil hard and true and many fortunes have been made by men who began a new life manacled by the King's iron. Whilst on board this ship you will be subject to the King's regulations and discipline. Mess Captains will be appointed from amongst you to be responsible for the conduct of six other prisoners. Daily they will draw rations for their mess mates and keep Deck Captains informed of any illness or ill discipline of those in their mess. Until we sail, those men, currently Deck Captains on board the hulk, will continue until a decision is made about new appointments. When we sail from these shores others among you will be given tasks such as barbers, tailors, scrapers, swabbers and caulkers. From the women on board we need cooks, seamstresses and cleaners. Discipline is now under the control of the marines who will not hesitate to test the cat o' nine tails on a deserving back. There will be no washing or drying of clothes between decks."

Henry's heart began to thump when he heard the words 'women on board'. What women? Was Susannah among them?

The men were given coarse cloth trousers and jackets emblazoned with a number and covered with broad arrows. They were made to change on the open deck in the freezing wind blowing in from the English Channel.

A sailor called out each man's name – in groups of six they were led into the holds and allocated specific spaces. Finally, Henry and two others were the last left on deck. Captain Walton, flanked by two hefty marines, spoke to them.

"You men are Deck Captains for the time being; you'll remain so until I decide whether you are fit to carry on. Remember, you share the punishments of those on your levels – one lash for every ten your men suffer! I'll also withdraw wittles to the same proportion."

"That hardly seems a fair cut of the cake, Sir – any man might get himself a lashing with the cat just to visit a few stingers on our backs!" The tall prisoner next to Henry spoke up.

"It'll be up to you to discourage any reasons for the marines to bring out the cat!"

"You mentioned women prisoners, Sir – is one named Susannah Holmes among 'em?" Henry asked.

"You'll be Kable I 'spect, I read about you and the girl in the London Gazette. Aye, she's on board, the Navy's not cruel enough to separate a couple with child."

Henry could not speak but a grin the width of the Plymouth harbour revealed his pleasure.

"Right you men, get yourselves below – we sail for Portsmouth in a few days!"

The people of Portsmouth were in a panic. For days rumours had been circulating of fever on one of the transports, and now their worst fears had been confirmed. The dreaded typhus was aboard the *Alexander*!

Captain Duncan Sinclair cursed the rag tag army of cold, wet, and underfed prisoners he had been forced to embark two weeks previously. The prisoners cursed the overcrowding – there were over two hundred and sixty prisoners and crew on a ship just one hundred and fourteen feet by thirty feet. The ship's surgeon blamed the lack of medical supplies but whatever the root cause the fever rampaged through the hapless creatures below decks.

Commodore Phillip and John Hunter raced by coach to Portsmouth when the news was received in London. By the time they arrived, three prisoners had died and dozens more were dangerously ill. Phillip ordered everybody ashore, separating those diagnosed as 'fevered' from the rest. Enlisted men fumigated the ship, soaking the timbers in creosote oil and quick liming the felons' quarters. Gunpowder was exploded in every part of the ship as a final precaution.

Despite this, within three weeks eleven men had died.

Phillip was furious, laying a great deal of the trouble on lack of fresh provisions. He dashed off a caustic communication to Evan Nepean and

Lord Sydney, blaming the Chief Contractor who was forced to release the fresh provisions which Phillip had been pressing for for so long.

Prisoners deemed well were re-embarked on the *Alexander*, to be gradually joined by the sick as they recovered. Nevertheless, a further five convicts would die before the fleet sailed. A woman on the *Lady Penrhyn* would also succumb to gaol fever.

The supply ships, the *Borrowdale*, *Fishburn* and *Golden Grove* arrived in Portsmouth a day or two earlier than the transports from Plymouth. By the middle of March 1787 the First Fleet had assembled at the Motherbank. The Naval ships *Supply* and *Sirius* anchored in the harbour were waiting for the signal to set sail. There were almost fifteen hundred souls aboard the eleven ships, including five hundred and sixty eight male and one hundred and ninety one female prisoners.

The *Charlotte* and *Friendship* were the only vessels with a mixture of prisoners. The *Charlotte* was to carry eighty eight men and twenty one women, the *Friendship* had seventy six men and twenty women.

Phillip and John Shortland were delayed in London ensuring that final supplies were dispatched to Portsmouth. These supplies, of necessity, were mainly bulkier items of ships spares, various stores of a personal nature for the officers and the vital fresh provisions.

Henry, who had found that a firm hand was the key to a quiet life on the hulk, quickly imposed himself over two or three troublemakers on his deck. Despite being the youngest deck captain, the others tended to follow his lead when dealing with the officers and crew. He was also busy making leather cuffs for fetters, which Surgeon Arndell declared 'saved me treating a great number of infections of the limbs'. Henry was more than happy to earn a crust.

Susannah was elated when she discovered Henry on board the *Friendship*. Although billeted in different parts of the vessel, they managed to spend a few minutes together with the connivance of the Surgeon.

The fleet had been issued with orders to keep prisoners ironed below until the flotilla was out of sight of land. However, there was a certain amount of leeway on board the *Friendship* where several married couples were incarcerated.

Captain Walton liked the forthright young man from Norwich who was not afraid to speak up for the convicts. Henry, he found, put in a harder day's work than many of his crew, and awarded him similar privileges to the married men on board.

Men and women were secured in different holds at night but married couples were allowed a certain amount of time together during the day. Not all the ships allowed convicts this daily liberty.

By mid April, a total of sixteen men had died aboard the *Alexander* as well as the woman on the *Lady Penrhyn*. The Commodore sent a final cutting letter to Evan Nepean pointing out that the deaths had occurred amongst 'hapless undernourished creatures embarked at Woolwich' from hulks owned and managed by Duncan Campbell. 'I have never seen such sickly unfortunates, as sparse as skeletons, as those from the infamous hulks of Woolwich," he reported.

There were only twenty women aboard the *Friendship* but this did not prevent the more brazen making their way into the crew's quarters actively assisted by sailors and marines. These escapades, although viewed seriously by the officers, were nothing compared with the wanton behaviour of women secured on the *Lady Penrhyn*.

Throughout the fleet there was a palpable frisson of excitement amongst prisoners, crew and marines; all were journeying to a mysterious land on the other side of the world. Amongst the crew there were many who had sailed to America on more than one occasion, but none had been on such a long voyage into unknown seas and strange lands.

When word spread on May 9th that Governor Phillip had embarked on the warship *Sirius*, excitement turned to tension as final preparations for the great journey were made. Two days later, HMS *Hyena*, which was to escort the fleet until it was clear of dangerous French waters, arrived at the Motherbank.

As tensions mounted, officers found it necessary to impose tighter controls. Strict instructions were issued to ensure that prisoners were not permitted lanterns nor candles, owing to the risk of fire, so below decks were as black as pitch and just as stifling. The lower, coffin-like holds had no outlets other than hatches to the decks, thus sickness flourished until officers were forced to allow prisoners a daily dose of fresh air and exercise.

Three days later, the *Sirius* hoisted the signal for the fleet to weigh anchor. Astonishingly the seamen aboard some of the transports went on strike, refusing to man the yards. They demanded their full wages and the opportunity to go ashore and purchase personal supplies.

Lt. Phillip Kirby, aide-de-camp to Governor Phillip, wrote in his private log:
'The seamen had reason on their side. They had been contracted upwards of seven months, during which time they received no pay excepting that of river pay and one month's advance. The great length of the voyage renders it necessary that they would have money to furnish themselves such necessaries as were indispensable; but it became the masters' interest to withhold pay from them, that they might be obliged to purchase those necessaries on the course of the voyage at a very exorbitant rate.'

The fleet dropped anchor again and Phillip sent furious messages to every Master demanding that they release the supplies the seamen wanted at a rate they could be purchased at in Portsmouth. He threatened to inform the ships' owners that the Masters were jeopardising bonuses promised by the Government. To save the officers' faces he ordered a few of the more belligerent seamen removed and sent ashore.

These actions broke the strike and at 10 a.m. on Sunday May 13th the sails cracked and billowed and the convoy wallowed and rolled its way towards a new world. It was the longest sea journey ever attempted by so large a number of people. The First Fleet had set sail on the greatest voyage in history.

Chapter Twenty Six

As the fleet entered the English Channel the ships began to pitch and roll in the huge sea swells. Seasick, homesick, wet and wretched, spirits plumbed the depths of despair in the close dark below decks. Water seeped through seams and soaked terrified prisoners; vomit and sweat seasoned the oppressive atmosphere in the black confusion. The stench was indescribable, even to convicts used to the noxious air of unsanitary prisons and hulks.

On the *Friendship*, Henry, who had spent months on fishing boats, belched and heaved, crammed like the others in a space so small it was impossible to sit up.

In the women's quarters, Liz Pulley was helping the ships' surgeon, Thomas Arndell, deliver a baby. The mother was barely sixteen years old, terrified both of the sea and of giving birth. The infant, a boy, was stillborn. While Liz washed the girl, Surgeon Arndell took the baby on deck where a seaman sewed it into a canvas bag and dropped it over the side.

Shortly after the fleet set sail, Commodore Phillip instructed all irons, except for those being used for punishment, were to be removed. This immediately raised him in the eyes of every prisoner.

For the first two days progress was slow. Captains were sizing up officers, the officers gauging crew and the seamen were getting used to the ships. The *Sirius* was constantly posting signals to ensure that the fleet 'crowded sails and kept close'; the *Charlotte*, in particular was several miles astern by the end of the first day. She was to prove a surprisingly slow sailor. As the fleet approached the Lizard, a great number of casks were spotted floating in the water. The *Fishburn* picked up thirty five and the *Scarborough* twenty five; even the *Friendship* snared two. They were casks of Geneva that proved to be a remarkably fine wine.

For the next four days, the fleet was lashed by moderate gales and constant rain until Phillip ordered the fleet to hove to about two hundred miles west of the Scilly Isles. There was a heavy sea running but the gales subsided at last. The Commodore felt it safe to order the *Hyena* to return to port, but then received a signal from the *Scarborough* that there was trouble aboard.

An informer told an officer that a mutiny was being planned and named the ringleaders as Thomas Griffiths and Phillip Farrell. They were taken to the *Sirius* heavily ironed and after a short court both were sentenced to twenty four lashes. The square-headed corporal, originally on board the *Dunkirk*, had the pleasure of laying into the prisoners with the cat o' nine tails. Afterwards they were transferred to the *Prince of Wales* and the informant, for his own safety, went to the *Charlotte*.

Despite their seasickness, the prisoners were benefiting from improved rations and being allowed on deck for exercise when weather conditions permitted. Captain Walton confirmed Henry as Deck Captain whilst allocating a number of tasks to other prisoners. Men were appointed caulkers, dry-stoners and pitchers, others had to perform scrubbing and scraping jobs and a few were permitted to help prepare food.

Life aboard the *Friendship*, as on all the vessels, was beginning to settle into a routine. As well as the relative freedom enjoyed by those given daily tasks to perform, all prisoners were permitted on deck to exercise cramped limbs. Women were allowed to wash clothing but had to enlist help from the crew to catch rainwater as salt water was unsuitable and cask supplies too precious. Following a storm the ship's rigging would be festooned with womens' clothing.

Sanitary arrangements on board were a constant source of aggravation. During the day, an open platform with holes cut in it was lashed to the outmost section of the bowspit – this was termed the 'heads'. Prisoners' daily body functions were a publicly hazardous operation as well as being the subject of much crude humour and derision.

At night, easing chairs – rough wooden commodes – were provided on each level. The most prized berths were those furthest away from the easing chairs.

Those selected as cooks had to be on deck by 4.30 a.m; messmen assembled an hour and half later, supervised by the deck captain.

At sunrise, bulkheads were thrown open and prisoners were made to line up by the bathing tub where salt water would be thrown over them by the bucketful. Breakfast would quickly be followed by the first of the prisoners' tasks – often holystoning the decks.

Surgeon Arndell insisted that any wine allowance was drunk after meals by means of a mug passed from one to the other to ensure that each prisoner drank their share and to prevent trafficking and hoarding.

Men shaved twice a week and had hair shorn fortnightly. Regular meals, frequent exercise and lack of irons improved the health of prisoners although sickness remained a constant companion of those locked below for eight or ten hours at a stretch.

Two weeks out from Portsmouth, a prisoner aboard the *Friendship* died of consumption, worsened by a fever that spread like wildfire through his deck. His body was washed and sewn in a canvas bag; and, watched by prisoners and crew, Captain Walton conducted a short funeral service. Afterwards, his body was thrown overboard where it followed astern of the ship for a considerable distance before disappearing beneath the waves.

Henry and Susannah, sitting together in the shelter of a pile of spars and canvas watched the body for some time.

In a nearby space, Liz Pulley and Ann Turner played with little Henry who, at fifteen months old, was curious about everything and mobile enough to need constant watching, particularly on board ship. Liz was singing a ballad popular among the prisoners:

'They go to an island to take special charge,
Much warmer than Britain and ten times as large,
No customs-house duty, no freightage to pay,
And tax free they'll live in Botany Bay.'

Henry smiled at Susannah, "Liz is a rum 'un, but she loves her songs and our baby too!"

"We've been lucky in many ways, Henry, sometimes I'm afraid that something awful will happen to part us."

"Stay clear of that tar, name of Robson," he answered sourly, his brow clouding over.

"He means no harm – he gives me goats milk for our child."

"I know what he's after," Henry said darkly.

Robson was a fine seaman, every finger a fish hook. Tall and strong, corn coloured hair tousled in loose curls to his neck. Barrel chested and broad, he looked, and was, as strong as a bull. His arms bulged with sinew and muscle. His face was a golden brown and a ready smile revealed brilliant white teeth. One powerful arm was adorned with a crucifix, done he said, with India ink by a skilled man in Le Havre. He was well-respected as a first class seaman, worth his weight in gold according to the Captain, and well loved by the ladies in port by all accounts.

Alas, when in port he was overly fond of supping ale and all manner of spirits which got him into numerous brawls. As often as he was given a senior role on board on account of his seamanship, he was reduced in rank by his many battles when in drink.

Many women prisoners were smitten by Robson's looks and charm.

In the hold that night Susannah, Liz and Anne whispered together.

"Has Robson been trying it on, Susannah?" Anne wanted to know.

"He's spared me a few kind words and a little milk and fruit for my boy."

"He'll be wanting something in return, mark my words," Liz said flatly.

"He wouldn't have to ask me twice," Anne whispered.

"Nor me, but he shouldn't be coming between two people who are as good as married – even if one of 'em is a surly sod," Liz answered.

Towards the end of May, the weather became changeable and crewmen were constantly occupied with scaling the rigging, putting up sails to catch light winds and bringing them down again to avoid overloading spars and masts.

The 27th was a fine day and the prisoners were amazed when a porpoise appeared at the bow of the *Friendship* and danced among the waves, splashing and spinning a few feet under the surface, catching the rays of the low sun, reflecting bright colours like a submarine rainbow. It was the first time they had seen such a creature, and were thrilled when four or five others joined the first and played leapfrog in the sea.

At every opportunity, officers and a few of the crew cast fishing lines into the waters baited with fish heads. Captain Walton caused a huge cheer to go up when he landed a large bonito and, shortly afterwards, another. The prisoners knew there was a reasonable chance some of the fish would find its way onto their plates come the morrow.

A few days later, the waters began to roar and heave, waves thrashed themselves into a frenzy of foam upon ships' sides. In bad weather the seamen tied hemp around their clothing, securing sleeves at the wrists and trousers at waists, knees and ankles to keep warm and dry.

Henry, jammed against the forecastle, was making leather ties for the crews. Spray hurled itself over the forecastle and stung his face in spiteful pellets. He shivered in his issued clothing consisting of duck trousers, coarse linen shirt with a blue cloth waistcoat, a pair of tan stockings and a woollen cap.

The wind began to howl in earnest so Henry made his way to the hold, but as he reached the hatch a splintering crack came from far above as the main topmast was carried away by a fierce gust of wind.

Captain Meredith, Commander of the Guards, had just emerged from the top deck and Henry saw his look of horror as sail and mast came crashing down in a knot of rigging. Instinctively, Henry launched himself at the officer, hurling them both behind and below a crate lashed to the deck. The topmast, thick as a man's body, smashed into the crate, showering them with ropes and shreds of canvass. The two men stared first at the broken mast and then each other. Untangling himself, Captain Meredith shook Henry's hand, blue lips clamped together in a face white as a hoar frost, unable to utter a word.

The fleet had been at sea for a little more than a fortnight and prisoners were beginning to find their sea legs. Most of the first week had been spent being sick below, but once they were allowed regular exercise, the majority began to take an interest in their surroundings.

Initially, the sea, fish and birds were the source of much wonderment then inclement weather caused a deal of terror, but as the month of June approached, a number of women turned their attentions to the crew and marines.

Of the twenty females on the *Friendship*, six or seven would regularly find their way through the bulkheads to fraternise with the free men.

Liz Pulley was one of those familiar with the men's quarters, having become attached to the boatswain whom she referred to as 'Freddie, a free man and fresh meat!"

These forays caused no problems as long as they went undetected but one night Liz found Freddie with another prisoner named Elizabeth Dudgeon. An almighty fight broke out which alerted Ralph Clark, Lieutenant of marines, who arrested the women as they fought and screamed. Later, he reported to Captain Walton that he had never heard 'such vile profanities from soldiers nor sailors as he had the misfortune to hear from those two whores!'

The two women were made to stand upright in a punishment box, arms outstretched and ironed to the top for six hours the next day. The box was bolted to the deck near the 'heads', so while the two under punishment enjoyed obnoxious airs from the makeshift lavatories, prisoners visiting the heads were entertained by their colourful profanities as they continued to curse each other throughout the day.

There was trouble amongst the male prisoners too, resulting in frequent fights and quarrels. Captain Walton was particularly hard on crimes arising from gambling; he often expressed the view that '*a man who loses his rations through gambling will steal another's.*' Nevertheless, dice, cards, pitch and roll continued to occupy a hard core of prisoners whenever they got the opportunity.

On the day that Liz Pulley was released from her punishment, Henry made her join him and Susannah amongst the crates stored at the rear of the ship.

"Liz, you must hold your tongue and temper, 'tis too easy for a troublesome prisoner to be cast overboard in the night!" he warned her.

"That bitch Dudgeon swiped my earrings! I'm not worried about that gutless boatswain but I 'int having her steal my gelt!"

Susannah, seeing her friend working herself up into a passion, handed little Henry to her. "Play with the boy awhile, Liz, he loves you."

The three of them sat for a time watching the nearby *Charlotte* ploughing through the glistening sea, bow waves father to restless rainbows.

"Will you look at the size of that!" whooped Henry, pointing at a dark shape in the water immediately astern.

The fin of a large shark, about nine feet long, cut through the surface of the dark waters. Suddenly a little school of bottle nosed porpoises appeared around the shark and began darting and diving at it.

"They are playing with the creature!" shouted Liz.

They looked up to see a marine standing nearby on one of the crates.

Susannah coloured up, "Robson," she said faintly.

Henry struggled to rise but Liz dumped the baby on his lap. "Piss off, Robson, you're not wanted, she said bluntly. Susannah clutched Henry's arm. The sailor grinned and jumped down, disappearing amongst the boxes. "Henry," Liz said in mock severity, "You must learn to hold your tongue and temper!"

Susannah smiled but Henry glowered in the direction Robson had taken.

"Land ahoy!" a sailor in the crow's nest bellowed.

The three friends stood up and shaded their eyes against the sun.

"I can just see a tiny rock on the horizon," Liz announced.

They were looking at the 13,000 ft. peak on Tenerife, the fleet's first port of call on its historic voyage; it was eighteen leagues away.

The next day all eleven ships were anchored outside the port of Santa Cruz, in the waters called Santa Cruz Roads. Senior officers for all the ships were summoned to a meeting aboard the flagship *Sirius*. It was a fine day so Commodore Phillip addressed them on the top deck.

"Over the last few months I met many of you at Woolwich or Portsmouth but time prevented me from speaking to you together before we sailed. Gentlemen, this is a voyage of considerable endeavour, never have so many souls been taken on so long a sea journey to a place unknown. We are making history gentlemen. I have asked – are we taking convicts or colonists? – the answer is we take convicts to become colonists. I am charged with conducting eleven ships and 1,500 souls safely to New South Wales, a free land. There can be no slavery on a free land, and consequently no slaves. Your task is more than conducting your ships safely to our destination; what you do and say each day sets standards at mastheads, gives aspiration to sailors, marines and prisoners. I urge you to remember the belly is more sensitive to encouragement than a prisoners back; the withdrawal of wages a greater stinger than the cut of a lash on a man's haunches."

Commodore Phillip sat down to a thunderous round of applause, his bald pate glistening with sweat in the sunshine.

Next, John White, Surgeon General to the fleet rose to address the officers. "Gaol fever is still with us gentlemen! We lost seventeen before sailing and a further nine at sea. Most of those were on one ship – the *Alexander* has lost twenty one prisoners since embarkation. It is imperative that quarters are scrubbed regularly – particularly prisoners quarters where overcrowding creates a fetid store of fever and noxious ills. Scurvy and the tropics will take their toll in the weeks and months ahead. At every port men, marines and prisoners must be made to consume fresh vegetables and fresh meat. Their lives, and ours, depend upon it!"

Lastly, Captain John Hunter, second in command to the Commodore gave detailed instructions to each ship's Master on what to purchase in Santa Cruz by way of fruit, vegetables and meat. Their buying allowance strictly linked to the ration of prisoners and free men on each vessel.

A great deal of the fruit that the prisoners received was unknown to them. Most had never seen bananas, figs, almonds and watermelons before, but tucked in gratefully when given the chance. A number of goats and poultry were bought and stowed on each ship, to be eked out as fresh meat over the coming weeks.

As darkness fell that night, a prisoner named Powers escaped from *Alexander* by sliding down the anchor chain to a jolly boat tied there and rowing to the shore. When word of this spread the next morning, the prisoners were agog with excitement and a number scaled the rigging to scan the shoreline for the fugitive. Within hours, Powers was discovered asleep by the upturned boat and was brought back to the *Alexander* by a party of Marines.

Although spirits amongst the convicts sank at the sight of the escapee being returned festooned with iron, a spontaneous cheer went up to acknowledge his daring. On board the *Alexander* he became a hero to his fellow felons and was feted as a man of courage for the remainder of the voyage.

During the few days that the fleet were in Santa Cruz Roads, temperatures soared. Even in the shade it was around seventy degrees. At night, in the holds occupied by the prisoners, the temperatures approached ninety. In the damp foul air tempers were even more frayed than usual and many squabbles occurred. Henry and other deck captains found it difficult to keep order. On the *Friendship*, Captain Walton would not hear of leaving the hatches open at nights – Powers, escape from the *Alexander* had put paid to that.

It was in this tetchy atmosphere that a fight broke out amongst the women. Liz had become convinced that Elizabeth Dudgeon, the woman who had usurped her in the boatswain's affections, was trying to foster Robson's friendship with Susannah. It was when Liz caught Dudgeon giving a note from the seaman to her friend that trouble flared.

Soon the two women were rolling about the deck screaming obscenities, punching at each other like prizefighters. Two other women joined in, and the cheering prisoners, glad of the entertainment, soon surrounded all four. Captain Meredith, Commander of the Guards, could do nothing until he had called for reinforcements. It took some time before the women were subdued but not before Dudgeon had cracked a lump of wood across the Guard Commander's head.

As the little procession of prisoners and marines passed Henry by the forecastle, Liz called out, "I gave the bitch a right pissbawler, Henry!"

Henry was trying to make out why she should single him out when Dudgeon, her left eye closed in testimony to the power of Liz's 'pissbawler' spat at him as she passed by.

All four women were sentenced to be ironed for ten days. Dudgeon, nose askew and bloodied, was also ordered to embellish the stocks for two days as a reward for her pugilistic endeavours upon Captain Meredith.

Lt. Clark wrote in his daily log.

'I am not convinced they will be long out of irons. There was never four greater whores living than they are. I wish all women were out of the ships.'

Chapter Twenty Seven

At first light on the 10th of June the fleet set sail from Tenerife. Riggings creaked and timbers groaned complaining to each other of the hardships of sea life. The *Friendship* nosed its way from the harbour, the sea a silver shield splashed with sapphires. Fresh winds filled canvas, sails crackled and bellied and blew the fleet towards the promised land. Temperatures were in the high seventies so sails were rigged above hatches to catch and deflect the wind to the hot and horrid hell below decks. Nonetheless, consuming heat sapped the strength and will of the wretched creatures trapped in steaming holds where movement was almost impossible.

Two days out, the fleet was almost becalmed so once lookouts reported 'no sharks' several sailors dived into the gentle waters to stir the blood and wash off the day's labours.

The blazing sun scorched the decks so pitch dripped through seams and burned prisoners below, where in oppressive heat there was only one word spoken or thought, 'Water!'

It was a relief to all concerned, when a gentle breeze allowed the fleet to move off towards the next port of call in the Cape Verde Islands. When the ships passed the equator on June 15th, convicts were kept below to avoid interference with the sailor's ceremony of ducking any of the ship's company who had not passed the line before. In view of the high spirits of the crew, aided by liquor, an extra guard was placed on the women's quarters.

On the day that Liz Pulley and the three other women were released from irons, the fleet rounded a reef off Port Praya, Sao Tiago, ready to take in fresh supplies of water and vegetables. After the Commodore had given the order to anchor, and a welcoming gun was fired from the forts, the wind suddenly dropped and caused a deal of consternation as several ships began to drift towards the eastern reef. A heavy swell threatened to crowd the convoy together until orders signalled them to stand off.

It was two hours before the danger passed, helped by a stiff breeze which enable the fleet to put clear water between ships.

On board the flagship, Commodore Phillip stared intently through a telescope at the harbour, watching the restless ocean breaking with thunderous roars upon the shore of Sao Tiago. Reluctantly, he ordered Captain Hunter to signal the fleet to proceed to Rio de Janeiro.

"'Tis a pity to miss the chance of buying fresh vegetables and fruit," Captain Hunter remarked.

"We're also missing the opportunity of dashing a ship or two on those rocks," Phillip growled. The second in command posted the signals and the convoy began the hazardous run across the Atlantic Ocean.

The prisoners were getting used to seeing dolphins and sharks and some attempted to match the sailors when they threw out lines to catch fish. On the *Friendship* there was a great deal of excitement when a large Albacore – the bosun estimated it at one hundred and fifty pounds – swam around the bows for a time. The seamen struck at it with a weight but with no success.

Ann Turner and Susannah watched the attempt to capture the Albacore sitting on a coil of ropes. Liz, released from the 'box' the previous day, had taken little Henry to the stern of the ship. Suddenly, there was a terrified scream from Ann as a fish landed in her lap.

"A fish that flies!" she shrieked, running to the other side of the deck in a fearful panic. To the astonishment of the prisoners other fish came sailing over to land on the deck. Nobody dared to touch them until the bosun declared that they were 'flying fish, frightened out of the water by a shark or porpoise.'

Sure enough, a shoal of porpoises were leaping and plunging in the sea, sending an amazing number of flying fish through the air for incredible distances.

As soon as they realised that there was nothing magical about the fish, the convicts set about grabbing those on deck as candidates for the cooking pot. Shortly after this incident, their daily rations were enhanced even further with the capture of a seven foot long shark, gaffed by a boat hook. When it was drawn up to the deck the fearsome beast had several sucking fish still attached to its body.

The fleet sailed on with the *Lady Penrhyn* being the slowest ship, several times the convoy had to lay-to to allow her to catch up. Slowly, the weather became unpredictable, with horridly humid days interspersed with thunderstorms. The temperatures brought new dangers to the fleet.

Vapours from rancid bilge water caused a rash of fevers to break out as an army of vermin multiplied in the foul blackness. Rats, cockroaches, bugs and fleas emerged to feed on the detritus of humanity crammed into the torrid hell that was below decks. Stench from the awful soup sloshing about in the bilges – sea water seasoned with pee, puke, oil, dead rodents, lice and sweat, caused even experienced seamen to vomit and many prisoners to swoon away.

On the *Alexander* another wave of fever felled prisoners as bilge water crept so far up the ship's sides that it turned wood panels and buttons black in officers' quarters. Here it was reported that when hatches were removed the stench was so powerful it was scarcely possible to stand over them. Throwing them open each morning became a regular punishment for marines who had offended in some way.

Rain, when it came, was in short heavy bursts, so when a deluge was spotted racing across the waves. the crews would rush around rigging up awnings to catch fresh water, regularly casking six to eight butts a time.

Nevertheless, on the *Friendship* water was short and so were tempers. Captain Walton, making a surprise inspection one night found that a few crew had broken through the bulkhead to the women's section.

He called Captain Meredith who turned out his marines. Soon four women were discovered in the seamens' bunks, engaged, in the words of Lt. Clarke *'in the most vile and depraved acts.'* Two were first offenders but the other two, Elizabeth Dudgeon and Liz Pulley, were well known to the officers.

In his diary Lt. Clark wrote *'Those damn troublesome whores are a disgrace to their sex, bastards that they are.'*

Lt. Clark, a pious man, frequently scandalised by the conduct and profanity of the women, kept a full account of his thoughts. Mainly, his fellow officers considered, showing to his wife on his return that he had remained untouched by immorality during the voyage.

The four women were ironed and thrown in the 'hole'.

When Captain Walton reported the matter to the Commodore,

the sailors caught with the women were sent across to the *Sirius*. The carpenter was fined and returned to the *Friendship* but the boatswain, steward and a seaman were kept aboard for flogging to be witnessed by the whole ship's company.

It was a calm day so crew and marines were formed in a square on deck around the three men sentenced to be flogged.

There was always a deal of resentment when crew or marines were flogged. Serving men usually received much harsher sentences than prisoners, sometimes as much as two or three hundred lashings, using the heavier military cat 'o' nine tails. On this occasion the men were sentenced to receive one hundred lashes, reduced to fifty lashes upon appeal.

The square-headed corporal was detailed to administer the punishment. First up was the boatswain, hands tied together and fixed to a rope stretched above head height across the deck. This allowed onlookers every opportunity to witness pain and punishment without hindrance. The corporal warmed up with a few stingers across the boatswain's back, drawing blood at the fifth stroke. The man, biting on a rolled up cloth, stared into the distance and said nothing. After twenty lashes the corporal switch his attentions to the boatswain's backside after having the victims' trousers removed.

This time he rushed at the man, whip in upstretched hand, bringing it down with all his weight behind the blows. In the ranks this caused a ripple of shuffled feet, where one or two began to mutter but were silenced by the Commander of the Guard.

As the corporal rested for a moment, a huge spider scurried out from a crack, seized and carried off a sizeable piece of flesh flayed from the boatswain's buttocks. Lt. Clark was sick over the side of the ship.

When the scourger began to lash 'close in' several watchers were provoked to cry out in protest, knowing it caused the knots on the end of the cords to curl round a man's chest. Captain Hunter made the corporal stand a fair distance.

For the last few lashes the corporal reverted to his 'rush and jump' way of bringing the cat down finally managing to wring sickening groans from the boatswain.

When the punishment was over there was a smattering of claps from the assembled men in acknowledgement of the victim's courage. The corporal, bespattered with blood and flesh like a careless butcher, grinned wolfishly, thinking the applause was for his efforts.

When it was the seaman's turn he screamed at each stroke putting every watcher's nerves on edge until finally being dragged off, crying pitifully.

Last up was the steward, his face a mask of sweat and legs trembling uncontrollably. He managed to hold out until halfway through then screamed horribly and fainted. The scourging stopped while a matelot threw a bucket of water over him under the watchful eye of the ship's surgeon. When revived he received the remainder of his rations. Finally, his body was dragged away giving the flogger time to wash the gore from his arms and face.

As the ship's company dispersed, the Captain's dog wandered over to lick the blood from the deck. It was a treat the mutt was to enjoy on a regular basis.

Commodore Phillip instructed all ships that the daily water ration was to be reduced from three pints to two pints to preserve supplies. This did not help the negative feelings that were building and Prisoner Dudgeon, when released from being ironed on the *Friendship*, gave the Commander of the Marines a volley of abuse. Captain Meredith immediately ordered her to be flogged.

Lt. Clark, scandalised by her profanity, relished the punishment, recording in his diary:

'The corporal did not play with her but laid it home, which I was very glad to see. Then he ordered her to be tied to a pump. She has been fishing for it, which she has at last got to her heart's content.'

In the doldrums, on some days, there was not a drop of wind to fill a canvas and the fleet wallowed in the empty ocean. Occasionally a ship would pick up a slight breeze and move a hundred yards or so but generally progress was slow. Seamen were kept busy scraping off bunches of barnacles from hulls. Prisoners were left to lie around in any pocket of makeshift shade they could rig. Despite the heat and shortage of fresh water the felons knew that they were better off on deck rather than remaining in the fetid atmosphere of the holds.

Towards the middle of July, prisoners on the *Friendship* were watching a burial taking place from the *Lady Penrhyn*. A woman named Beckford, one of the oldest prisoners at eighty two years, had died of dropsy.

Henry and Susannah, together at every opportunity, watched the canvassed body splash into the deep where it was instantly surrounded by curious sea birds. The dead never went willingly under the water, often floating in full view for ages.

"Another poor soul will never see Botany Bay, Henry."

"At this rate of knots, nobody will see anything," he replied gruffly.

Susannah had the baby in a canvas sling tied around her neck.

"Who paid for the sling?" Henry asked, noticing it for the first time.

"I've had it a week, it's a clever thing, it leaves my hands free to do other chores."

"Who gave it to you?" Henry persisted.

"Just one of the men, I did some sewing for him."

"Who?" He demanded truculently.

"Robson."

"I told you to have nothing to do with that bastard!" he shouted.

"He means no harm, Henry, he's just being kind."

"Being kind, my foot!"

Several prisoners looked up at the raised voices and then turned away, tempers were always short in the heat. Susannah didn't reply, knowing that when Henry was angry he was best left alone.

"Here, give me the sling, I'll tell Robson he can stick it where the monkey sticks his nuts!"

"No, it's mighty useful, especially on a ship that rolls about. I need my hands free to keep from falling.

They struggled together until Henry shoved her away and stomped off, his face a furious red.

Henry sought out Redmond McGrath, known as 'Red', being the owner of an unruly mop of flame red hair. Red was a fourteen year man, convicted in his home town of Glasgow for robbing the local magistrate of a handsome pocket watch. He and Henry had become friends when thrown together in the cramped space for sleeping below decks.

"What's troubling you, Henry?"

"That bastard Robson's been after my woman again!"

"What's he done this time?"

"Gave her a present for my boy; he knows she won't refuse anything for the kid."

They found a space in the steerage, strewn with coils of rope, spare sails and piles of stores too mysterious to fathom.

"You've got a problem there, Henry. When Robson throws his cap at a woman, not many will resist."

"I've got plans, Red. Some say those who are a fair way through their sentence will be free men when the time is up. If they don't make us start the sentences afresh when we reach Botany Bay I've only a few years left to serve. It'll all come to naught if I lose Susannah and my boy."

"The girl will stick by you, Henry."

"I've a notion Robson knows Susannah's got a bit put by to start a new life."

"Has she, how much?"

Henry bit his lip in the darkness. He and Susannah had vowed not to say anything about the collection made by Lady Cadogan.

"Tis nothing to write home about, I'll deal with Robson one of these dark nights."

On the quarterdeck, Liz found Susannah staring out to sea, her eyes wet with recent tears.

"Is it Henry?" she asked. "He's a surly sod sometimes!"

"He tried to take this baby holder the sailor gave me."

"That'll be Robson I 'spect! Don't be worried little Angel, you can't trust any man."

"I am worried, Liz, there's going to be trouble."

"Where men are there's always bleeding trouble."

A few days later, a brisk breeze heralded the start of the southerlies and the fleet picked up a collective rate of knots, making between seventy and a hundred miles each day over the next week.

Gradually, the weather changed and the fleet endured heavy squalls with the occasional day of calm in between. The 22nd of July was a relatively moderate day and the prisoners were able to spend most of it on deck. Ann Turner and Liz were trying to cheer up Susannah who was feeling low spirited because Henry had not spoken to her since their quarrel. Nearby, an officer was teaching a group of prisoners to read.

Suddenly, the sea parted between the *Friendship* and the *Lady Penrhyn* and a huge black shape rose menacingly from the water. The prisoners were terrified, running from the sides as the monster, as long as the ship itself, blew a great trumpet of water into the air.

A sailor on the rigging roared out "Whale amidships!"

The beast eyed the vessel bleakly, its head covered in crusty ridges of barnacles, it was an awesome creature. It blew several more spouts before plunging head first into the swell, displaying a massive tail half the height of the topmast before disappearing gracefully beneath the water.

The prisoners were amazed that such an enormous creature even existed.

A little later, as Susannah, Ann and Liz sat by the forecastle scanning the seas for more 'sodding great monsters of the deep' as Liz called them, Henry appeared.

"I've bartered an apple for you," he informed Susannah. It was a wizened little fruit but Susannah took it gratefully.

"I haven't got anything for you," she said.

He looked at her blankly. "It's your birthday," she informed him.

He was twenty three years of age on the day the whale appeared. Henry and Susannah went off together, holding hands.

Drenching cold rain, least liked by sailors, persisted for the next few days. The crew, at the end of each watch, went below to wring out their clothes. Sometimes two men would work together to wring out a pair of trousers, one at each end. But in the absence of a little sun or drying wind there was no alternative at the beginning of the next watch but to select the least wet of their clothes, clap them on and go out onto the deck to begin their duties, already cold, miserable and damp.

Despite the appalling weather – three ships lost sails or topmasts and the *Friendship's* caboose was swept overboard – spirits amongst crew and prisoners slowly rose. At every opportunity a crewman would be sent aloft to scan the horizon for land. On the first day of August, Captain Walton, in common with the rest of the fleet, gave orders for the ship to be cleaned and painted in anticipation of their arrival in Rio de Janeiro.

Excitement mounted the next day when a Portuguese ship passed close by; signals between them indicated that she was carrying slaves from Guinea on the coast of Africa. In the afternoon, a great cheer went up from the crew – quickly followed by another from the prisoners – when a signal from the *Supply* told them that she had sighted land.

Within two hours all of the ships had glimpsed land; Commodore Phillip flagged for the fleet to reduce sails and keep close to the *Sirius*.

The thought of being able to write again to his wife when they reached Rio led Lt. Ralph Clark to add even more anguished notes in his diary. He frequently referred to her as '*my dear beloved Alicia, my virtuous wife, my best friend*' and kissed her picture '*a hundred times.*' But the pious Lieutenant coupled his sentimental thoughts with a vicious diatribe against the women convicts.

'*Sarah McCormack taken very ill this afternoon – the doctor has been obliged to bleed her twice a day and says she will not last the night out. She is now quite speechless and I am apt to think (God forgive if it is not so), that she is eaten up with the pox. She is one of them that went though the bulkhead to the seamen – I hope she has given them something to remember her – never was there a set of greater rascals together than they are. They are ten thousand times worse than male convicts and if the convicts had any thought to make their escape they would assist them.'*

Despite land being tantalisingly close, calm weather prevented the fleet from making much headway for the next three days. However, by the 6th August, the fleet began to approach the harbour of Rio de Janeiro. All prisoners were ordered below – land being a magnet for those in captivity.

On the *Friendship*, Liz and Ann Turner, hanging back as the felons filed down the gangway were rewarded by the sight of a long canoe crewed by four naked slaves carrying three gentlemen in strange garb. They were invited to come on deck but declined, explaining that *'until every ship had been inspected by the health boat the Viceroy would permit nobody to board nor sailors go ashore.'*

Liz, being last down from the hatchway, nearly fell the final few feet when the *Sirius* suddenly fired a 13 gun salute, shortly answered by the fort guarding the entrance to the city.

Chapter Twenty Eight

The Viceroy knew Commodore Phillip from his years of service in the Portuguese Navy and honoured him by having a number of prominent buildings illuminated as the fleet was rowed into the harbour and safely anchored.

After customs men had come aboard in galleys and the formalities of mooring in a foreign port had been completed the Commodore and Captains went ashore to pay their respects at the Viceroy's Palace. The Captain of the Guard there made a little speech of welcome in which he said they were at liberty to go where they wanted in Rio.

It wasn't long before Phillip sent the Captains off to purchase fruit, vegetables and fresh meat whilst he remained behind to catch up on the latest news, a valuable commodity for seamen, whenever they reached port.

Despite being late for that day's market, the Captains were able to purchase a wide variety of fresh food. They went about their business separately, each man responsible for his own ships' company and, more importantly, for managing his own allowance in dealings with local traders.

The market place was particularly rich in fruits – they bought limes, bananas, and enormous oranges – some almost a foot in circumference. Some of the yams weighed more than ten pounds each.

Out in the harbour a flotilla of small craft plied their trades around the ships. Officers, crew and marines were able to bargain with traders in the canoes, invariably rowed by naked slaves. Everything was remarkably cheap, sixpence bought forty eight oranges, which, after gorging themselves, the men stowed away for future use.

The next day most of the officers and some crew were allowed ashore.

They found the streets near the harbour reasonably wide and straight with many fine houses on either side.

Lime and orange groves, in full fruit, refreshed nostrils that had become used to the awful effluvia of the prison ships. The refreshing scents were the subject of much comment and appreciation.

Wherever they went the locals, who seemed to have a fine regard for the British, greeted them pleasantly. Commodore Phillip in particular was to attend many functions over the next month and a number of officers quickly made new friends amongst the local gentry and visited their homes around the harbour. A great deal of entertaining was also done on board ships and the occasional visitor stayed overnight.

Even the serious Lt. Clark found the lusty local girls disturbingly attractive. Thoughts of them kept many of the men warm and cosy during cold nights.

Rio's bright beauty, surrounded by cloud-topping mountains was deeply appreciated by the sailors and marines who had endured the hardship and grind during the nine weeks since their last landing.

After two days in Rio, Commodore Phillip called a meeting aboard the *Sirius* to discuss the fleet's progress and future plans. John White, who was to be Surgeon General when they reached Botany Bay, was first to address the senior officers.

"Gentlemen, we have lost seven more souls since Tenerife, five from the *Alexander*, one of whom was lost overboard. There are eighty one on the list of sick including a seaman from the *Alexander* who fell from the main yardarm and broke his skull. Although venereal complaints continue to plague us I consider the work of the ships' surgeons to be very well done. I remind you of the continued vigilance by way of good hygiene and ensure men and prisoners receive as much fruit and green stuffs as can be digested – 'tis little enough money in this port! Every man and woman must be given 2lbs of fresh meat or fish a week – no short measures if you please. We will be quick liming the felons quarters on the *Alexander* – and creosoting the timbers again so we will need to move the prisoners, possibly to other ships."

All except the *Alexander*'s surgeon received this intelligence well.

Major Alexander Ross, Deputy Governor of the new colony, said a few words about security with particular emphasis to 'keep sharp' in port. This was followed by detailed instructions concerning the amount allowed for crews', marines' and prisoners' rations, together with dire warnings of who would pay if the monies were exceeded. Finally, Commodore Phillip rose to address the meeting.

"Evan Nepean, deputy to Lord Sydney, said in Parliament that the new colony would absorb a dreadful banditti. He was right of course, God knows the numbers we have flogged and cut flesh from; even female prisoners thieve and fight amongst themselves with conversation most abandoned, their conduct shameless. But there is a greater sin that pervades this expedition that is not confined to criminals but is also rife amongst the ships' Company and it must be stamped out! I refer to buggery, Gentlemen!If we do not eliminate this foul practice I fear a moral stain of the deepest dye may be impressed upon the new Colony, perhaps irrevocably and thus become attached to the name of Englishmen everywhere."

The meeting shuffled uneasily, the Commodore had hit upon conduct that many detested but had often closed an eye to.

Captain Walton spoke from the crowd of officers at the back of the cabin. "Sir, this problem exists, there is no denying the matter, but it remains a difficult one to overcome. We crush these creatures in cheek by jowl, forcing four men to sleep in a space seven feet wide. It is impossible for a guard to go down there in the blackness amongst the rabble – a man's throat could be cut in that maelstrom of bodies and even the prisoners themselves wouldn't know who wielded the fatal weapon."

This brought nods of agreement from several officers, a number of whom then added their opinions of how to deal with 'unnatural practices' aboard ships. After discussing the subject for some time it was clear that nobody had a sure-fire way of solving the matter so it was left to individual officers to isolate known offenders and keep them in irons.

Commodore Phillip agreed to allow prisoners regular daily exercise whilst in port, provided the marines doubled the usual guards. This concession was more to do with the worry of what was going on below rather than concern for the convicts' health.

The business of cleaning and repairing the fleet went on apace. There were the usual major tasks, such as refurbishing masts which had strained or cracked, painting the ships inside and out, replacing or repairing damaged sails and a great deal of carpentry where prisoners and crew had broken through bulk heads. A thousand other jobs occupied the crew – rigging to be coiled, spars set, rusting chains scraped, frayed rigging replaced, chaffed gear similarly treated, pumps rigged, worn coverings renewed, slack rigging 'tauted', cleats cleaned and of course decks holystoned and re-pitched. All devices to keep deck hands busy less they stand about in meagre shelter from wind and rain. It was the Officers' duty to keep men employed and it was a task they carried out with a high degree of efficiency.

Eventually, following inspections by the Chief Surgeon, all prisoners' quarters on every ship were fumigated, smoked and creosoted, despite his original instructions that only the *Alexandra* was to be so treated.

The prisoners were overjoyed at being allowed on deck – albeit for a strictly limited time – to see and smell the strange city of Rio de Janeiro. Many also gladly volunteered to help kill the myriad forms of bugs and lice that still infested their living space.

The officers went ashore or visited other officers at every opportunity. The physician of the *Lady Penrhyn* – commended by Commodore Phillip as the best behaved ship in the fleet – described a day in his log of 14th August 1787.

'*Went on shore and purchased some medicines for use at sea. This day one of the Portuguese officers dined on board with us, was a very civil, polite, behaved man; greatly delighted with my phosphoric tapers, broke one to show him the nature of these and made him a present of one in a tin case. This day purchased thirty one plumes of birds native of Rio de Janeiro of the Brazilian magpie kind, very beautiful. This evening Signor ll deffonso, a Portuguese physician with six other Portuguese gentlemen came on board with Major Ross and drank tea; nobody on board but Captain Campbell, myself and Mr Antis, the Chief Mate. All other gentlemen being gone on the shore opposite to drink tea in Orange Grove – Signor ll deffonso is the Chief Physician at Rio and upon the first vacancy is to be appointed Physician to the Queen of Portugal. He gave a very polite invitation to me to visit him and to see all the curiosities which the Queen's Museum in this place consists of, and which I should gladly have accepted of, but unfortunately a sister of the Physician happened to die the next day, therefore he could not make his appearance in public for some considerable time after without the greatest decorum, he appeared to be an intelligent good man of about forty years. Previous to his leaving the ship he left a considerable sum of Portuguese money (not less than forty shillings English) for the convicts to be expended for their use in such articles as the Captain should think most beneficial to them in their unhappy predicament.*

This afternoon a Snow from the coast of Guinea moored very near us with a cargo of some hundreds of black slaves for the slave market in Rio. At daylight in the morning I was awoke with their singing, as is their custom previous to their being sold or executed – they all naked. In the evening the party returned from drinking tea in the Orange Grove – the account they gave of the country was enchanting – within one hundred yards of the beach they were surrounded by orange, lemon and lime trees, also indigo, pineapples and many other kinds of plants and fruit all which they may have for getting. There were also great numbers of birds and enormous butterflies, both extremely beautiful of their kind. This evening a large monastery, situated on the left side of the bay was superbly illustrated in honour of some one of their Saints, and many curious fireworks displayed, the best of which undoubtedly were the sky rockets which mounted a great height and some gold and silver rain, others very good stars.'

Arthur Bowes Smith.

The prisoners of course saw none of this in their limited periods on deck. However, on the *Friendship*, Henry and Susannah were grateful for opportunities to be together, even for a few minutes. Henry was still well thought of by Captain Walton and the Commander of the Marines, Captain Meredith, whose life he had saved when the mast crashed on the deck.

His previous experience as a seaman aboard fishing boats in Lowestoft qualified him to assist in jobs such as holystoning decks. Two men slid a roped, smooth bottomed holystone back and forth over wet sanded decks. Others manned 'prayer books' – small hand sized stones to holystone awkward spots, behind spikes and places too small for the roped holystone. After this work sand was washed off the deck then swabbed down and dried as much as possible. The work he did and his position as deck captain enabled Henry to spend precious extra minutes with Susannah and their son.

Their previous quarrel was forgotten and they spent a deal of time in planning and dreaming about their future together. Henry was all for starting a leather business as soon as he was free.

"There must be animals in Botany Bay – else how will people eat – where animals live there are bound to be skins. Skins mean leather and I can make things from leather!" he told her.

"And I can get work as a servant, there's a good chance one of the officers will need a person to clean and cook." Susannah replied.

When they dreamed together anything seemed possible; with no place for fetters and hard masters.

Whilst in port, periods on deck allotted to prisoners were severely limited for reasons of security. Nevertheless the felons enjoyed the feeling of being near land. They could see the distant shore and make out free people moving around the harbour; the delicious smell of citrus trees reached them and they absorbed, through contacts with the ships' company, the feeling of friendliness and goodwill arising from the citizens of Rio de Janeiro.

Generally, seamen were pleased to have prisoners aboard. Any tasks given to prisoners, often just to keep them occupied, allowed the crew a sight more liberty so they were not averse to making friends with the felons.

Even mending and making clothes, which on a normal voyage would occupy a hefty portion of sailor's watch below, would be done by the women for a small fee or favour. It also afforded opportunities to strike up friendships that the crew could develop to profit their carnal desires.

Time spent in a place like Rio benefited everybody in the fleet – crew, marines and felons. The abundant fruit, vegetables, meat and fish were a godsend after the scant rations they had had at sea.

Some convicts even renewed their old professions whilst in port. On board the *Charlotte* a forger named Barrett started striking quarter dollars out of spoons and shoe buckles. John White wrote of the amazing ingenuity of the forger's ring after discovering him and his partners in the enterprise.

'*The impression, milling character was so inimitably executed that had the metal been a little better, the fraud, I am convinced, would have passed undetected. How they could effect it all is a matter of the most inexpressible surprise to me, as they were suffered never to come near a fire, and a sentinel was constantly placed over their hatchway which surely rendered it impossible for either fire or fused metal to be conveyed to their quarters. The adroitness, therefore, with which they managed, in order to complete so complicated a process, gave me a high opinion of their ingenuity, cunning, caution and address.*'

The forger, Barrett, got off lightly but was made to witness the two hundred lashes a marine was awarded for trying to use the coins on shore.

Reverend Johnson, Chaplain to the Fleet, took the opportunity in Rio to visit every ship and conduct a service. On the *Friendship* he urged prisoners to '*not lead the life of the vile, the lowest of the low, be not barbarous of society but hold true to God. Those that are married hold true to your vows, abominate neither self, nor animal, nor shipmate.*'

Chapter Twenty Nine

ugust passed swiftly and the first few days of September was spent in a bustle of preparation to cross the ocean again to the Continent of Africa.

As a compliment to Commodore Phillip, the Governor dispensed with port duties that amounted to the enormous sum of £155. All vessels were subject to a daily charge of five shillings plus £5 entering and £5 departing, except the *Sirius* and *Supply* which, being the King's ships, were exempt.

Commodore Phillips bought one hundred sacks of tapioca, which could be used in place of flour. However, he also intended the burlap sacks to be used to make up for women's clothing that had disintegrated since leaving England. The women were grateful for anything that helped to improve their dreadful apparel, and set to with the greatest degree of imagination to create outfits of burlap trimmed with pieces of whatever they had left of their tattered clothing. Ann Turner also made clothing for some sailors, being known as uncommon quick with a needle and someone who could 'run up a nightshirt in half a glass!'

Excitement reached fever pitch when the order to resume the voyage came on 4th September 1787. Once anchors were weighed, Henry was one of the few prisoners allowed on deck to join the sailors in waving to the local populace who had been so kind to the fleet.

Songs are as vital to sailors as muskets to military men. They cannot haul in rhythm nor pull with a will without a song. Songs with a lively chorus puts vigour and strength into every sinew. Usually one man sings alone and the rest join in the chorus, often loud enough to raise the deck.

So it was as the fleet left Rio de Janeiro the locals were treated to a full repertoire of seafaring songs.

Captain Walton, Master of the *Friendship*, stood before the main mast, enjoying the songs and the prospect of battling the ocean. A Captain at sea is Lord of all he surveys, accountable to nothing but conscience and judgement, obeyed by all, dealing out praise and punishment at will.

Two days after leaving Rio, the weather suddenly changed for the worse. The strumpet wind, not caring where she bestowed her favours, blew from all quarters. Sailors were kept busy day and night.

On the *Friendship* the cry "All hands! Tumble up and look lively!" brought every crewman on deck.

The sea, cold and sullen, rose up before the ship and struck the bows with the sound of a sledgehammer upon solid wood. Even experienced hands looked taut-faced at this chilling reminder of the sea's power. Top gallant masts bent like whips before the howling gale.

Henry's experience aboard the Lowestoft fishing boats was known to Captain Walton who called him up to help the beleaguered crew. On deck, wind and rain stung into him, pinning his body against rigging, holding him helpless against its relentless onslaught. It took time for him to get used to the sails billowing and snapping against the tall masts with thunderous cracks.

The ships pitched and rolled in the heavy seas as terrified prisoners crouched together in the pitch black below decks. Bilge water, stirred to a foaming frenzy by the violent storm, sent a sickening stench over petrified prisoners.

A dark mass of clouds came rolling up from the south, highlighted by distant flashes of lightning. Within minutes the sea began to heave and for a moment the ship balanced on the crest of a huge swell then plunged into the chasm yawning before it, burying bowsprit and forward deck into the seething foam. Angry water surged over the deck and out of ports and hawse holes, flinging every loose piece of equipment against the bulwarks. As the vessel lifted its nose, the waist of the ship was awash with three feet of icy water which was forced down every crack and crevice to the fearful felons below. Large nets which had been slung over the bulwarks strained out the seamen unfortunate enough to be washed across the treacherous decks by the giant waves.

The storm lasted all night and sometimes laid the ship down so much that sea leaked into the leeward portholes. In the holds the prisoners clung to anything that was fixed, and to each other, in an agony of panic that was to last until eight o'clock the following morning.

It was the first of many storms as the fleet ran before the westerlies to the Cape of Good Hope. There was little respite from the fearsome weather for more than three weeks. Even those days that were spared the full-scale gales were filled with fierce squalls and high winds. Small batches of prisoners were allowed on deck, when fleeting opportunities arose, to allow fresh air into them and the stinking holds.

The *Friendship* sailed well in strong winds and once managed one hundred and eighty eight miles in one twenty four hour period. Bad weather and seasickness meant less trouble from the prisoners, although two women were ironed following a fight.

Susannah and Henry saw nothing of each other until the end of the month when, totally out of the blue, the sea became calm. Prisoners were given deck time in two batches and the rigging was soon alive with washing; fresh water was plentiful following the storms.

The surgeon took the opportunity to commit the son of one of the convict women to the deep. The boy, who had died during the night had been sick ever since they had sailed from Portsmouth. Susannah was with the boy when he died, having been sent for to help calm the distraught Mother. She had sobbed helplessly until Susannah held her in a fierce hug, feeling her pain.

"The Lord will take care of your little lad, he goes to a better place than this stinking hole." Susannah turned her face away so that the woman could not see her own tears.

When the surgeon had finished his short service over the swaddled corpse, the prisoners soon drifted back to their bunks.

Death was not an unfamiliar companion to most on board.

As soon as they could, Henry, Susannah and their son got together to watch the seamen spearing fish with a long handled prong. Amidships, two whales were spouting by a dozen dolphins, dancing and cavorting as elegantly as anything they had ever seen. Susannah leaned forward and kissed Henry on the mouth; it was soft and warm and full of love. Henry, the hard deck master, was suddenly soft as putty in her embrace.

"What was that for?" he grinned.

"Nothing, I just felt like it."

"I wouldn't object if you felt like it again."

She took his face, thick with stubble, in her hands.

"I love you, Henry."

Before he could reply, the leather bound end of a thick rope struck him on the leg.

"Sorry, didn't see you under the lee of the forecastle," Robson's eyes belied the apology.

Henry jumped up, hampered by Susannah clinging to his shirt. The two men squared up to each other.

"Robson, you scraggy pile of dog shit, what are you doing here?" Liz Pulley appeared as if by magic. She jumped down from a box to stand in front of him, peering intently at his startled face. "'Ere, is that a pustule of the pox on your scrawny neck?"

Robson swore and went off, shining his cap badge on his sleeve and using the reflection to examine his neck.

"Ta, Liz," Susannah smiled.

"Anything for you, Angel."

Henry growled and looked darkly in the direction the seaman had taken.

"Kable, sit your arse down and look after that girl! Robson ain't worth a pot of piss!" Liz poked him fiercely in the chest until he slumped back on the deck.

Satisfied, she wandered off, having bestowed a conspiratorial wink on Susannah when Henry wasn't looking.

They had barely time to settle down again when a commotion at the gangway heralded the arrival of Reverend Johnson. He gave a number of combs, to be distributed to those women who had behaved well in the storms. He also carried the news that a convict had been lost overboard from the *Charlotte* a week or so earlier. The Captain had ordered a search but it had been impossible to see more than a few yards in the driving rain, and it was too dangerous to linger long in the heavy seas.

Communication between the ships was difficult and was mainly conducted by flag signals or occasionally by shouted instructions when they were close enough. On rare occasions, it was possible to row a long boat from one vessel to another, but only on calm days when the fleet was making little or no progress. Often, during violent storms, the fleet was scattered several miles apart and it took a great deal of time for Commodore Phillip to muster them back into some semblance of order.

The prisoners knew only what they were told and what they overheard. There were constant quarrels amongst prisoners, being so closely confined for the most part. However, relations between the ships' company were also beginning to chaff. Familiarity was apt to breed discontent, and so irritations turned into bickering and open quarrels broke out.

It was the same on every ship but on the *Friendship* Henry witnessed the normally placid Surgeon Arndell almost came to blows with Captain Meredith. An argument about a misplaced piece of kit rapidly became heated between two men who had been particular friends up to then.

Henry recounted all this to his friend, Red, who considered himself genteel, not a common criminal, although he had every qualification of one, being a habitual housebreaker.

Listening to Henry's description of the fracas with one ear cocked, Red consumed his food, as usual at breakneck speed. He had a habit of wielding his spoon as if engaged in his profession, ramming the implement into his victuals as a burglar might attack a sash with a crowbar, levering food into his mouth in the manner of forcing a window.

"Serve him right, it was him who got me my stripes!" Red said through a mouthful of pie.

Early in the voyage, Red, who was overly fond of liquor and fighting when drunk, had been awarded fifty lashes as a recipe for sobriety. Henry had found him weltering in his squalid space, shoes filled with blood, his back a jellied mess. Horrified at the sight of the man's ribs through his lacerated back, Henry had taken care of him, closing the wounds and binding them with a shirt torn into strips. They had been firm friends ever since.

"How's that little lad of yourn?" Red asked, managing the difficult task of belching and breaking wind at the same time.

"He's fine, it's difficult to keep him still on this ship."

"And your woman?"

"I've no grumbles there."

Red detected the slight hesitation in Henry's voice.

"Come on, out with it!"

"Truly, I've nought but good to speak of Susannah, it's that bastard Robson, he's always hanging around her."

"You two have always seemed closer than a leech on a man's arse."

"When we reach Botany Bay I've to work for nothing – he's got a job with money coming in, and prospects," Henry said gloomily.

"What about the pile of money you two have got stashed away?"

"Susannah had money collected for her and the child – it makes her a better prospect as a wife."

"I'd make the best of that young girl, she seems a good' un to me."

"That's what a fiend of mine, John Euston, said afore I left Norwich."

"Then cheer up and pay attention to your betters you gloomy bugger."

Despite the inclement weather and the surliness creeping into the crew, the westerlies were driving the fleet at a good speed to the Cape. The *Friendship* sailed particularly well in stiff winds and had to stand to allow the slower ships to catch up.

Commodore Phillip was pleased at the progress the fleet was making and grateful that all the ships were still intact. However, he had not anticipated the frictions that were being reported to him from all the ships; he had himself witnessed several fractious incidents between officers on the *Sirius*.

Confirmation that tensions were arising came early in October when Captain Sinclair signalled trouble aboard the *Alexander*. A convict told an officer of a plot to escape when they reached the Cape of Good Hope. The man the prisoners looked up to, John Powers – who had escaped at Tenerife – was the ringleader. He and others had obtained a crowbar and other tools from some seamen who also intended to jump ship at the port.

Captain Sinclair had four of the felons ironed; three to be locked in the hold and Powers stapled to the deck. Three seamen were transferred to the *Sirius*, later to be flogged and fined.

The Commodore, Major Ross, and Captain Hunter discussed the problems of the fleet over dinner that night. Phillip was particularly concerned about the officers aboard the *Alexander*. One of the lieutenants reported that Captain Sinclair did not have full control of the ship, with prisoners refusing to do anything when ordered.

"And now we have a threatened mutiny on board," Phillip stared gloomily out of the porthole.

"It can hardly be called a mutiny," Major Ross protested.

"When a man refuses a Captain's orders – that's mutiny at sea!" Phillip said grimly.

The discussion went on for nearly an hour until finally Phillip instructed Major Ross to organise inspections of the *Alexander* whenever weather permitted and said he would change personnel when they reached Cape Town. Word of the troubles aboard the *Alexander* spread round the fleet during the next few days of calm weather, carried by the well-meaning Reverend Johnson.

To the relief of all, the winds picked up and the fleet moved off once more upon the forbidding ocean where wind, water and sky merge as one. The crew knew every new wave thrown aside drew the vessels nearer Cape Town and safety. Fortunately they were only five hundred miles from the Cape.

The fleet covered the distance in four days.

Their welcome at Cape Town was to be entirely different to the one they had enjoyed at Rio.

Chapter Thirty

T
he *Sirius* took the lead as the fleet sailed into the gentle waters of Table Bay during the evening of Saturday 13th October 1787. Prosperous looking houses nestled at the base of Table Mountain, so called because the peak appeared to have been lopped off by a mighty hand, leaving it flat along the top. The sun was slipping under the sea to the west, vermillion-tinged frothy furrows of cloud crinkled across the clear sky; blue-green waters a sea of shimmering sapphires in the setting sun. As the last vestige of sunlight dipped below the horizon, red edged clouds changed to grey within moments, as if some Godly hand had turned down the wick of a gigantic lantern.

The next morning, after customary salutes were exchanged between the *Sirius* and the fort, Commodore Phillip and the senior officers went ashore to present the King's compliments to the Dutch Governor.

Along the shore, a great number of gallows and implements of torture were erected, graphic reminders that misdemeanours and crime were savagely punished in that place. Near the main landing point, several wheels for breaking felons were occupied by crooked bodies, grey faces contorted in agony – all missing a hand which was nailed prominently to the device.

To a man the officers covered their faces with nosegays as the smell of death assailed their nostrils.

"God almighty, what kind of place is this?" exclaimed Reverend Johnson who had gone along out of curiosity.

"No worse than public hangings at Tyburn gallows!" Phillips replied.

"But so many, and all mutilated!"

A guard of twelve men from the fort marched ahead, leading the party.

They were dressed in loose fitting white trousers with dark blue jackets that sported deep red cuffs and a red breast. Their red knee high boots were made of leather. All wore a stiff hat with a blue and red feather sticking out from the top. On the front of the hat the emblem 'VOC' was embroidered.

Captain Hunter, seeing the Reverend's puzzled look explained, "That's the Dutch equivalent of our East India Company – theirs is the United East India Company."

They were escorted to a five sided fort with a bastion built on every corner. Through the centre a large building ran, with every window protected by latticed ironwork, looking out into the courtyard.

Governor Cornelios Jason van Graff, a short man wearing a high-buttoned blue coat and a large broad brimmed hat, greeted them. He stood on a balcony and addressed them from above, flanked by officers of the fort. When he had finished reading from a prepared speech, he disappeared inside the building, never to be seen again by most officers during their visit.

One of the officers emerged from the building and offered to show them round the fort. Commodore Phillip, nettled that the Governor had not deigned to join them, stiffly agreed.

The first place they were shown was a dungeon set in the corner. The officer explained that they had received a prisoner that morning so they would have the privilege of seeing how Dutch law operated. A slave named Jephta had been found with many stabbings to his stomach, intestines protruding through his wounds. Another slave, a man called July of Java was now in the dungeon.

The officer told them that the law required that a criminal confess before sentence was passed so July of Java was being interrogated. The questioning consisted of five stages – the first involved tying the prisoner by the wrists and suspending him from a hook in the ceiling. The next, having his hands tied behind his back and suspending him – straight-armed, from another hook. Failure to confess meant that the prisoner was then suspended from yet another hook, this time upside down. If this did not elicit a confession, the man was dropped on his head from the hook and if the unfortunate creature then did not, or could not, confess, he was thrown into an adjacent 'black hole' until he bled to death.

Thus enlightened, the officers were shown back into the sunshine of the courtyard. Commodore Phillip thanked the Dutch officer for his assistance and told him they needed to make contact with merchants of the town to buy fresh supplies.

Once outside the fort the Commodore, still seething from the slight by the Governor, stormed off with Major Ross. The rest of the party went to locate supplies and begin negotiations.

Cape Town was a sombre place, full of clean, neat houses, mainly two storey homes with flat roofs. A few of the larger properties had thatched, pitched roofs and were built in the shape of a flat 'H'. The middle bar was the main room of the house with four doors leading off. One door concealed the kitchen and the other three, bedrooms. Families spent most of their time in the main room, which served as a place in which to greet and entertain callers.

There were two churches, one Calvanist and the other Lutherian. The town had none of the lighter places of relaxation or enjoyment they had found in Rio. There were no coffee houses nor taverns, and nowhere to sit, talk and drink fruit juices. It was a town of work or worship with nothing much between.

Later that day, the Commodore held a meeting on the *Sirius*. All who had gone ashore had found the Dutch merchants dour and uncompromising. Prices quoted for essential supplies were three or four times what had been expected.

Phillips reckoned the British were being treated badly because of the recent war with France – the French had an agreement with the Dutch to place a staging post on the Cape for French ships.

Major Ross thought the Dutch were protecting their Far East trade with India and Indo-China and charged exorbitantly to any other trading nation to deter them from using the route. Whatever the reasons, Phillip knew that a large proportion of the currency that he had been allowed for the fleet would remain at Cape Town.

It was the last port before the long and dangerous route to the unknown land called New South Wales. As well as the usual supplies, the fleet had to purchase stock for the new lands. It was imperative to the success of the whole enterprise that they obtain good breeding cows, sheep, fowl, horses, seeds and plants.

Commodore Phillip realised they had to spend at least four weeks in Cape Town in order to build up the health of crew, marines, and prisoners. Any less and he would lose dozens, possibly hundreds, to the scourge of scurvy. Just about the last thing they needed was to be held to ransom by hard-nosed Dutch merchants.

The Commodore told the meeting of the plot discovered aboard the *Alexander* in the mid-Atlantic. Information extracted from the crewmen, who had already been removed from the ship, meant that three more seamen were transferred in irons to the *Sirius*. A trial of all concerned would be held later.

Surgeon White, himself sickly pale, informed the gathering that more than thirty aboard the *Charlotte* were seriously ill with putrid fever and he expected some to die within twenty four hours.

The mood was sombre when the meeting ended. Everyone realised that Cape Town was a harbour of necessity, quite unlike Rio, which the officers had been reluctant to leave.

Crew and prisoners alike were set to clean the fleet. They creosoted quarters, quicklimed cracks and exploded gunpowder in the holds to kill bugs, fleas and legions of other vermin. In the *Alexandra*, a fire of charcoal, birch bark and camphor oil was lit to fumigate the ship. The fire also pinpointed places that were likely to leak. Everywhere that a puff of smoke was observed filtering out between boards was caulked and stoppered.

As no officer could bear the sight of an idle seaman, orders would spill out and send men scampering to new tasks. The Second Mate on the *Friendship*, Patrick Vallance, was no different and relished finding men jobs. He was a long-serving man devoted to the sea and inebriety in equal measure. When 'in drink' he was coarse in manner and language.

He was no friend of Liz Pulley, who had once told him that he had 'more edges than a broken piss pot.' Lately he had taken to watching Susannah when she washed her undergarments in a bucket and tied them to the riggings. He regularly came to stare insisting he was only watching them dry.

Henry, alerted by Liz, watched him like a frigate bird trawling the ocean for fish, ready to take drastic action if the Mate approached Susannah.

Susannah and Henry managed to spend a few minutes alone some seven days after the fleet anchored at Cape Town. Holding hands, they sat amongst mounds of tackle crammed on the poop deck watching a sailor perched on a plank painting the side of the ship.

"It's a rum thing to feel land about us after being at sea so long," Susannah looked across at the houses crouched between the mountain and the sea. "I wonder what my brother is doing at this moment, what sea he is on. I know I'll never see him again."

"When the new colony is settled you'll be able to write." Henry said.

"I don't know where he is nor what ship he sails in."

Together they stared across the still waters at the flocks of sheep grazing on the slopes of the mountain the seamen called the 'Lion's Rump.' To the north lay a long stretch of sparkling white sand, beyond which the land was covered with bright green bushes. They could hear the bleat of the sheep and the croak of frogs clearly over the water.

"Do you think we'll be happy in Botany Bay, Henry?"

"We are transported as felons, outcasts of our mother country but this is a new beginning. We know what cast us down in England and now we have a chance to start anew. We know how to suffer, we know how to survive, we need only to learn how to prosper."

"Perhaps the new land will be our Eden, Henry."

They clung together in love and fear at the prospect before them. Henry felt her firm breasts through his thin shirt and sudden warmth began to pervade his body. Susannah too felt a dart of desire and together they rolled back against a large crate, kissing deeply, only to be interrupted by a shout from below.

The seaman on the plank, legs dangling in the water, had spied a pilot fish. Pilot fish were never far ahead of a shark and, anxious to retain his feet for walking, he had shouted to Henry to keep a sharp look out.

Henry helped Susannah to her feet and they stared down at the man below.

"Will we ever get time together?" he said sadly.

Commodore Phillip, his feelings assuaged by an invitation to dine with Governor von Graff the following week, had met a Dutch merchant who indicated that he would be able to supply all the cattle the fleet required. Phillip took Major Ross and John Hunter along to the merchant's house to discuss the business.

Fortuin de Waal was a large man but only half the size of his French wife, a very formidable looking woman of about forty five years. They were startled to discover that the couple had twenty children. Mr de Waal told them he had contacts in the area inhabited by a number of Huguenots. The place was the 'French Quarter' known locally as Franschoek. The Huguenots, deeply religious Protestants, had been driven from France and Belgium, prevented from freely practising their religion by the ruling Catholics many years before. The officers were formally introduced to a raft of younger children, all dressed identically in dungarees of a rough blue cloth they called denim.

"It is the cloth of my town of birth, called de Nimes," Madame de Waal explained proudly.

Before business began, the officers were treated to glasses of local wine and a small dish of spicy meat. Their cook, like the other servants, was from Asia, hence the spicy food.

"Better to have servants from India or the Asian islands," confessed Madame de Waal, "otherwise they would just melt into the bush and never be seen again."

There were indications that economy was a religion in the de Waal household, even the candles were placed before mirrors to double the light.

Finally the dishes were cleared away and servants dismissed, helped by Madame de Waal thumping one young girl with a hand as coarse as rope. Phillip's feeling of foreboding was confirmed when Fortuin de Waal began by asking a figure some five times the usual value for a flock of sheep.

Three hours later, the officers stumbled out into the daylight having agreed to pay three times what they considered fair worth for sheep and feed.

"You may feel we've been robbed," Major Ross told Phillip, "but the fact is we have no choice but to buy their damned stock."

"The Major is right," Hunter added, "those merchants have us over a shipload of barrels!"

Victualling the fleet proceeded slowly owing to the high costs, but Phillip insisted serving men and prisoners were well fed with fruit, vegetables and fresh meat. The passage to New South Wales was to be the most dangerous part of their epic voyage and nobody was sure how long it would take.

Reverend Johnson had been called to the *Friendship* to conduct a service. Afterward Henry heard the Minister talking to the abstemious Lieutenant Clark. Reverend Johnson was scandalised, having just learned that some women on board the *Lady Penrhyn*, as a reward for good behaviour, had been allowed to earn money through prostitution in Rio de Janeiro. Locals had been rowed to the ship to be entertained by the women in a specially constructed caboose on the deck. As one pinnace left another was allowed to proceed from the dock, the operation supervised by marine guards.

Lieutenant Clark was glad to discuss his thoughts about the women with Reverend Johnson, whom he considered to be the only one in the fleet as God-fearing as he himself was. Religiously every Sunday he would take out the picture of his wife (he kept it in a cloth bag hanging by a ribbon round his neck) and kiss it fervently – usually a hundred times. He was subject to the most extraordinary dreams, details of which he faithfully recorded in his diary, once waking up Captain Meredith with his crying. Rarely did he drink alcohol, preferring lemonade, and he avoided carousing with other officers.

A few days after his discussion with Reverent Johnson the high-minded Clark demanded a court martial when his friend Lieutenant Faddy '*came on board very much in liquor and began to abuse me in a very public manner to Captain Meredith and another officer and gentleman.*'

Major Ross, on receiving the complaint, moved swiftly to avoid the embarrassment of a court martial. Nevertheless, he had to assemble nine officers on the *Friendship* to examine evidence and determine what to do about the complaint. In the end Lieutenant Faddy had to acknowledge his bad behaviour and apologise to Clark. Relations between Clark and the other officers remained stiff for some time after the hearing but it did not prevent the unbending Lieutenant from having two women prisoners – Barbour and Dudgeon – ironed for fighting three days later.

Henry had received permission to spend more time with Susannah as a reward for preventing some equipment from being lost overboard. Their talk, as always, was of the future. The nearer the New Lands loomed, the larger their apprehension grew. However, sharing their fears drew them closer together. Little Henry, now nearly twenty months, was a bonny baby who added greatly to the feeling that as a family they could overcome any difficulties that lay ahead.

Little did they know that their hopes would receive a terrible blow before the fleet left Cape Town.

Liz, Anne, Susannah and the baby were still confined together in their few feet of sleeping space every night.

"Is Robson still bothering you, Susannah?" Anne whispered in the darkness one night.

"He brought me a present from Cape Town, I dare not tell Henry."

"I've been heading him off as much as I can," Liz informed them. "He's a queer cote, usually all mouth and trousers but I reckon there's something soft about him."

"He's not as odd as Lt. Clark," Anne replied, "he's alus calling us bastards and whores but these last two nights he's asked me to wash and darn for him."

"He just wants someone to skivvy for him, that's not odd," Susannah said.

"I felt his hot hand touch my arse a couple of times," Anne said.

"You're pulling my pisser," Liz said bluntly.

"I thought it was just the closeness of the cabin at first," Anne grinned, "but when he had a good rummage around the second night I knew he was feeling frisky."

"I can hardly credit it," Susannah grinned.

"Did he invite himself aboard?" Liz said.

"I don't think he knew how."

The three women laughed.

The next evening Liz, Susannah and the baby were enjoying the last rays of sun, sitting in the lea of the main mast. They gazed at the sea, a phosphorescence of firewater dappling in the evening light.

Liz Pulley had been much quieter than usual since the fleet had arrived in Cape Town but was still frequently in the company of the crew. She was inordinately fond of Susannah and delighted in helping her to look after little Henry.

"'Ere, hang on to young Samson, I've got to feel the wind on my fanny," Liz exclaimed, handing the baby to Susannah. It was her way of saying she was going to the 'heads' to have a pee.

Fifteen minutes later, Susannah became worried, the 'heads' were perched on the bowsprit and it was easy to lose a footing in the fading light. Henry was below helping to re-arrange the prisoner's bedding, to create more space for the extra stores that they were taking on boards, and Anne was on some mysterious quest of her own. Just then, to Susannah's relief, Liz appeared out of the gathering gloom.

"Where have you been? I was getting worried."

"Don't worry about me, little Angel, I did a little trade by the forecastle there. One of the tars minded the wheel and one of them minded me, then they changed over. Both were better for the experience and I'm a mite richer too!"

"Liz, how could you! I thought you'd changed these last weeks!"

"Little Angel, I feel no shame in what I do. Many a time the only way I could survive was to give men the pleasures of my body. When your guts are aching for a bit of bread there's a lot you'll do to live. I've whored, I've pinched, but Botany Bay will give me a chance to change, perhaps the last chance I'll get to do something worthwhile with my life."

They sat together in silence for a while, listening to the sea slapping against the ship's sides. From the distant shore, strange sounds sped across the water from animals concealed in the thick bush.

"Do you think Botany Bay will be like this place, full of animals and forest?" Liz asked.

"They say no one knows because the Captain who found the place never stepped ashore to find out."

"Should I find myself someone to get hitched to when we reach Botany Bay?"

Susannah, taken aback by Liz's sudden change of conversation, studied her friend for a while.

"Are you serious?"

"It's crossed my mind a few times lately."

"Anne reckons there are seven or eight men to every woman on the ships."

"I know I need to change, getting married would be a big change. I just don't know if it's the thing to do."

Susannah instinctively grasped her friend in a fierce hug and was astonished to discover hot tears soaking her dress on the shoulder. She had never known Liz to cry before. "What's the matter Liz?"

"I'm up the gut, little Angel, I'm having a baby."

"Are you sure, Liz?"

"I saw the doctor when we came into the harbour."

"Who is the father?"

Liz looked up at the stars, "Buggered if I know," she sighed slumping back against a mast. Tears squeezed through her fingers. "I'm a silly sod. Sometimes I don't know if you're my sister or my daughter."

Susannah held her tight. She didn't know either.

Commodore Phillip and the ships' masters were having no success in their negotiations with the tight-fisted Dutch. It seemed they had a policy of charging a minimum of three times the usual price for everything ranging from a pound of nails to cattle and horses. Chickens were two shillings and sixpence and geese five shillings. The Dutch, having learned the purpose of the fleet, never passed an opportunity to extract money from the English sailors. A lot of the crew, and many officers too, never went ashore in Cape Town, declaring it a *'town of skinflints and bible bashers.'*

On Thursday 25th October, Henry and Susannah were to receive news that would strike them like a sledgehammer.

The female felons were lined up on the quarterdeck watching men brought up in batches to have their hair cut. The convict barber was a gardener by trade who clipped away as if thinning a hedge. The women shrieked with delight at every tufted head revealed by the amateur barber.

He had taken to ripping the sheet from each victim to reveal his handiwork to the women, as a matador might snatch his cape from the face of a bull, and bowing to the audience.

The first mate, supervising the operation, also enjoyed the spectacle, having instructed the barber to 'shear 'em short.'

In recent days there had been a great deal of inspections of ships by senior officers. Only that morning Major Ross and Captain Hunter had inspected the *Friendship* to see where the sheep and cattle could be accommodated if the convicts were moved elsewhere. As they had openly discussed the possibilities with Captain Walton as they moved amongst crew and prisoners, everyone quickly became aware of the intended changes.

When a boat bearing Major Ross came alongside, the women stopped taunting the latest batch of shorn prisoners and waited expectantly when he conferred with Lieutenant Clark – the other officers having gone ashore in the ships' pinnace.

Immediately the Major departed, Lieutenant Clark commanded that all of the women be assembled on the quarterdeck. It didn't take long as only Elizabeth Dudgeon was missing but was quickly discovered in the ship's galley with the cook and his mate.

There were twenty one women on the *Friendship* – a few had been exchanged with other prisoners whilst they were in the harbour of Rio de Janeiro. Lieutenant Clark stood on a small box and made them crowd around in a semi-circle. He seemed inordinately pleased with himself.

"I am," he announced, "delighted to inform you that you will all be transferred to other ships. You are to gather together all of your belongings ready to move tomorrow or the next day."

"We know that you silly sod, we want to know which ship," someone called from the back.

"You will be dispersed amongst several ships," he replied grandly.

Suddenly panic gripped Susannah and she pushed to the front. "The men," she gasped, "when will we know where the men are being put?"

"Can't you think of anything else, you harlot? Isn't it enough you rut like beasts of the forest and blaspheme worse than King's troopers?"

Liz Pulley appeared by Susannah's side and linked arms with her. "You pious bastard! The lass only wants to know if her Henry is going on the same ship – you know they're a pair and no trouble to no one!"

Lieutenant Clark, hot under the collar, sneered down at the two women.

"All the men are staying on this ship – only women are changed for sheep and cows, and damned glad I am of it!"

Susannah sank back in Liz's arms, her face a deathly white. Liz lowered her to the deck and prised little Henry from her grip. "Don't worry, little Angel, I'll stick by you, we can't be far from Botany Bay."

The news spread like wildfire and when Henry heard he was furious. "I've not come this far to lose Susannah and the baby now!" he stormed.

'Red' McGrath calmed him down. "If you rampage about shouting your mouth off you'll only make things worse. What you've got to do is pull in your favours – the Captain and Meredith both owe you! Ask 'em if you can go with the girl and your boy – surely they ain't flint-hearted!"

Henry held his head in his hands, willing his temper to simmer down. He had, after all, saved the Guard Commander's life.

It was evening before he could get an audience with James Meredith. The Captain took him to the cabin used by ship's surgeon and listened with sympathy to Henry's request.

When James Meredith went off to consult with Captain Walton, Henry waited impatiently watching the Atlantic surf boom against the white beach with rolling acres of fynbos beyond. Stretching back as far as he could see, dark green trees crept from the greenery to the foot of stark mountains rising in the distance. Birds kept up a blanket of sound, occasionally showing bright plumage in short wheeling flights.

Time passed with no word from Captain Meredith. Henry's heart felt like lead in his chest.

The lookout, a young boy, new to sailoring, strode confidently the length of the deck, keenly aware of the importance of his duties. He was mildly surprised when the regular salt who took his place, stowed himself behind a pile of rigging for a nap. Sufficient, he felt, for a fine night in harbour.

The sharp edge of the sea against a blood red sky caught Henry's attention, but did nothing to rouse his spirits. The sky was afire as far as the eye could stretch, becoming a layer of light blue against the darkening night as the sun sunk below the horizon.

An old hand Henry knew well stood nearby watching the sun set.

"There's nothing to beat nature's show, lad."

Henry nodded but could not bring himself to reply.

"Kable, come here lad," Captain Meredith called to him from the shadow of the forecastle.

"Can I go with Susannah and my son?"

"Sorry, nothing can be done to change the Commodore's orders. You are needed here on the *Friendship* – it's no coincidence that prisoners on this vessel are among the best behaved of the whole fleet. The run to Botany Bay is likely to be the roughest part of the whole expedition, we can't afford to lose you now."

Henry pressed his fist against his mouth, forcing back rage and disappointment.

"Look Kable, we think it's going to be ten to twelve weeks before we get to Botany Bay, it's not long to wait to see your woman and boy again – then you can have the rest of your lives together."

"That's ten or twelve weeks when she could meet a marine or tar when I'm not around to look after her."

"The girl dotes on you, everyone knows that."

"I've got no prospects, no chance of a regular income. A marine taking the Kings shilling, week in and week out, must be a temptation to any woman!"

"Kable, you've been a good man aboard this ship, I'd say you've done duty as well as any man, and I'll not forget you risked your life to save mine. I can't alter orders but I'll write you a reference when we reach New South Wales so you and the girl get a comfortable billet."

Silently, the two men shook hands and Henry turned to go.

"Wait Kable, there's something I have contrived for you."

Captain Meredith left Henry in the cabin and returned moments later with Susannah!

"Make sure you tidy this berth before the doctor sees it tomorrow morning. He's staying in Cape Town tonight," he grinned, closing the door behind him.

Ralph Clark, who shared a cabin with James Meredith, was outraged when he learned what he had done. "The least I can do is to double the deck guard," he said, struggling into his top boots.

"Get back to your hammock, man, their child is locked in the hold, they'll go nowhere without the child!"

Liz Pulley made sure she, Susannah and Anne went everywhere together. She reasoned that when the women were separated into groups to be transferred to different ships it would be done on the spot. By keeping together they were more likely to find themselves on the same ship.

She was wrong; Susannah and Elizabeth Pugh – who also had a baby – together with Elizabeth Thackeray and the notorious Elizabeth Dudgeon were allocated to the *Charlotte*. Four others went to the *Lady Penrhyn*. Liz Pulley and Anne, with the remaining eleven women were sent aboard the *Prince of Wales*. Some sailors were also transferred to other ships.

Henry and Susannah, since their night in the doctor's cabin, had spent only a few minutes together before she was taken to the *Charlotte*. It had been long enough for them to promise everlasting love and devotion.

Chapter Thirty One

The fleet was suddenly busy cramming prisoners even closer to make room for hundreds of animals and their feed. Pens and stockades were constructed on already overcrowded decks. Only fowl and smaller animals could be kept in the holds. Horses, cows and a few goats were banged up in wooden crates, which were bolted and chained to ship's decks and sides. It was a dangerous operation to ferry the stock across the harbour; each beast had to be hauled aboard using canvas slings under their bellies, two or three men strained on a rope attached to a pulley to lower the terrified animals to deck or hold. Table Bay echoed to the sound of pigs squealing and complaining about their new accommodation.

Most of the stock was bought with Government funds for the new settlement but a number of officers had purchased animals for themselves.

One stallion, three mares and three colts were hauled aboard the *Lady Penrhyn* for Commodore Phillip, who felt he would have need of such animals when he was Governor of the New Lands. Henry and other trusted prisoners helped load the animals and secure them in pens.

Lieutenant Clark, having overseen a flock of sheep shipped aboard the *Friendship* in place of the women, confided in his diary, '*I think we will find them much more agreeable shipmates than they were.*'

A seamen aboard the *Sirius*, which had been filled with a flock of sheep, was discovered 'abominating a merino.' He was sentenced to fifty lashes, the loss of a week's pay and transferred to the *Prince of Wales* as a reward for his romantic endeavours. Thereafter, whenever he appeared on deck he was greeted with cries of 'baa baa' and gales of laughter. Later, the prisoners changed this to 'pa pa', indicating that his union with the unfortunate sheep had borne fruit.

The tough work in getting the fleet ready for the arduous run to New South Wales claimed another life when Patrick Vallance, second mate on the *Friendship*, having imbibed too freely after grafting hard all day, fell overboard from the 'heads'. He was never seen again.

Commodore Phillip, after many battles with the tightwad Dutch, was glad to give the signal to weigh anchor on the 11th November. He had, at great cost, provisioned the fleet for the final leg of the journey to give the fledgling colony a reasonable start in New South Wales. Rigorous inspections ensured prisoners and serving men had been well fed with fresh meat and vegetables.

However, the wind was against them and the fleet was unable to sail. The *Scarborough* and the *Friendship* found themselves hovering head to head in the bay, bowing and curtseying at each other like a coquettish couple of would-be lovers.

The Commodore ordered the fleet to wait for better weather. Nobody was sorry to leave Cape Town. However, before them were unknown seas and an unknown land. The inhabitants of Cape Town, for all their faults, were the last civilised people they could hope to meet for years ahead.

On the day that the fleet was to sail to the new lands, Henry, as had been his habit since Susannah had been transferred, strained his eyes toward the *Charlotte*, bobbing about in the sea not fifty yards away. To his great joy he spotted Susannah waving from the quarterdeck.

Vigorously he signalled back, jumping up and down in excitement. As he watched a seaman joined her but to his astonishment they held hands and waved together. Dumb-founded he shaded his eyes against the setting sun, hoping that he was mistaken. He was not, and to complete his agony, Susannah kissed the sailor on the cheek.

The wind changed and swung the *Charlotte* away so that the two of them were hidden from his devastated gaze.

He would not see either of them again for over three months.

His friend, Red, found him a little later in the hold. "It's not like you Henry, to be skulking down here when there's a breath of fresh air to be had on deck."

"She's gone, Red, I'll never see her again."

"Susannah? You'll see her when we reach Botany Bay."

"She's got herself a sailor, I saw them together, they even kissed in front of me."

"Not that bugger Robson I hope."

"I expect so, he's been after her ever since we sailed."

"Look, Henry, she's probably just hitched up with him temporarily like, just to get a few extra victuals for the boy."

"She looked happy, she wasn't putting it on."

Red left him there, kicking a hole in the wooden partition at the entrance to their quarters.

Chapter Thirty Two

For over a week, the fleet battled against a head wind, making little progress. Mountainous waves towered above ships' cross trees, the height of which even long serving seamen had not seen before.

The laden vessels were making heavy weather of it, weighed down with supplies and plagued by a thousand adjustments needed to make the improvised pens safe for frantic cattle.

The ships laboured up spumy walls only to crash down troughs of frightening steepness, the decks were awash with angry seas, icy water was forced down every crevice, soaking petrified the souls who were crouching in black holds where candles and lanterns were forbidden – the fear of fire was just as real as the threat of capsizing. The sea-sick prisoners were wet and cold, and crammed into confined spaces but they were unusually glad to be close-packed with fellow beings.

Howling gales swept across the ocean, slamming into the puny craft, vicious pellets of rain nailed the crewmen against rigging until a slight shift freed them to tighten a sail or adjust a stay.

Eight days from Cape Town, the weather moderated enough for Commodore Phillip to signal every ship to pass in succession under the stern of his ship. Officers from the *Sirius* were sent on board each vessel to acquaint them with Phillip's new plan. It would not be well received by everybody.

The Commodore wanted to proceed with all haste in the *Supply* – being the fastest vessel – together with three other swifter ships – the *Alexander*, *Scarborough* and *Friendship*. The objective was to prepare Botany Bay by cutting timber and erecting shelters for the rest of the fleet. To this end any prisoner skilled in carpentry and agriculture was to be transferred to the four fleetest craft.

Whilst Phillip would go in the *Supply*, Captain Hunter would remain on the *Sirius*. Lieutenant Shortland, the naval agent, was to be in overall command of the three transports. These decisions were fiercely argued over by the Officers on the different ships. Daily hardships were enough to keep the prisoners from being too concerned with the rumours which circulated on every vessel.

One of the women transferred from the *Friendship* in Table Bay died on the *Lady Penrhyn*. She left a boy of three years who was immediately adopted by one of the female prisoners who had lost her own child earlier in the voyage.

Henry Kable lay violently ill in his space, having been bilious since the fleet met the giant rollers a day out from Table Bay.

One curious piece of intelligence reported to the *Sirius* was that all the ships had lost a number of fowl every day since their departure from Table Bay.

The planned transfer of personnel could not be made immediately as the weather suddenly became changeable; one day the fleet was driven along with a fair wind, another would see ships rolling violently in the swell, lacking a steadying breeze.

Commodore Phillip was concerned that his plan to forge ahead would have to be revised as the *Supply*, which sat low in the water when fully loaded, lagged behind. On a number of occasions, the fleet had to shorten sail so the laden vessel could catch up. Although it had previously proved to be the speediest vessel in the fleet, it did not travel well in a stiff breeze.

However, Sunday 25th November was a fine calm day so the Commodore decided to press ahead with dividing the fleet into two groups. He intended to plot as much of the coast of the New Lands as possible before reaching Botany Bay.

Several officers were not convinced of the wisdom to split the fleet, as they had come this far with no major mishaps. Some felt that the Commodore was abandoning the slower vessels and didn't like losing the senior officers who were going in the vanguard.

There was also a feeling of vulnerability; indeed two days after the 'racers' had disappeared over the horizon, the Captain of the *Lady Penrhyn* reported a huge rock in the sea ahead. It proved to be a dead whale of a most enormous size which in all probability had been dead some time. The beast was prodigiously swelled and stripped of much of its skin. It was a great height out of the water and at first sight had every appearance of a rock, especially as it was covered with a variety of sea birds. Despite the fact it was at least half a mile from the ship, the stench was almost intolerable.

Henry rose from the mortuary of the lower decks on the *Friendship* and felt well enough to be sick in the foaming ocean. He gripped the rigging and bent his green face to the green waters and retched violently. The bile was bitter in his mouth, his stomach empty of anything else. A frigate bird, cruising serenely overhead, screeched its contempt for all to hear. Red McGrath watched him from the forecastle, aware that Henry had been devastated to see Susannah hand in hand with the sailor aboard the *Charlotte*, and this had played its part in keeping his friend below for so long. He had never known Henry to languish in his space before.

The volatile weather continued to tax the crews, some days sullen seas surged and roared, laying the ships so low that ice cold water poured into the portholes soaking miserable prisoners and throwing meagre possessions around dark holds. Another day would bring bright sunshine and steady winds.

Despite dreadfully cold wet conditions, and apart from seasickness, prisoners were generally in good health. Bowes Smyth, the surgeon on the *Lady Penrhyn*, that this was as consequence of the generous rations allocated to prisoners.

The Master of the ship disagreed, "What about all those deaths on the *Alexandra*"? He demanded.

"Many convicts were embarked on that vessel from different gaols with malignant disorders upon them, and consequently many died on board, but the *Scarborough* has not lost a single person during the passage."

"The good health of prisoners is because officers pay strict attention to keeping them and their berths well aired and perfectly clean." The Master replied.

"Responsibility for that lies with the Surgeons on every ship and on this vessel only two women have perished, one of eighty two years of a dropsy which had long reigned upon her."

Bowes-Smyth was proud of the extraordinary health record of his ship but did not mention the glut of venereal diseases, nor had he ventured much down into the bowels of the ship. There the gut-wrenching stench of vile bilge water constantly plagued those locked in its heady thrall.

The prisoners were, if anything, more trouble than they had been at the start of the voyage. The first mate on the *Friendship* opined this was due to 'too much grub.' Most of the trouble occurred between prisoners. There were many petty thefts which led to fights and outbursts of appalling language.

Punishments meted out were thumbscrews, or wrist fetters consisting of iron cuffs joined by a solid shaft. Women hated having their heads shaved and whilst this punishment was being inflicted they invariably abused the officers, which drew the extra humiliation of being gagged.

On the *Friendship*, just before Christmas Day, two prisoners complained to Lieutenant Clark that the rest '*detained their food allowance and gave them what they pleased.*' They told him that certain prisoners had stolen and stored beef and wood.

Lieutenant Clark mounted an inspection and soon found the beef and 29 large billets of wood. He was not slow to inform the Captain of the Marines.

"I found Henry Lovell and Henry Kable, two prisoners who have the liberty of going about the ship have stolen beef and wood when they were sent to pump water. Both are damned, I will keep a sharp look out for them when at Botany Bay otherwise they will take the teeth out of my head."

Bowes-Smyth recorded almost the same sentiments about females on the *Lady Penrhyn*:

'*I believe there was never a more abandoned set of wretches collected in one place than are to be met in this ship in particular.* . . . . *The greater part of them are so totally abandoned and calloused to all shame and common decency that it frequently becomes indispensably necessary to inflict corporal punishment upon them.* . . . . *They perpetually thieve the clothes from each other, nay almost from their backs.* . . . . *Nor can their matchless insincerity be equalled except by their base ingratitude; many of them plundering the sailors (who have at every port spent almost the whole of the wages due to them in purchasing difference articles of wearing apparel and other things for their accommodation) of their necessary clothes and cutting them up for some purpose of their own.*'

Henry was brought before Captain Meredith, ankles and hands manacled. "You are a damn fool Kable, your record on this ship has been exemplary until we left Cape Town. Since then you've been surly and uncooperative.

Now we find you've been using your position of trust to steal food from the mouths of fellow convicts. This is the action of a stupid selfish person, have you no common decency?"

He waited a moment but Henry said nothing. "Prisoner McGrath tells me the mother of your child has hooked up with a sailor on the *Charlotte*, which I know is a blow to any man."

Henry stared ahead, stone-faced, gulping down equal measures of anger and sorrow.

"I know you can be a good man Kable, I've seen the work you've put in since we left England, but this is your last chance. Anymore tomfoolery of this nature and you'll lose all your privileges. Seven days of reduced rations."

Two marines marched Henry to the forecastle and unlocked his chains. "You're a lucky sod Kable, any soldier would have got fifty of the best."

Henry said nothing, the Captain's remarks about Susannah and his son had stirred emotions he preferred to keep hidden.

The *Friendship's* Master, Captain Walton, acknowledged Christmas Day by giving the ships company and prisoners raisins to be put in a pudding along with molasses he had brought in Rio de Janeiro. In addition, the crew and marines were allowed a double ration of grog. It was a sentimental time, particularly for the felons, remembering family and friends back in the old country.

Lieutenant Clark was touched to hear carols sung in the prisoners hold, accompanied by two fiddlers using instruments retained for religious services.

Henry ate his Christmas pudding thoughtfully, listening to the carols – it brought to mind Liz Pulley and Susannah singing so beautifully in Norwich Castle one Christmas so long ago.

That evening he stood alone staring into the gathering mist as the *Friendship* slipped through the water with hardly a sound. The sea was remarkably smooth as if quietened by a covering of oil. Now and then a long low swell lightly lifted the ship and tipped it forward without seeming to disturb the milky surface.

Out in the ghostly mist Henry could sense a whale nearby, breathing deeply and evenly, somehow like the ocean's bosom rising and falling in steady passion. No matter how hard he tried, he couldn't get out of his mind the image of Susannah, laughing, waving and holding hands with the sailor on the *Charlotte* in Table Bay. He could not understand her betrayal so soon after they had pledged their love for one another.

Over the next fortnight, the divided fleet was subjected to a dozen different facets of weather, ranging from being so hot that men were obliged to walk about bare-chested, through days of rain, hail and ferocious winds that laid some vessels almost flat against the surface of the sea, to bouts of forked lightning the like of which nobody had seen before.

On one occasion women on the *Lady Penrhyn* were sluiced out of their berths by freezing seas raging over the decks. For days afterwards the main sail was snagged with weeds washed from the bottom of the vessel. Violent storms on New Years Day 1788 saw the assistant surgeon almost flung overboard; he just saved himself by clutching the mizzen mast and hanging on for grim death. The water smashed into the officers' cabins and left bedding entangled with sundry bits of equipment strewn about the deck.

On the *Friendship*, Captain Walton was called to the forward hold by Captain Meredith. Most of the fowl had died since Cape Town and two more sheep had perished.

"What the devil ails the livestock?" Captain Walton wanted to know.

"I've talked with officers on the other ships about this every time we've been becalmed. Beasts and fowls die on all ships in calm weather and bad weather." Captain Meredith told him.

Red and Henry stood nearby having just finished mucking out the sheep pens. "They've been poisoned," Henry said shortly.

"Poisoned? How do you know?"

"I've worked on farms, look at the animals' mouths, you'll find a deal of foaming – it's a sure sign they've eaten something bad."

"Good God, could the Dutch have sold us poisoned feed?" Captain Walton asked.

"Officers on other ships have made the same suggestion," Captain Meredith replied, "and now we are running out of hay."

"Issue instructions to wash the grain feed, it can't do any harm. I'll signal the rest of the fleet," Captain Walton climbed wearily to the deck.

Red turned to Captain Meredith, "Is there anything we can do?"

"We must battle on, come what may," the weary Captain replied.

Four days later a great cheer went up on the *Friendship* when Van Diemens Land was seen to windward. They were not near enough to make out details, only that the cliffs were steep and mountains rose beyond. Lieutenant

Clark, aware the fleet was still eight hundred miles from Botany Bay, was inspecting livestock with Captain Meredith.

"I wish to God we were at anchor, these poor sheep have hardly hay sufficient to keep life in them. If we stay out much longer they must all die and us too. For the last three weeks its common knowledge there is insufficient firing in the ships and we'll be obliged to eat our provisions without cooking."

"Do cheer up you miserable bugger, we are all in the same predicament." The Captain walked off to find more cheerful company.

The next day, ships in the slower pack also spotted land. It was a fine day so they were able to discern ground thickly populated with trees and many grassy acres between. A large fire raged on one of the hills far inland.

During a brief lull in the weather a few days later, the masters of the six ships were summoned aboard the *Sirius* to decide whether to put in boats to collect grass for the remaining stock. The *Sirius* had lost almost all sheep, thirteen goats out of fifteen, one cow and their entire flock of fowl. Reluctantly, after studying huge breakers crashing on the rocky shoreline, it was considered it too dangerous and they decided to press on.

Within half an hour of the masters returning to their respective stations, the ships were engulfed in a ferocious hurricane. It was a chaotic scene with ships being driven in all directions. The *Fishburn* and *Lady Penrhyn* almost collided and the *Golden Grove* narrowly escaped jagged rocks. Every vessel sustained damage except the *Sirius*. The storm ripped the *Fishburn's* jib sail and tore the *Borrowdale's* fore top sail to pieces; the *Golden Grove* lost both foresail and main topsail, the *Charlotte* saw no more of her main sail and the *Prince of Wales* suffered damage to main yard and sail, and main topsail. It was a terrifying half an hour for crew and prisoners alike.

The *Lady Penrhyn*, laid almost horizontal by fierce winds, was in imminent danger of capsizing. Bowes-Smyth recorded the women prisoners' reaction in his diary:

'During the storm the convict women in our ship were so terrified that most of them were down on their knees at prayers, and in less than an hour after it had abated, they were uttering the most horrid oaths and imprecations that could proceed out of the mouths of such abandoned prostitutes as they are!'

Within days, temperatures were climbing, seventy five degrees Fahrenheit one day and eighty the next. It was a mixed blessing to the prisoners. Damp, wet quarters were suddenly transformed into steaming spaces, unhealthy and airless, so they were glad to spend as much time as possible on deck.

Henry helped rig sails above hatches to divert fresh air into the fetid holds. His friend, Red McGrath, found him one day standing on a crate staring into the vast waste of water beyond the stern.

"Still worried about that matelot with your woman, Henry? Don't worry lad, we'll reach dry land soon, then you can sort it out."

Henry grunted, but said nothing.

"I've not yet seen a seaman who can stand up to you, Henry."

"There's no taste in nothing, Red. If Susannah doesn't want me, it doesn't matter if I fight the whole King's Navy, nothing will signify."

"That sailor means nothing to her. The women just take 'em on temporary like – they have to have someone looking after 'em. Better a sailor who can get extra grub! She'll need it for the boy."

"We'll see," growled Henry, "we'll see."

Chapter Thirty Three

The next day, a roar of relief came from every quarter when land was sighted. The joy of crew and prisoners was unconfined; convicts and tars danced jigs together. Men who had been at loggerheads hugged one another; Officers shook hands and hurried to bring out the bottles of liquor that they had been saving. Relief and rejoicing ran hand in hand throughout the three transports in the vanguard that had, at this time, lost sight of the *Supply*.

Twenty four hours later they ran into Botany Bay, delighted to find the *Supply* anchored by the shore, having arrived the previous afternoon. At eight o'clock the next morning, the remaining seven ships rounded Solander Point and entered Botany Bay.

The greatest sea journey ever undertaken was over. They had travelled over fifteen thousand miles and not lost a ship. It was eight months and seven days since they had left England. By any standards it was a masterpiece of seamanship and planning.

Just as astonishing was the safe arrival of so many souls. Since sailing they had lost just twenty three prisoners and five convict children with three deaths amongst crew and marines. Most of the prisoners' deaths had been due to illnesses that they had had when they embarked. Commodore Phillip was not slow in calling a meeting aboard the *Sirius* and congratulating the officers for their diligence in looking after so many prisoners on the historic journey.

Soon officers, accompanied by marines, went ashore for their first look at the new land. Around the harbour every nook, every cranny, every rocky promontory teemed with seals. These, together with numerous whales in the nearby ocean, were to form the basis for the New Lands' fortunes for decades to come.

In the bush, baked bronze by the blazing sun, lurked strange creatures that bounded away with prodigious leaps when disturbed. White cockatoos roosting in tall trees wheeled and shrieked away in the clouds, like throngs of lost souls.

Governor Phillip – his appointment began the moment he stepped ashore – organised a proper inspection of harbour and surrounds. Accompanied by Captain Hunter, Lieutenant Shortland, Major Ross, Captain Meredith and a party of marines he set off in a longboat. The Governor had been ashore twice already and his first impressions of Botany Bay as a future settlement were not good. He wanted to make an inspection accompanied by officers who would not be afraid to voice their own opinions.

Ever since the first ship had appeared, natives had begun to assemble in greater numbers. As soon as the rowing boats reached dry land, a group of natives approached, finely muscled and slender, with very dark skin. All were entirely naked and carried long lances tipped with sharpened bones. Each had a thin stick threaded through their septum and every one was missing a front tooth. Their bodies were decorated with ridged scars from self-inflicted wounds. Some made threatening gestures with spears whilst others were clearly curious about the white men. They had fashioned their thick black hair to leave a sort of hollow in the middle, which they appeared to use as a handy receptacle for anything they wanted to transport. Several carried dead fish in the hollow; the sweltering sun sending rivulets of oil from the stinking fish down faces and backs.

Governor Phillip issued strict instructions that any threats from the natives were to be answered with smiles and gifts; only if life was threatened should resort be made to firearms. Several tribesmen menaced them with spears, jabbing the points at the landing party, indicating the weapons would be used if they came any closer. One flung a lance at a nearby tree where it lodged, quivering. Another broke from the black ranks and threw his spear at a marine who discharged his musket in the air. The natives ran off with great speed.

Governor Phillip enticed them back, waving ribbons and beads in the air. Before long, the curious natives returned to accept the gifts, amazed by the variety of coloured baubles and astonished by the heavy uniforms worn by officers and men. In no time at all they were swarming around the boat, poking clothing, touching buttons and delighted whenever an officer lifted his hat.

It was some time before the officers could begin their inspection of the harbour. The ground was scattered with tall trees, not closely packed, which Major Ross thought could easily be cleared to provide open ground for planting.

"Not with soil as poor as this," Lieutenant Shortland demonstrated the point by scraping the dust with his heel, it was thin and sandy and supported sparse grass. The party examined the soil in several places around the harbour and found it equally thin and light.

Captain Meredith voiced the opinion that the earth would turn to dust once the trees were cleared. Captain Hunter thought the trees were not hardy enough to support buildings or even wooden huts, pointing out that eucalyptus did not have enough strength for construction purposes.

Governor Phillip gathered the officers around him, "Gentlemen, I am concerned about the harbour, plumb lines dropped yesterday indicate many shallow coves. The open mouth of the bay might well allow heavy swells to push ships on to rocks in no time at all!"

After more discussion the Governor decided that he would take more soundings in the harbour and ordered Captain Meredith to provide three or four prisoners to cut down trees the following morning.

"Make sure at least one of the convicts is a carpenter so we can test if the timber is good enough for building," he ordered.

Henry and Red McGrath, together with two carpenters, Ed Pugh and Moses Tucker – all from the *Friendship* were sent ashore with a guard of marines the next morning.

Captain Meredith and the Governor watched as Henry and Red got to work on one of the grey green eucalypts that surrounded the harbour. The two prisoners were startled when a large stone fell from a branch above as their axes bit into the trunk.

"We saw several stones stored in branches by the natives when we arrived," explained Phillip, "we believe they use them to drop on kangaroos – it's their method of capturing the creatures."

Captain Meredith looked dubiously up at the branches.

"Tis true," Phillip went on, "in many ways the native is a crude hunter. Yesterday we watched his use of the fire stick, they set fire to a rotten tree and club whatever emerges – snake, bear, beetle – it makes no difference – they eat the lot!"

Henry and Red looked at each other with amazement. When allowed a rest after the first tree was felled, Henry went into the bushes and set a snare using a thin cord that usually secured the bottom of his trousers.

After a second tree was felled the prisoners were allowed a pannikin of water. Suddenly there was a thrashing noise from the bush nearby.

"My snare!" Henry shouted, leaping up to investigate. Moments later he emerged holding a large lizard, about three feet long and quite dead.

As Meredith and Phillip crowded round to examine the weird creature the bushes parted and two natives leapt out, menacing them with spears. The marines, sitting under a tree nearby, were startled into action but fell over themselves, scattering their muskets in the confusion. The Governor, contemplating a vicious looking lance not twelve inches from his nose, fell back in terror.

Henry felled the nearest native with a violent blow, grabbed the lance and broke it over the second native's head. The man ran off howling into the thick scrub.

Captain Meredith organised the marines to form a circle round the Governor, who had recovered his composure, and his hat, which he placed carefully over his bald pate.

"Well done, Kable," Meredith growled, looking angrily at the marines.

"There was no way I was going to let them bugger off with my catch."

Phillip picked up the lizard by the tail and brought it over to Henry. "Do you want this creature cooked for your supper?"

"It don't look the most 'ansomest of morsels, Sir, now I study it close."

The Governor took a mug of water and poured it over the unconscious native. When he had recovered enough to sit up, Phillip tossed the lizard into the man's lap. They left him there, rubbing his jaw and staring at the dead creature as if it had dropped from the heavens above.

At the water's edge, Phillip and the officers talked together for some time. The marines were getting the boats ready to return to their respective ships when Meredith addressed them.

"The Governor will be exploring an inlet a few miles up the coast first thing tomorrow. Kable, you are to accompany the Governor – he reckons you'll be a useful man to have around."

A few minutes later, Captain Meredith drew Henry aside. "Kable, I've given you a good character with the Governor, don't let me down!

Remember, he'll be keeping an eye open for likely servants – you won't get a better billet!"

As the oarsmen pulled the rowing boat across the rippling waters they passed the *Charlotte*. Henry stared intently at the decks but there was no sign of Susannah. The Governor noticed Henry squeezing his eyes at the ship.

"Captain Meredith tells me you have a woman aboard the *Charlotte*."

Henry nodded miserably, cupping his chin in his hands, but said nothing.

Gangs of male prisoners, under the close watch of marines, gathered as much fresh vegetation as they could for the remaining animals. Women felons were kept on the ships until a place of settlement had been established. More and more natives gathered to watch the strange ships and men. They were very curious about hats worn by officers and frequently tried to snatch them from their heads.

Lieutenant Phillip King, leading a party to gather wood found himself surrounded by natives who poked and pulled the men's clothing, particularly their trousers. Gradually it became clear they desired to know what sex the strange white creatures were. The Lieutenant made one of the marines undo his fly buttons and reveal all to the natives. Upon discovering that the man was similarly endowed to themselves, the natives let out a great shout of delight, made crude gestures and went around shaking hands with the whole party.

Then they gesticulated to their naked women, standing some way off, to come down to the beach. Using signs and grotesque pantomime, the natives made it clear that the women were at the service of the white men.

Lieutenant King declined, not least because the women, covered in fish oil, were strangers to personal hygiene, sporting noses coated with bubbles of congestion. Rotting fish oil and wood smoke seemed to be the womens' favoured perfume and, although the visitors were not straight out of the washtub themselves, the prospect of intimate contact did not appeal.

Fish and molluscs were the favoured diet of the Botany Bay locals; huge mounds of shells and bones on the shore confirming their preferences. When fishing in the harbour they carried fire in their canoes, burning on a bed of sand and seaweed. Fish was cooked immediately after being caught although many were observed eating the flesh raw.

The following day Henry found himself seated next to Governor Phillip in a longboat as they made their way to the shore in the new harbour. Captain Cook had noted the inlet in 1770 but had not explored it. Phillip was desperately hoping for a better place in which to begin the new Colony. When the boat touched gravel some twenty feet from the shore, Phillip insisted on going ahead of his men as he had at Botany Bay. However, as he was wearing a favoured pair of buckled shoes he ordered Henry to carry him through the surf. Henry got the Governor to a dry spot on the beach before lowering him down on the sand.

The land was covered in ferns and pink eucalypts, and a stream of clear water flowed serenely into the bay. Nearby, the harbour seemed deep enough to allow ships to be tied to trees growing by the water's edge.

Phillip was jubilant after the disappointment of Botany Bay. Immediately, he declared the place should be known as Sydney Cove, 'in honour of the man who sent us here.'

The place was thickly wooded with lush ferns and shrub interspersed with other areas covered in thick grass and an occasional tall tree disturbing the open scene. To Henry, it was a wonderful change from the stifling confines of the prison ships, especially the suffocating space below decks. The sheer size of the place with the clear blue skies above was overpowering. Henry took in the fresh water and lush greenery; it reminded him of his carefree days in Norfolk. Strangely he was suddenly more hopeful of the future than he had been since he saw Susannah with the sailor in Table Bay.

"This is a handsome place to make a new life, don't you think Kable? A place to smell the sweet aroma of freedom, to cast off the shackles of the past," Captain Meredith said.

"Aye, 'tis heady enough to give a man fresh dreams of the future, right enough."

The two men stood together for a moment contemplating the blazing blue of the bay, the clarity of the immense sky, and ground covered in crackling leaves and thick grass. Their reverie was disturbed by the exuberant Governor.

"Right, you men," Phillip declared, rubbing his hands together, "let's plumb the depths of the harbour. There's work to be done!"

Every man worked all day, testing water, wood, soil and harbour. The

Governor was overjoyed, declaring it the grandest mooring he had seen anywhere which could conceal a thousand ships in the coves and no enemy would be any wiser.

When they returned to Botany Bay the next day, the Governor called senior officers to the *Sirius*.

"It is, gentlemen," he told them, "one of the finest harbours in the world. It is well protected from swells and winds, the bays are deep and capacious and we'll have no trouble getting in or out – unlike Botany Bay! Fresh water runs freely into the bay and although the soil seems no different to this place, it grows fern and trees most luxuriant. Even the rocks about the bay are similar to Portland stone and that, as we know, is excellent material for constructing buildings and making roads. Gentlemen, tomorrow we sail for Sydney Cove!"

The sailors set to work preparing the vessels for the move. All female and most male prisoners were kept below for the greater safety of the fleet. But heat and lack of air meant conditions in the stinking holds went from bad to worse. The fetid atmosphere drained strength from already feeble bodies and maladies proliferated. The women were prone to fainting and fits, and many of the male convicts suffered similar seizures. The old refrain of 'water, water' became a constant cry from the steaming spaces below.

Worsening weather prevented an early start the next morning, then, astonishingly, the sails of two ships were seen in the distance. A stiff wind blowing out of Botany Bay prevented the vessels from coming in, so Governor Phillip sent the *Supply* out to investigate. He issued orders that nobody was to go aboard the vessels when they came in to Botany Bay, nor reveal that the fleet was on the point of leaving for a better anchorage.

The *Supply* returned, unable to find out what flag the two ships sailed under but reported that they were certainly not English. The wind strengthened the vessels were unable to make headway and disappeared from view in the afternoon haze. It also prevented the fleet from leaving the harbour as intended.

Knowing it was vital to get to the new harbour before the strange ships, Phillip made everyone aware that he would definitely leave early the next day, whatever the difficulties. The rest of the fleet were to follow as soon as the *Supply* cleared the mouth of the bay.

The two strange ships managed to enter Botany Bay around midday despite the fierce gale. They were French ships on a voyage of discovery – the *Compass* and the *Quadrant* – commanded by an explorer named Jean-Francois de la Perouse. They had lost two boat crews, torn to pieces by natives on the Navigators Isles, including the Captain of one of the vessels. The arrival of the French ships put the fleet in a desperate haste to get out of Botany Bay despite the dangerous wind.

Captain Hunter, although he received La Perouse with civility, was in a tearing hurry to join Governor Phillip in the new harbour. He promised the French explorer as much help as he could muster, although he was unable to supply food, spares, weapons or stores of any kind!

To Hunter's great embarrassment, the fleet treated the French to an astonishing display of ineptitude. The *Friendship* sailed straight into the *Prince of Wales* and lost the whole of her jib boom, rending to pieces the *Prince of Wales'* mainsail and top mast stay sail; the *Charlotte* glanced off the *Friendship* and had most of the curved work ripped from her stern, then narrowly avoided smashing into the rocks. The *Lady Penrhyn* almost rammed the careering *Charlotte*, only changing course at the last minute.

Swearing and cursing, the crews showed the cowering prisoners that they knew a thing or two when it came to nautical profanities. The officers blamed Phillip for the debacle, having been ordered to sail 'without fail.'

Eventually they got out and it was late evening when the fleet entered Port Jackson, named by Cook but never entered by him. Eight miles further they came to Sydney Cove where the *Supply* lay at anchor.

For the next ten days, the male prisoners, supervised by marines, set to work establishing the first rudiments of the new settlement. Gangs chopped down trees and cleared shrubs, others dug virgin soil, levelling and digging out roots. Everywhere fires blazed, some burning debris, others providing heat for blacksmiths to forge necessities and sharpen tools. Cooks set up crude ovens to serve both the sweating labourers and the supervising marines.

Stones were hauled and sorted, some to harden the 'dockside', others to be laid down and battered into rough roads and paths. In neatly planned sections, wooden huts began to appear, along with rows of tents.

Some officers had brought their own marquees that were pitched some way from the areas that were allocated as convict compounds. Marines marched about and military discipline began to get back to a barrack-like normality.

A few prisoners escaped, trekking through the bush to Botany Bay, where they begged the French to give them passage, but were sent back. The astonished natives watched all this activity, having no idea what it meant. Governor Phillip ensured that they were treated well and many beads and trinkets were given to the onlookers.

Henry was put to work erecting the Governor's marquee and marking out a large garden. The new colony was short of professional gardeners but Henry, being a countryman, had a fair idea of how to plant the seeds the Governor had brought from Cape Town.

As he worked, Henry was watched every day by a muscular native with gleaming teeth who wore his hair in a top knot he used for storing arrow heads. On one occasion, Henry disturbed a black snake as thick as his wrist and a yard in length. The muscular native hopped over the fence, picked up the creature by the tail and nonchalantly cracked it like a bull whip. With a great show of indifference, he tucked it into his top knot so it hung limply down his back. Then without a word he ambled back to his previous perch, squatted on his haunches and resumed his watch.

Henry had his own daily vigil to make. Every day he sat on a rock after work to stare at the *Charlotte*. Never once did he spot Susannah, nor the hated Robson. He had his own patch of canvas in the Governor's garden pitched under the branches of a thick shrub, alongside another tent housing other prisoners working nearby. Whenever possible, Henry would spend time with Red McGrath who was billeted in a compound patrolled by marines every night.

During a break in the weather – a moderate storm had lashed the encampment for two days – Red hurried down to a rock where he knew Henry would be scanning the *Charlotte* that lay a hundred yards from the shore.

"Henry, I've got news for you, the women are being brought ashore tomorrow!"

"How do you know?"

"There's a meeting in the Governor's marquee, you can hear everything through the canvas."

Henry paced about the flat rock before sitting down to stare at the *Charlotte*. "She won't want me, not if she's got a sailor."

"Don't be daft, Henry, I told you it's bound to be a temporary thing – nothing to worry about."

"I'll take care of Robson, the bastard," Henry drew a wicked looking knife from his boot.

"Don't be a fool, man. You haven't come all this way to hang from a gum tree."

"We'll see."

"I heard your name mentioned, Henry."

"How so?"

"Governor Phillip informed everybody how history would show he was the first white man to set foot in Sydney Cove, but I heard Captain Meredith tell Major Ross that Henry Kable planted the very first foot upon the land, seeing how you carried the Governor ashore."

Henry was staring at the *Charlotte* again and didn't seem to take in what his friend had said.

"Red, I've to go with a party to cut down trees first thing tomorrow, they say some are twenty five feet around the trunk, I'll be there all day. If you're back before me, keep an eye open for my son."

"Count on it, Henry."

The next day, Henry found it hard to concentrate on cutting down trees. Thick branches had to be lopped before teams tackled the massive trunks. It was hard work for the prisoners, most having 'gone soft' during years in prison and aboard ship.Frequent rests were needed and a system of one hour on and two hours off gradually evolved.

During rest periods, Henry spent time setting snares in the undergrowth, anything to keep busy. Once he was startled to find the native who watched him in the Governor's garden standing right behind him.

"God, you gave me a fright," Henry growled.

The man, not understanding a word, flashed his white teeth in a wide grin and beckoned Henry to follow him. Within a few yards, he spotted a bee gathering nectar from a flower and from his topknot produced a burning ember of wood. Carefully, he blew smoke at the bee until it tumbled, stunned, to the ground. Using a sliver of sap, he attached a piece of fluff from a feather to the bee. Within moments the bee recovered enough to take off in heavy flight. Grinning, the native crooked his finger at Henry and they set off, following the white fluff through the bushes. A hundred yards away, it disappeared into a hole in a rotten trunk, whereupon the native began smashing his way into the tree. Amazingly, he didn't seem bothered by the seething swarm, intent as he was in rifling honey from the nest. Henry stood some way off, wary of the angry bees.

When he returned the corporal asked him where he had been. "A native showed me how to find honey," he answered.

It was knowledge he would find useful if he escaped into the bush. It was something that had been on his mind ever since he had seen Susannah holding hands with the sailor in Table Bay.

Transporting female prisoners from the ships began early that morning. Women were ferried in longboats from the *Prince of Wales*, *Charlotte* and *Lady Penrhyn* in a process that took all morning to complete.

All were strictly searched to recover items stolen during the journey but little was found. The few that possessed good clothes put them on and 'scrubbed up' for the occasion. The surgeon on the *Lady Penrhyn* grudgingly conceded that '*some might be said to be well dressed.*'

The masters of the merchant ships were glad to be rid of the prisoners as they were under a penalty of forty pounds for everyone who was missing. It had been a thankless task for the officers to keep women and men apart during the voyage so they too were heartily glad to see the back of them.

Once ashore, the first task for marines was to help the women to finish erecting tents. Male prisoners had been flattening the ground and clearing the area of bushes since the previous day. The women were anxious to secure decent bed places and store what meagre possessions they had.

Trouble began when black clouds ran in from the west and the wind rose powerfully. Great heavy drops of rain began to fall, soon to beat down in fearful torrents. Male prisoners fell over themselves in coming to the aid of the women when their poorly erected tents began to sag and flap. When the storm began in earnest, incredible forked lightning and the most tremendous claps of thunder vied with incessant rain to turn the whole area into a quagmire. Sullen seas roared and crashed onto the nearby shore. Bowes-Smyth thought it the most violent storm he had ever experienced; the thunder even '*shook the ship*'.

In the rain-lashed confusion it was impossible for marines to mount an adequate guard and soon the male prisoners got amongst the women and a terrible scene of debauchery, violence and drunkenness began. Within a short time the marines, realising they had lost control, joined in. On the ships, sailors asked for grog so they too could 'make merry' with the women.

The women didn't stand a chance – those who were unwilling were raped. Others made the most of the bedlam to line up men and maximise their earnings. Quarrels and fights broke out in the rain lashed anarchy and some took the opportunity to loot what goods they could. Reverend Johnson, appalled by the mayhem, took his wife to the Governor's marquee for sanctuary. He found Major Ross there, reporting the situation out of control.

"We must stop this bestial behaviour," the Minister insisted.

"Is there nothing the marines can do?" Governor Phillip demanded.

"It's bedlam down there, Jack Tars are fighting marines, marines strike prisoners and the women mix it up. 'Tis better to let these wanton fires burn themselves out and regain control when this blasted storm ceases," Major Ross replied.

"I must at least try!" Reverend Johnson strode to the canvas opening and plunged into the howling rain.

By the guard post, a woman, wearing the remnants of a dress stood with her back against a tree, white legs showing either side of a marine. She seemed oblivious as she nonchalantly shielded a cheroot from the downpour, carefully holding it away from her lover's bobbing head. Two sailors waited in line for their turn.

The Minister hurried on but nobody paid a bit of attention to his pleadings to 'desist from foul lust.'

It seemed that everywhere he looked, men were chasing barely clad women, some laughing, some screaming; others scrabbled and rolled together, punching, biting and kicking in the slimy earth.

Sliding and skidding, he fell down by a tent, his lantern revealing a prisoner mounted on a naked woman, bare backside going like a fiddler's elbow. Behind him swayed a drunken sailor, preparing to take his own unnatural pleasure from the unsuspecting prisoner.

The holy man was sick on the black earth; thunder roared and lightning lit his frenzied flight back to the Governor's marquee. Major Ross and Captain Meredith, embarrassed by the Minister's earlier show of bravado, had just got back from a tour of the women's compound too.

Meredith was emptying water from his top boots when the mud-caked vicar fell into the tent. He was almost crying with fear and disgust.

"It's Soddam and Gomorrah out there, I've never dreamed such gross lewdness could exist on God's earth. Men are raping women, men ravish one another! This damn storm is to blame! It's uncorked the desires of a thousand men, and the women are no better!"

"Poppycock! I never heard such senseless drivel. Get hold of yourself man!" Major Ross replied angrily.

"I suggest we cool our tempers and wait out the storm here. There is nothing to be done until first light tomorrow," Phillip banged his fist on a table. "We have the reading of the King's commission tomorrow – nothing must spoil that."

The entrance to the marquee flapped open and an officer stumbled in to report that he had brought back the wood cutting gang in view of the storm.

"Is Kable with you?" Phillip asked.

The officer nodded.

"Bring him in."

Henry arrived, soaking wet, wondering why he had been summoned.

"Go to the women's camp, Kable, it's an unholy madhouse down there."

Without a word, Henry took off at top speed. Reaching the women's enclosure his heart sank at the chaos before him. Soon he was running from tent to tent shouting, "Susannah! Susannah! In one tent he came upon Liz Pulley struggling with a burly man wearing a vest. The man was so drunk he could not get up. Henry dragged Liz from the partially collapsed tent.

"Have you seen Susannah and my boy, Liz?"

Liz wiped the teeming rain from her eyes with the bottom of her skirt.

"I've seen her."

"Where, Liz, where?"

She peered round the camp, it was impossible to see more than a few yards except when a bolt of lightning lit up the scene. "I've seen her," she repeated.

"For god's sake, Liz, where?"

Liz began to cry, hanging on to Henry in the wind and rain, squinting this way and that. "I don't know, lad. I don't know if I'm on my arse or elbow in this pissing rain."

Henry sounded his frustration into the black skies.

"I'm sorry, lad, everything looks the bleeding same."

He thrust her away from him and she almost fell in the mud.

"Henry, Henry, get rid of that great lummock in there, my head's fit to bust."

Henry hauled the man from the remnants of the tent and dumped him twenty yards away. The man crawled away, his great white backside streaming with water. By Liz's tent another fight had broken out. Robson was battling with another sailor. Liz joined in, hitting the second man with an iron spar.

Suddenly, all three fell over the adjoining tent to reveal a near-naked Ann Turner astride a uniformed figure sprawled on the ground.

Ann rolled off, cursing the three figures fighting in the mud. The sprawled figure sat up, desperately trying to cover his manhood with his hat. Henry was astonished to recognise the pious Lieutenant Clark.

Disgusted, he pulled his boots from the sticky ground and squelched off to resume the search for Susannah. He went from tent to tent, invariably to be cursed by the occupants, gradually realising that he had no hope of finding Susannah and his son. A log jam of humanity ran, shouted and fought within the camp, mud-caked ghosts in the darkness. No one paid the slightest attention to the tempest, stupefied by grog and lust.

By the edge of the enclosure, Henry tripped over a guy rope and fell on a tent. From within a man cursed and thrust his head out of the flap. "Who's that lumbering about – can't you get your own woman?"

"Red, Red, is that you?" Henry shouted at the figure. It was almost impossible to see, even up close.

"Henry Kable, come in man."

Henry slid in next to Red, who didn't bother getting off the woman, locked as they were in sexual combat.

"Red, have you seen Susannah?"

"I saw her up by the top of the camp. A young sailor was looking out for her. He was taking a hell of a pasting from two marines!"

"Red, you should have taken care of her!"

"I kicked one bloke in the nuts and cracked the other over the head with a lump of wood."

"What happened to Susannah?"

"Went off with the tar, I suppose."

Henry crawled out of the tent, knowing there was nothing he could do, he had only recognised Red from the sound of his voice and they were just inches apart.

Slowly, he made his way out of the women's camp and back to his tent in the Governor's garden. As he stepped over the rough fence a flash of lightning revealed two men fighting by his billet. In frustration, he cracked one of them over the head with a broken branch and seized the other by the throat. Suddenly a voice screamed from his tent.

"Henry, no, Henry!" It was Susannah.

"Is this your sailor boy?" he shouted furiously.

"He's my brother!"

"Brother? brother?"

He's been looking after me, let him go, Henry!"

The sailor slumped to the ground when Henry released his grip. Susannah ran to Henry, laughing and crying in the pouring rain. They clung together, oblivious to the tempest. Lightning flashed and the heavens roared but it was of no consequence to Henry and Susannah.

"Are you silly buggers going to come in out of the rain?" Susannah's brother called from the safety of the tent.

They tumbled in through the sodden flap, squeezing together in the cramped space.

"Henry, this is my brother, Harry."

"What happened to Robson? I saw you with him on the deck of the *Charlotte* in Cape Town harbour."

"That wasn't Robson, he wasn't even on the *Charlotte*, that was Harry. I was so pleased to find him on the ship, I haven't seen him since he went off to be a sailor at Lowestoft."

"It was nothing to my astonishment at finding you, Sis, I had no idea you were amongst those convict women."

"Harry, I didn't want you to know."

"Where's our son?" Henry asked.

Susannah carefully moved a pile of clothes from the side of the tent. Little Henry lay sleeping soundly.

Kneeling they kissed each other deeply.

"I love you, Henry."

"I love you, Susannah."

"I'd better make myself scarce." Harry struggled to his feet but Henry stopped him.

"Stay and look after the boy a moment, there's something I must do." Wrapping Susannah's shawl around her head he pulled her towards the flap.

"Where are we going?"

"You'll see."

They ran through the pelting rain to the Governor's marquee. A bolt of lightning lit up their bedraggled figures as they arrived in the startled presence of the Governor and senior officers.

"What the devil is this, Kable?"

"Sir, we want to get married."

"Your department, I think, Reverend Johnson."

The Minister took them both by the hands. "Thank God for a Christian thought! I was losing my faith in humankind after that orgy of depravity in the encampment."

He turned to the Governor. "Do I have your permission?"

The Governor nodded. "Did you find your boy, Kable?"

"He's safe, Sir, can Susannah Holmes stay in my tent tonight?"

"Aye, they'll be safer there than in the mayhem down by the harbour."

At first light next morning, Henry and Susannah went down to the women's enclosure to search for Liz and Anne. Collapsed tents and sundry bodies lay strewn about, most still sleeping from the drunken orgy the night before. A few marines were harassing prisoners to get up and wash. The whole place was a sea of mud; personal possessions, tents and empty bottles lay haphazardly everywhere.

Eventually Henry took to calling out, "Liz Pulley, Anne Turner, make yourself known," as loudly as he could. Astonishingly, from a partially collapsed tent not five yards away, Liz Pulley's face emerged.

"Henry Kable, will you keep your bleeding voice down, my head's throbbing."

They ran over and squatted beside their friend. "Liz, are you alright? We've been worried about you."

"Apart from this hammer in my head I'm as right as ninepence."

"Have you seen Anne?"

"She's around somewhere, I saw her last night busy with that righteous bugger Lt Clark. He was trying to cover himself with his cocked hat; it seemed the right thing to use. She'll be alright, she's a survivor."

"Come with us Liz, Henry thinks he can get you a job at the Governor's place."

"Not before I get married I ain't. Here, meet my husband to be."

She lifted the tent flap to reveal a figure snoring blissfully. Susannah stared at the man. "Isn't that Robson?"

"It is, he was on my ship since Cape Town and we've been getting real friendly. He's signing off seafaring duties and staying in the new colony with me."

"Does he know about the baby you are carrying?" Susannah whispered.

"Of course he does, it's his."

"His?"

"Definitely, sure as eggs are eggs." Liz gave the most enormous wink.

Henry and Susannah looked at each other, open-mouthed. Laughing, they kissed their friend.

"Well done," Susannah whispered.

"I certainly have been," retorted Liz, scratching her nether regions.

"We are getting married too," Susannah said.

"The authorities have finally come to their senses then." Liz hugged them both.

Astonishingly, after the chaotic rioting and rutting of the night before, the entire Company assembled for the official ceremony to install Commodore Phillip as Governor the next afternoon, 7th February 1788.

The prisoners were formed into a circle with an opening on one side. Next the marines in the red, white and blue uniform marched in bearing their muskets. The convicts were made to squat and all gentlemen present were requested to make their way to the front and form a respectable guard around a table set up in the middle.

Phillips, accompanied by the Lieutenant Governor, Clergyman, Surgeon General and other officers, solemnly entered the human arena to be greeted with a stirring march from the band.

From two red cases, documents were opened and unsealed, witnessed by all present. The Judge Advocate, Captain Collins, read out the new constitution:

"I officially appoint Arthur Phillips Esquire as Governor General, Commander-in-Chief over all the territories called New South Wales, belonging to his Brittanic Majesty George the Third, King of Great Britain, with full powers to build forts, castles and towns and to appoint and constitute officers of every kind as he should judge proper," he announced in ringing tones.

The declaration gave Governor Phillip more powers than ever before granted to an individual under the British Crown.

Phillip stood to the ringing cheers of the disparate audience of prisoners, marines and sailors seated and standing before him. The first thing he did was to harangue convicts and crews for the crushing disgrace of the night before.

"Any man who attempts to get into the women's enclosure again will be shot!" he thundered. "I vow those who do not strive industriously in this new Colony will starve. Any misdemeanours will be rewarded with loss of rations. Poultry and animal stock are vital for breeding and sustaining our new Colony, thus theft of these precious animals will bring punishment of death on those responsible."

He paused, waiting for the message to sink in.

"For those that work and strive together to build this new Colony I promise a comfortable and happy existence. I urge you all to make our new community a happy and prosperous place to live and grow."

The ceremony ended with 'God Save the King' and three volleys from the marines.

Three days later, Henry and Susannah, transported as felons, outcasts of the old country, began a new life under the clear blue skies of New South Wales.

They were the very first to be married in the new Colony being the first in a line of four other couples, under the shade of a glorious eucalyptus tree, to the delighted laugh of a watching kookaburra bird.

The End

Footnote

Henry and Susannah Kable became one of the best known and most successful couples in the First Fleet.

When it was discovered that their precious package had been stolen from the hold of the *Alexander*, they successfully sued Captain Duncan Sinclair for fifteen pounds, creating a precedent for all prisoners. It was the first civil case ever held in the new country and publicly vindicated the rights even of prisoners, to use the legal system.

In 1791, Henry was granted his 'ticket-of-leave' and awarded thirty acres. He went on to accumulate more and more land.

He teamed up with another prisoner, James Underwood, and they built the first ocean going vessel in the Colony (the *Contest*). At one time, Henry was reported as being the proud owner of twenty five ships, and later went into the whaling and sealing trade and became even wealthier.

In 1794, Henry was appointed Chief Constable of Sydney and, two years later, Keeper of the Gaols. He was the first person to begin a mail service in New South Wales.

Of the four couples wed in the first marriage ceremony, Henry and Susannah were the only couple to produce descendants in Australia; they had ten Colonial-born children.

In later years, stories of Henry and Susannah's successes were to inspire many free settlers to migrate to the new country.